THE MEGA
BOOK OF
Crosswords

First published in Great Britain by
Arcturus Publishing Limited
for
Bookmart Limited
Registered Number 2372865
Trading as
Bookmart Limited
Desford Road
Enderby
Leicester
LE9 5AD

This edition published 2002

Printed and bound in Great Britain

© Arcturus Publishing Limited

ISBN 1 900032 83 X

THE MEGA
BOOK OF
Crosswords

ARCTURUS

CONTENTS

SECTION ONE

The Crosswords

SECTION TWO

The Solutions

SECTION ONE

The Crosswords

1

ACROSS

3 Vital organ (5)
8 Pits (5)
10 Mistake (5)
11 Small child (3)
12 Excite (5)
13 Bands (7)
15 Domesticates (5)
18 Umpire (3)
19 Go back (6)
21 Supposed (7)
22 Attack (4)
23 Ring of light (4)
24 Chief city (7)
26 Servant (6)
29 Weep (3)
31 Choose (5)
32 Inhabitant (7)
34 Performed again (5)
35 Gratuity (3)
36 Tooth (5)
37 Narrow (5)
38 Religious song (5)

DOWN

1 Song (5)
2 Went to bed (7)
4 Cupid (4)
5 Relaxed (6)
6 Handle (5)
7 Grass-cutter (5)
9 And not (3)
12 Denial (7)
14 Energy (3)
16 Wall painting (5)
17 Pry (5)
19 Edited (7)
20 Desire (5)
21 Wash out (5)
23 Natural surroundings (7)
24 Provides food (6)
25 Weight (3)
27 Apportion (5)
28 Discard (5)
30 Drive back (5)
32 Face (4)
33 Fastener (3)

2

ACROSS
1 Hurry (5)
6 Loans (5)
9 Not tested (7)
10 Minor (5)
11 Zodiac Sign (5)
12 Sugary (5)
13 Torrid zone (7)
15 Number (3)
17 Agents (4)
18 Go to bed (6)
19 Quilt (5)
20 Adviser (6)
22 Curve (4)
24 Regard (3)
25 Mocks (7)
26 Custom (5)
27 Intolerant person (5)
28 Open area (5)
29 Argument (7)
30 Golf cup (5)
31 Alloy (5)

DOWN
2 Onto land (6)
3 Flowers (6)
4 Finish (3)
5 Increases (5)
6 Young Hare (7)
7 Revise (4)
8 Knife (6)
12 Search (5)
13 Tidies (5)
14 Give an opinion (5)
15 Weary (5)
16 Requirements (5)
18 Readjust (5)
19 Giver (7)
21 Creepily (6)
22 Halve (6)
23 Snuggle (6)
25 Frogman (5)
26 Aspiration (4)
28 Belonging to him (3)

ACROSS

1 Mourn (6)
7 Wool (8)
8 Tub (4)
10 Black magic (6)
11 Encipher (6)
14 Agent (3)
16 Wanderer (5)
17 Dregs (4)
19 Gem (5)
21 Log (5)
22 Custom (5)
23 Treads quietly (4)
26 Pale (5)
28 Enclosure (3)
29 Robust (6)
30 Haggle (6)
31 Burden (4)
32 Plea (8)
33 Slumbers (6)

DOWN

1 Grit (6)
2 Avoids (6)
3 Resound (4)
4 Solvent (7)
5 Broom (5)
6 Yielded (5)
8 Drill (4)
9 Summit (3)
12 Mountain pass (3)
13 Old-fashioned (5)
15 Subtract (5)
18 Be (5)
19 Injection (3)
20 Damp (3)
21 Wax lights (7)
22 That woman (3)
23 Scan (6)
24 Insects (4)
25 Undresses (6)
26 Poplar (5)
27 Injures (5)
28 Criticise (3)
30 Lads (4)

4

ACROSS

4 Difficult to detect (6)
7 Monk (8)
8 Man's name (6)
10 Upright (5)
13 Key (4)
14 Schedule (4)
15 Region (4)
16 Animal's foot (3)
17 Ballpoint pen (4)
19 Cart (4)
21 Acrobatic movement (9)
23 Unaccompanied (4)
24 Skeleton part (4)
26 Wager (3)
27 Tidy (4)
29 Peer (4)
32 Expensive (4)
33 Willow (5)
34 Facial hair (6)
35 Number (8)
36 Joins (6)

DOWN

1 Navigate (5)
2 Military student (5)
3 Notice (4)
4 Musty (5)
5 Expert (4)
6 Room (6)
9 Heavy (6)
11 Argument (3)
12 Group of intriguers (5)
13 Jemmy (7)
15 Painting, music, etc. (3)
16 Friend (3)
18 Pressed (6)
20 Staggers (5)
21 Bed (3)
22 Very warm (3)
23 Harsh (6)
25 Mineral (3)
28 Relaxes (5)
30 Lubricated (5)
31 Take in liquid (5)
32 Pull (4)
33 Darts-player's line (4)

5

ACROSS

3 Grasps (5)
8 Desire (5)
10 Ogles (5)
11 Frozen water (3)
12 Drinking tube (5)
13 Sluggishness (7)
15 At no time (5)
18 Male sheep (3)
19 Calm (6)
21 Liable to change (7)
22 At that time (4)
23 Certain (4)
24 Floor coverings (7)
26 Assemble (6)
29 Equal (3)
31 Mexican plant (5)
32 Brittle material (7)
34 Vital fluid (5)
35 And not (3)
36 Television, newspapers, etc. (5)
37 Viper (5)
38 Step (5)

DOWN

1 Fetch (5)
2 Invaded (7)
4 Schedule (4)
5 Celestial body (6)
6 Drain (5)
7 Colour (5)
9 Expert (3)
12 Alike (7)
14 Pitch (3)
16 Aphrodite (5)
17 Allude (5)
19 Broke (7)
20 Male deer (5)
21 Airs (5)
23 Abandons (7)
24 Underground room (6)
25 Listening organ (3)
27 Helped (5)
28 Custom (5)
30 Temptress (5)
32 Musical tailpiece (4)
33 Rockers' enemy (3)

6

ACROSS

1 Rubbish (5)
6 Join (5)
9 Tranquillised (7)
10 Wind instrument (5)
11 Wash out (5)
12 Understood (5)
13 Informed (7)
15 Domestic fowl (3)
17 Relate (4)
18 Tune (6)
19 Hood (5)
20 Women (6)
22 European capital (4)
24 Before (3)
25 Dining room (7)
26 Child (5)
27 Wading bird (5)
28 Antitoxin (5)
29 Artist (7)
30 Total (5)
31 Poplar (5)

DOWN

2 Cat-like (6)
3 Of the stars (6)
4 Shelter (3)
5 Cold dish (5)
6 Deserved (7)
7 Revise (4)
8 Spurted (6)
12 Aquatic birds (5)
13 Musty (5)
14 Evade (5)
15 Residence (5)
16 Man-made fibre (5)
18 Tooth (5)
19 Lesson (7)
21 Stop (6)
22 Freshwater mammals (6)
23 Vegetable (6)
25 Hackneyed (5)
26 Behave sullenly (4)
28 Body of water (3)

ACROSS

1 Card suit (6)
7 From across the pond (8)
8 Portent (4)
10 Reprimand (6)
11 Widely scattered (6)
14 Anger (3)
16 Implore (5)
17 Day (4)
19 Tag (5)
21 Ague (5)
22 Yielded (5)
23 Provide food (4)
26 Teacher (5)
28 Staff (3)
29 Deprive of food (6)
30 Building material (6)
31 Honest (4)
32 Calmed down (8)
33 Range (6)

DOWN

1 Divided equally (6)
2 Reserved (6)
3 Rational (4)
4 Hunter (7)
5 Twenty (5)
6 Finished (5)
8 Death notice, in short (4)
9 Stretch (3)
12 Everyone (3)
13 Sword (5)
15 Black bird (5)
18 Concerning (5)
19 Guided (3)
20 Cot (3)
21 Ardent (7)
22 Expression of surprise (3)
23 Incite (6)
24 Biblical garden (4)
25 Discover (6)
26 Russian rulers (5)
27 List (5)
28 Agent (3)
30 Cipher (4)

8

ACROSS

4 S American country (6)
7 Turn up again (8)
8 Morals (6)
10 Deal (5)
13 Ticket money (4)
14 Champion (4)
15 US coin (4)
16 Moist (3)
17 Close (4)
19 Mimics (4)
21 Remarked (9)
23 Complain (4)
24 Has to (4)
26 Summit (3)
27 M East country (4)
29 Beers (4)
32 Smile (4)
33 Slumber (5)
34 Showed mercy (6)
35 Young relative (8)
36 Squirm (6)

DOWN

1 Anger (5)
2 Navigation aid (5)
3 Church recess (4)
4 Freshwater fish (5)
5 Pain (4)
6 Units of length (6)
9 Handles (6)
11 Colour (3)
12 Giver (5)
13 Emergency services worker (7)
15 Barrier (3)
16 Marry (3)
18 Sovereignty (6)
20 Flower part (5)
21 Headwear item (3)
22 Devout woman (3)
23 Metal (6)
25 Insect (3)
28 Crest (5)
30 Minimum (5)
31 Backbone (5)
32 Gravel (4)
33 Transmitted (4)

ACROSS

3 States positively (5)
8 Broaden (5)
10 Type of duck (5)
11 Zero (3)
12 Relative (5)
13 Set alight (7)
15 Observable (5)
18 Obtain (3)
19 Surreal (6)
21 Talked informally (7)
22 Warmth (4)
23 On one occasion (4)
24 Covers thinly (7)
26 Fruit (6)
29 As well as (3)
31 Devil (5)
32 Detailed (2-5)
34 Fasteners (5)
35 Decay (3)
36 Skiing slope (5)
37 Change (5)
38 Confuse (5)

DOWN

1 Lotto (5)
2 Elation (7)
4 Invalid (4)
5 Disc (6)
6 Strain (5)
7 Reload (5)
9 Noise (3)
12 Stinging plants (7)
14 Beverage (3)
16 Deserves (5)
17 Sorts (5)
19 Humbles (7)
20 Hooligans (5)
21 Gem's unit of weight (5)
23 Tidy (7)
24 Aired (6)
25 Conclude (3)
27 Wireless (5)
28 Italian food (5)
30 State (5)
32 Object of worship (4)
33 Cooking vessel (3)

10

ACROSS

1. Metalworker (5)
6. Excite (5)
9. Narrator (7)
10. Relative by marriage (2-3)
11. Arched cellar (5)
12. Tag (5)
13. Satire (7)
15. Body of water (3)
17. Freezes (4)
18. Nut (6)
19. Streams (5)
20. Courageous (6)
22. Location (4)
24. Attempt (3)
25. Opportunist (7)
26. Shade of brown (5)
27. Relative of the weasel (5)
28. Den (5)
29. Hereditary (7)
30. Performed (5)
31. Bronze-medal winning position (5)

DOWN

2. Madman (6)
3. Vagrants (6)
4. Chop (3)
5. Couch (5)
6. Discloses (7)
7. Spoken (4)
8. Morose (6)
12. Reasoning (5)
13. Fair (5)
14. Cheerful (5)
15. Of sound (5)
16. Snake (5)
18. Greek letter (5)
19. Fascinated (7)
21. Amorous (6)
22. Grab (6)
23. Offer (6)
25. Apple drink (5)
26. Wise man (4)
28. Be seated (3)

11

ACROSS

1 Duties (6)
7 For eternity (8)
8 Unit of land (4)
10 Reimbursed (6)
11 Seem (6)
14 Finish (3)
16 Coin (5)
17 Compass point (4)
19 Brimless cap (5)
21 Satisfied (5)
22 Thong (5)
23 Layer (4)
26 Church table (5)
28 Illuminated (3)
29 Pests (6)
30 Warning devices (6)
31 Dutch cheese (4)
32 Grow in number (8)
33 Vow (6)

DOWN

1 Fee (6)
2 Retract (6)
3 Plant ovule (4)
4 Ensnared (7)
5 Group of witches (5)
6 Fruit (5)
8 Mimics (4)
9 Free (3)
12 Favourite (3)
13 Corner (5)
15 Flower part (5)
18 Nimble (5)
19 Exclude (3)
20 Agent (3)
21 Footballer (7)
22 Man's name (3)
23 Angry outburst (6)
24 Unit (4)
25 Save (6)
26 Avert (5)
27 Vestige (5)
28 Cover (3)
30 Ooze (4)

12

ACROSS

4 Clergyman (6)
7 Encore (8)
8 Merited (6)
10 Steeple (5)
13 Metrical foot (4)
14 Prong (4)
15 Too (4)
16 Ruminant (3)
17 Bucket (4)
19 Overwhelming defeat (4)
21 Copy (9)
23 Assist (4)
24 Young male horse (4)
26 Brick-carrier (3)
27 Den (4)
29 Paradise (4)
32 Nuisance (4)
33 Prostrate (5)
34 Niche (6)
35 Learned (8)
36 Severe (6)

DOWN

1 Faith (5)
2 European country (5)
3 Dossier (4)
4 Entreaties (5)
5 Yugoslav (4)
6 Feline (6)
9 Unprincipled (6)
11 Mine (3)
12 Drive back (5)
13 Illegal (7)
15 Afflict (3)
16 Snooker stick (3)
18 Fruit (6)
20 Aquatic animal (5)
21 Colour (3)
22 Expression of surprise (3)
23 Truthful (6)
25 Enclosure (3)
28 Something of value (5)
30 Eccentric (5)
31 Requirements (5)
32 Fairy (4)
33 Select (4)

ACROSS

3 Pamphlet (5)
8 Tree (5)
10 Relaxes (5)
11 Spoil (3)
12 Precipitous (5)
13 Sharp reply (7)
15 Watch faces (5)
18 Snake (3)
19 Neatly (6)
21 Furniture item (7)
22 Stop (4)
23 Applaud (4)
24 Prolific (7)
26 Ridiculous (6)
29 Before (3)
31 Sheriff's men (5)
32 Shake (7)
34 Listens (5)
35 Consume (3)
36 Sherry-producing town (5)
37 Beneath (5)
38 Harvests (5)

DOWN

1 Shy (5)
2 Tumbler (7)
4 Routine (4)
5 Believe (6)
6 Lukewarm (5)
7 Stand (5)
9 Knock (3)
12 Tarnished (7)
14 Weep (3)
16 Church passage (5)
17 Graceful woman (5)
19 Examiners (7)
20 Inexpensive (5)
21 Form (5)
23 Moderate (7)
24 Chill (6)
25 Anger (3)
27 Crates (5)
28 Guide (5)
30 Change (5)
32 Stumble (4)
33 Wicked (3)

14

ACROSS

1 Clan (5)
6 Nip (5)
9 Embankment (7)
10 Absolute (5)
11 Performer (5)
12 Soup (5)
13 Sparkle (7)
15 Damp (3)
17 Tear (4)
18 Gratify (6)
19 Frighten (5)
20 Respiration (6)
22 Dregs (4)
24 Gender (3)
25 Contrition (7)
26 Cutlery item (5)
27 Paddle boat (5)
28 Caper (5)
29 Sleeping loudly (7)
30 Hood (5)
31 Warehouse (5)

DOWN

2 Baby's toy (6)
3 Chest (6)
4 Listening organ (3)
5 Reject (5)
6 Gossip (7)
7 Irritation (4)
8 Duties (6)
12 Long seat (5)
13 Snatches (5)
14 Alphabetical list (5)
15 Common liquid (5)
16 Taut (5)
18 Primp (5)
19 Clergyman's salary (7)
21 Redeem (6)
22 Living room (6)
23 Igloo-dweller (6)
25 Bellows (5)
26 Average (2-2)
28 Also (3)

15

ACROSS

1 Tension (6)
7 Business (8)
8 Continent (4)
10 Pub (6)
11 Metal (6)
14 Moose (3)
16 Irritable (5)
17 Strays (4)
19 Wild (5)
21 Marine animal formation (5)
22 Initial (5)
23 Unsullied (4)
26 Indian dresses (5)
28 Weight (3)
29 Number (6)
30 Law-enforcement agency (6)
31 Leave out (4)
32 Definite (5-3)
33 Bedlinen items (6)

DOWN

1 Colonise (6)
2 Artists' stands (6)
3 Read closely (4)
4 Corrupt (7)
5 Sneaked (5)
6 Passenger ship (5)
8 State (4)
9 Annoy (3)
12 Friend (3)
13 Anaesthetic (5)
15 Poetry (5)
18 Former Indian ruler (5)
19 In favour of (3)
20 Rodent (3)
21 Water tank (7)
22 Tree (3)
23 Well-mannered (6)
24 Item (4)
25 Occurrences (6)
26 Adhere (5)
27 Got up (5)
28 Male cat (3)
30 Cooking vessels (4)

16

ACROSS

4	Public quarrel (6)
7	Intrude (8)
8	Stink (6)
10	Suspicious (5)
13	Saucy (4)
14	Insect (4)
15	Gaelic (4)
16	Snoop (3)
17	Rant (4)
19	Encounter (4)
21	Optical device (9)
23	Arm or leg (4)
24	Certain (4)
26	Racket (3)
27	Always (4)
29	Revise (4)
32	Parched (4)
33	Willow (5)
34	Reps (6)
35	Collided (8)
36	Absentee (6)

DOWN

1	Rod (5)
2	Contract (5)
3	Nimble (4)
4	Donkeys (5)
5	Units of length (4)
6	Take (6)
9	Quake (6)
11	Sick (3)
12	Seraglio (5)
13	Ironed (7)
15	Previous day (3)
16	Diocese (3)
18	Watch chain (6)
20	Fencing swords (5)
21	Can (3)
22	Dog (3)
23	Loiter (6)
25	Bind (3)
28	Call (5)
30	Tune (5)
31	Deal (5)
32	Indian coin (4)
33	Gemstone (4)

17

ACROSS

3 Couples (5)
8 Italian island (5)
10 Sharp (5)
11 Meadow (3)
12 Goddess of hunting (5)
13 Presumptious (7)
15 Box (5)
18 Untruth (3)
19 Man's title (6)
21 Interfered (7)
22 God of thunder (4)
23 Pudding ingredient (4)
24 Insects (7)
26 Hurried (6)
29 Scull (3)
31 Place (5)
32 Number (7)
34 Shuts with force (5)
35 Lubricate (3)
36 Greek character (5)
37 Deceived (5)
38 Correct (5)

DOWN

1 Claw (5)
2 Fishing boat (7)
4 Parched (4)
5 Sour (6)
6 Marks (5)
7 Declare (5)
9 For every (3)
12 Dug (7)
14 Assist (3)
16 Book of maps (5)
17 Mistake (5)
19 Advisers (7)
20 Celebrities (5)
21 Type of code (5)
23 Grave (7)
24 Confusion (6)
25 Boy (3)
27 Absolute (5)
28 Speed (5)
30 Valleys (5)
32 Sign (4)
33 Pinch (3)

18

ACROSS

1 Era (5)
6 Senior (5)
9 Silhouette (7)
10 Dirt (5)
11 Old-fashioned (5)
12 Started (5)
13 Duellists (7)
15 Wager (3)
17 Part of the eye (4)
18 Calm (6)
19 Berate (5)
20 Hit (6)
22 Crooked (4)
24 Golf peg (3)
25 Mischievous spirits (7)
26 Gum (5)
27 Tropical bird (5)
28 Gemstone (5)
29 Trespass (7)
30 Unfeeling (5)
31 Command (5)

DOWN

2 Doorman (6)
3 Children's magazines (6)
4 Shade (3)
5 Insects (5)
6 Suffered (7)
7 Slender (4)
8 Cricket team (6)
12 Building material (5)
13 Initial (5)
14 Gunpowder ingredient (5)
15 Brimless cap (5)
16 Canvas shelters (5)
18 Incline (5)
19 Bony (7)
21 Occupant (6)
22 Larger (6)
23 Snuggle (6)
25 Wading bird (5)
26 Ache (4)
28 Fuss (3)

19

ACROSS

1 Tropical grass (6)
7 Refill (8)
8 Stopper (4)
10 Hot and humid (6)
11 Cook (6)
14 Age (3)
16 Performer (5)
17 Read closely (4)
19 Deal (5)
21 The ones over there (5)
22 Actions (5)
23 Utters (4)
26 Agreeable (5)
28 Jewel (3)
29 Sluggish (6)
30 Oarsmen (6)
31 Paradise (4)
32 Paintings (8)
33 Examiner (6)

DOWN

1 Explodes (6)
2 Town in Greater Manchester (6)
3 Wild party (4)
4 Travesty (7)
5 Characteristic (5)
6 Less (5)
8 Entreaty (4)
9 Vase (3)
12 Expert (3)
13 Regretful (5)
15 Wear away (5)
18 Tropical tree (5)
19 Definite article (3)
20 Donkey (3)
21 Boring (7)
22 Immerse (3)
23 Drains (6)
24 So be it (4)
25 Nurse (6)
26 Desists (5)
27 Cost (5)
28 Deity (3)
30 Remainder (4)

20

ACROSS

- 4 College (6)
- 7 Pull back (8)
- 8 Avoids (6)
- 10 Stern (5)
- 13 Sugar plant (4)
- 14 Japanese drink (4)
- 15 Barrels (4)
- 16 Fish (3)
- 17 Precipitation (4)
- 19 Shortly (4)
- 21 Imperils (9)
- 23 Ran away (4)
- 24 Slippery fish (4)
- 26 Tibetan ox (3)
- 27 Nobleman (4)
- 29 Finished (4)
- 32 Spheres (4)
- 33 Sleep noisily (5)
- 34 Edible root (6)
- 35 Decide against (8)
- 36 Inferior (6)

DOWN

- 1 Small branches (5)
- 2 Cut of beef (5)
- 3 Hand tool (4)
- 4 Sugary (5)
- 5 Warmth (4)
- 6 US state (6)
- 9 Container (6)
- 11 Uncooked (3)
- 12 Jules, French novelist (5)
- 13 Flags (7)
- 15 By way of (3)
- 16 Lettuce (3)
- 18 Vipers (6)
- 20 Mr Welles, actor (5)
- 21 Moose (3)
- 22 Solidify (3)
- 23 Front (6)
- 25 That woman (3)
- 28 Detest (5)
- 30 Fashion (5)
- 31 Insurgent (5)
- 32 Lubricates (4)
- 33 Certain (4)

ACROSS

3 Red Indian trophy (5)
8 Type of element (5)
10 Angry (5)
11 Gear (3)
12 Middle East inhabitant (5)
13 Dried grape (7)
15 Relative (5)
18 Curve (3)
19 Bishop's headdresses (6)
21 Lured (7)
22 Injure (4)
23 Greek letter (4)
24 Dreary (7)
26 More miserable (6)
29 And not (3)
31 Alloy (5)
32 Tool (7)
34 Party (5)
35 Charged particle (3)
36 Unit of a gem's weight (5)
37 Commencement (5)
38 Tears (5)

DOWN

1 Happen again (5)
2 Tramp (7)
4 Short (4)
5 Fluid (6)
6 Photographic image (5)
7 Took unlawfully (5)
9 Hill (3)
12 Tooth (7)
14 E.g. painting (3)
16 Ruthless (5)
17 Treatise (5)
19 Souvenir (7)
20 Board game (5)
21 Wear away (5)
23 Scorching (7)
24 Cross out (6)
25 Enemy (3)
27 Book of maps (5)
28 Exclude (5)
30 Prongs (5)
32 Single item (4)
33 Distress call (3)

22

ACROSS

1 South American animal (5)
6 Noblemen (5)
9 Month (7)
10 Grin (5)
11 Stringed instrument (5)
12 Harbours (5)
13 Stress (7)
15 Consumed (3)
17 Revise (4)
18 Shameless (6)
19 Sleep noisily (5)
20 Emphasis (6)
22 Gaelic (4)
24 Regard (3)
25 Colonist (7)
26 Liberated (5)
27 Desolate (5)
28 Deceives (5)
29 Student (7)
30 Bore (5)
31 At no time (5)

DOWN

2 Walked irregularly (6)
3 Accost (6)
4 Expert (3)
5 Punctuation mark (5)
6 Reprimand (7)
7 Minerals (4)
8 Water down (6)
12 Indicate (5)
13 US state (5)
14 Relative (5)
15 Shade of blue (5)
16 Go in (5)
18 Plait (5)
19 Breathing device (7)
21 Underground room (6)
22 Guarantee (6)
23 Harsh (6)
25 Fruit (5)
26 Drop (4)
28 Lair (3)

ACROSS

1 Light shoe (6)
7 Senior council member (8)
8 Playing cards (4)
10 Modern (6)
11 Face (6)
14 Concealed (3)
16 Young women (5)
17 Let it stand (4)
19 Fruit (5)
21 Managed (5)
22 Start (5)
23 Ruminant (4)
26 Petty officer (5)
28 Guided (3)
29 Cooks (6)
30 Mother or father (6)
31 Norse god (4)
32 Enough (8)
33 Wobble (6)

DOWN

1 Rations (6)
2 Fraud (6)
3 Final (4)
4 Minor deity (7)
5 Bedaub (5)
6 Mountain range (5)
8 Pain (4)
9 Conclude (3)
12 Transgress (3)
13 Clearing (5)
15 Lukewarm (5)
18 Forbidden (5)
19 Record (3)
20 Males (3)
21 Mythical creature (7)
22 Public vehicle (3)
23 Scoff at (6)
24 Paradise (4)
25 Cad (6)
26 Wide (5)
27 Rescues (5)
28 Boy (3)
30 Bard (4)

24

ACROSS

- 4 Endure (6)
- 7 Large mammal (8)
- 8 Loved (6)
- 10 Slip (5)
- 13 Exsanguinated (4)
- 14 Timbre (4)
- 15 Sense (4)
- 16 Suitable (3)
- 17 Tack (4)
- 19 Single entity (4)
- 21 Alienated (9)
- 23 Worry (4)
- 24 Digits (4)
- 26 Dog (3)
- 27 Frozen (4)
- 29 Journey (4)
- 32 Network (4)
- 33 Stage whisper (5)
- 34 Tower (6)
- 35 Ejection (8)
- 36 Appeared (6)

DOWN

- 1 Minimum (5)
- 2 Start (5)
- 3 Footwear item (4)
- 4 Musty (5)
- 5 Nourishment (4)
- 6 Excused (6)
- 9 Flood (6)
- 11 Auction item (3)
- 12 Thick (5)
- 13 Overdue (7)
- 15 Tree (3)
- 16 Help (3)
- 18 Apparel (6)
- 20 Birds' homes (5)
- 21 Stray (3)
- 22 Signal assent (3)
- 23 Yet to come (6)
- 25 Offer (3)
- 28 Quoted (5)
- 30 Stiff (5)
- 31 Coin (5)
- 32 Unit of weight (4)
- 33 Curved structure (4)

25

ACROSS

3 Holds firmly (5)
8 Provide food (5)
10 Reason (5)
11 Tear (3)
12 Heathen (5)
13 Intoned (7)
15 Sailing boat (5)
18 Vehicle (3)
19 Scold (6)
21 Footballer (7)
22 Mountains (4)
23 Inquires (4)
24 Instruct (7)
26 Stirs (6)
29 Strike (3)
31 Detested (5)
32 Food fish (7)
34 Toxic vapours (5)
35 Plural of is (3)
36 Navigate (5)
37 Sea (5)
38 Prepared (5)

DOWN

1 Seraglio (5)
2 Portrays (7)
4 Street (4)
5 Musician (6)
6 Navigation aid (5)
7 Vision (5)
9 Spasm (3)
12 Lengths of time (7)
14 Pitch (3)
16 Motive (5)
17 Anxious (5)
19 Long seats (7)
20 Capture (5)
21 Nozzle (5)
23 Draw (7)
24 Last (6)
25 Tune (3)
27 Hurry (5)
28 Allude (5)
30 Creep (5)
32 Pay attention to (4)
33 Anger (3)

26

ACROSS

1 Employment (5)
6 Group of witches (5)
9 Public speech (7)
10 Sphere (5)
11 Rustic (5)
12 Chairs (5)
13 Takes (7)
15 Golf peg (3)
17 Flesh (4)
18 Astounded (6)
19 Gemstone (5)
20 Posture (6)
22 Nourishment (4)
24 Was seated (3)
25 Equilibrium (7)
26 Senses (5)
27 Blemish (5)
28 Howls (5)
29 Trod heavily (7)
30 Revises (5)
31 Examines (5)

DOWN

2 Comfort (6)
3 Drinking vessel (6)
4 Before (3)
5 Pig-pens (5)
6 Funeral procession (7)
7 Responsibility (4)
8 Rubs out (6)
12 Performing area (5)
13 Hoard (5)
14 Gem's unit of weight (5)
15 Claw (5)
16 Short musical piece (5)
18 Book of maps (5)
19 Emphasises (7)
21 Sampled (6)
22 Front (6)
23 Feline mammal (6)
25 Culpability (5)
26 Clenched hand (4)
28 Moist (3)

ACROSS

1 South American cowboy (6)
7 Depicting rural life (8)
8 Leporid mammal (4)
10 Cricket side (6)
11 Limited (6)
14 Guided (3)
16 Helicopter blade (5)
17 Snakes (4)
19 Drain (5)
21 Sacked (5)
22 Quick (5)
23 Type (4)
26 S American monetary units (5)
28 Soft bread roll (3)
29 Confectionery (6)
30 Royal residence (6)
31 Verbal (4)
32 Shining (8)
33 Steal (6)

DOWN

1 Swiss city (6)
2 Desires (6)
3 Honest (4)
4 Dressed (7)
5 Characteristic (5)
6 Change (5)
8 Assist (4)
9 Colour (3)
12 And not (3)
13 Turret (5)
15 Deserve (5)
18 Scatter (5)
19 Drink daintily (3)
20 Married (3)
21 Attaches (7)
22 Fish eggs (3)
23 Seasoned sausage (6)
24 Gemstone (4)
25 From there (6)
26 Religious song (5)
27 Joins (5)
28 Obstruct (3)
30 Mail (4)

28

ACROSS

4 Quick look (6)
7 Restorer (8)
8 Evades (6)
10 Wash (5)
13 Examine (4)
14 Gaelic (4)
15 Experts (4)
16 Elderly (3)
17 A great quantity (4)
19 Certain (4)
21 Fascinate (9)
23 Country road (4)
24 River deposit (4)
26 Professor (3)
27 Title (4)
29 Paradise (4)
32 Appends (4)
33 Prostrate (5)
34 Overnight case (6)
35 Secret phrase for admission (8)
36 Flaw (6)

DOWN

1 Clan (5)
2 Notices (5)
3 Monetary penalty (4)
4 Elegance (5)
5 Soon (4)
6 Hug (6)
9 Subordinate (6)
11 Limb (3)
12 Muscular male (2-3)
13 Divisions (7)
15 Perform (3)
16 Mineral (3)
18 Overturns (6)
20 Total (5)
21 Tin (3)
22 Contend (3)
23 Find (6)
25 Enclosure (3)
28 Skilful (5)
30 Giver (5)
31 Poor (5)
32 Assistant (4)
33 Nuisance (4)

ACROSS

3 Fashion (5)
8 Warehouse (5)
10 Edible bulb (5)
11 Sweet roll (3)
12 Extent (5)
13 Obedient (7)
15 Principle (5)
18 Twitch (3)
19 Scan (6)
21 Tree (7)
22 Breed (4)
23 Enquires (4)
24 Interval (7)
26 Improved (6)
29 Auction item (3)
31 Partly frozen rain (5)
32 Went back (7)
34 Heaped (5)
35 Signal assent (3)
36 Step (5)
37 Viper (5)
38 Thick (5)

DOWN

1 Refute (5)
2 Controller (7)
4 Work (4)
5 Linger (6)
6 Go in (5)
7 Musical sounds (5)
9 Place (3)
12 Match (7)
14 Fish's appendage (3)
16 Sister (5)
17 Abrupt (5)
19 Populated (7)
20 Snatches (5)
21 Social group (5)
23 Is present (7)
24 Go to bed (6)
25 Charged particle (3)
27 Exclusive (5)
28 Lukewarm (5)
30 Yielded (5)
32 Agents (4)
33 Deity (3)

30

ACROSS

1 Mistreat (5)
6 Implore (5)
9 Competent (7)
10 Command (5)
11 Finished (5)
12 Wide (5)
13 Return (7)
15 Prosecute (3)
17 Insects (4)
18 Relaxed (6)
19 Cubed (5)
20 Became calmer (6)
22 Metal (4)
24 Tear (3)
25 Furniture item (7)
26 Frivolous (5)
27 Planet (5)
28 Closes (5)
29 Remainder (7)
30 War-horse (5)
31 Snooped (5)

DOWN

2 Load (6)
3 Perfumes (6)
4 Listening organ (3)
5 Sword (5)
6 Gratified (7)
7 Loan (4)
8 Tree-lined street (6)
12 Plait (5)
13 Navigational aid (5)
14 Thong (5)
15 Blemish (5)
16 Decree (5)
18 Recompense (5)
19 Contrived (7)
21 Cut in half (6)
22 Stringed instrument (6)
23 Snuggle (6)
25 Assert (5)
26 Certain (4)
28 Drink (3)

ACROSS

1 Tropical tree (6)
7 Explorer of caves (8)
8 Ashen (4)
10 Riddles (6)
11 Morals (6)
14 Rodent (3)
16 Wearies (5)
17 Give out (4)
19 Aspirations (5)
21 Afterwards (5)
22 Ancient Italian (5)
23 Relax (4)
26 Devil (5)
28 Dreadful (3)
29 Cower (6)
30 Matures (6)
31 Norse god (4)
32 Became milder (8)
33 Abandon (6)

DOWN

1 Antipodean, commonly (6)
2 Neckwear item (6)
3 Mimics (4)
4 Gossip (7)
5 Talent (5)
6 Scum (5)
8 Fairy (4)
9 Permit (3)
12 Of him (3)
13 US coins (5)
15 Utter (5)
18 Tooth (5)
19 Bad actor (3)
20 Enclosure (3)
21 Yearning (7)
22 Managed (3)
23 Sword (6)
24 Paradise (4)
25 Examined (6)
26 Twenty (5)
27 Cash registers (5)
28 Offer (3)
30 Staffs (4)

32

ACROSS

4 Type of fruit (6)
7 Warn (8)
8 Sour (6)
10 Requires (5)
13 Ball-point (4)
14 Only (4)
15 Extremely (4)
16 Colour (3)
17 Manner (4)
19 Poke (4)
21 Happy (9)
23 Baptismal bowl (4)
24 Ado (4)
26 Part (3)
27 Revise (4)
29 Journey (4)
32 Join together closely (4)
33 Willow (5)
34 Intones (6)
35 Giggled (8)
36 Poplars (6)

DOWN

1 Aches (5)
2 Force (5)
3 Responsibility (4)
4 Seat (5)
5 Three-piece band (4)
6 Joined (6)
9 Church vaults (6)
11 Age (3)
12 Devil (5)
13 Advantage (7)
15 Animal doctor (3)
16 Staff (3)
18 Meaning (6)
20 Relaxes (5)
21 Bed (3)
22 Kernel (3)
23 Struggles (6)
25 Expire (3)
28 Records (5)
30 Shotgun (5)
31 Conceit (5)
32 Leg joint (4)
33 On one occasion (4)

ACROSS

3 Distress signal (5)
8 Autographs (5)
10 Come in (5)
11 Wager (3)
12 Deadens (5)
13 Crossed out (7)
15 Prophet (5)
18 Hiatus (3)
19 Hi-fi (6)
21 Cold-blooded creature (7)
22 Fur (4)
23 Equipment (4)
24 Invigorate (7)
26 Of salt (6)
29 Spirit (3)
31 Exhausted (5)
32 Feline (7)
34 Young women (5)
35 Decay (3)
36 Stately home (5)
37 Man-made waterway (5)
38 Belief (5)

DOWN

1 Roman river (5)
2 Number (7)
4 Clamorous (4)
5 Refund (6)
6 Follow (5)
7 Scene of action (5)
9 Solidify (3)
12 Planet (7)
14 Knock gently (3)
16 Colour (5)
17 Bellows (5)
19 Sleds (7)
20 Board game (5)
21 Shotgun (5)
23 Officer (7)
24 Whole (6)
25 Contend (3)
27 Horrify (5)
28 Gold bar (5)
30 Deadly (5)
32 Piece of information (4)
33 Unit of weight (3)

34

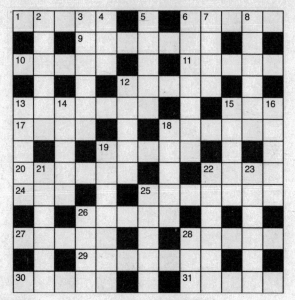

ACROSS

1 Attain (5)
6 Nobleman (5)
9 Fracas (7)
10 Metal fastener (5)
11 Stale (5)
12 Ceases (5)
13 Argument (7)
15 Expert (3)
17 Painting, sculpture, etc (4)
18 Frightens (6)
19 Lamp (5)
20 Cowardly (6)
22 Greek letter (4)
24 Slippery fish (3)
25 At an unspecified time (7)
26 Handle (5)
27 Small bird (5)
28 Slides (5)
29 Dream (7)
30 War-horse (5)
31 Misdemeanour (5)

DOWN

2 Panacea (6)
3 Sneaks (6)
4 Shed (3)
5 Condition (5)
6 Agreement (7)
7 Burden (4)
8 Spot (6)
12 Blemish (5)
13 Movement to music (5)
14 Take unlawfully (5)
15 Weapon-bearing (5)
16 Treatise (5)
18 Fire (5)
19 Educated (7)
21 Holiday spot (6)
22 Cup (6)
23 Two-seater bicycle (6)
25 Rescued (5)
26 Weary (4)
28 Thus (3)

ACROSS

1 US state (6)
7 Leaflet (8)
8 Disgusting (4)
10 Compels (6)
11 Pub (6)
14 Body of water (3)
16 Evaluates (5)
17 Mark (4)
19 Shelter (5)
21 Insurgent (5)
22 Nine-piece band (5)
23 Routine (4)
26 Counterfeit (5)
28 Agent (3)
29 Shed (4-2)
30 Powerful (6)
31 Incline (4)
32 Accuse (8)
33 Yearly (6)

DOWN

1 Dwellings (6)
2 Shudder (6)
3 Mimics (4)
4 Dress (7)
5 Half-frozen rain (5)
6 Amazes (5)
8 Travel permit (4)
9 Meadow (3)
12 Vehicle (3)
13 Respond (5)
15 Tag (5)
18 Paddle-boat (5)
19 Domestic fowl (3)
20 Animal doctor (3)
21 Platform (7)
22 Sister (3)
23 Keep (6)
24 Honest (4)
25 Impose (6)
26 Knife-edge (5)
27 Profits (5)
28 Fish eggs (3)
30 Entreaty (4)

ACROSS

4 Abduct (6)
7 Hopping marsupial (8)
8 Nearly (6)
10 Prig (5)
13 Dash (4)
14 Prophet (4)
15 Bridge (4)
16 Be victorious (3)
17 Egyptian goddess (4)
19 Contest (4)
21 Rebuke (9)
23 Cipher (4)
24 Praise (4)
26 Timid (3)
27 At the summit (4)
29 Small case (4)
32 Smile (4)
33 Fashion (5)
34 Sturdy (6)
35 Tolerance (8)
36 Tenant (6)

DOWN

1 Misses out (5)
2 Unwarranted (5)
3 Crippled (4)
4 Arborial marsupial (5)
5 Curse (4)
6 Descend using a rope (6)
9 Carriage (6)
11 Colour (3)
12 Desiccated (5)
13 Greek letter (7)
15 Man's form of address (3)
16 Marry (3)
18 Weapons (6)
20 Below (5)
21 Man's name (3)
22 Chart (3)
23 Opt (6)
25 Star (3)
28 Name (5)
30 Aquatic birds (5)
31 Lazes (5)
32 Pistols (4)
33 Slender (4)

37

ACROSS

3 Drops (5)
8 Allude (5)
10 Chose (5)
11 Tear (3)
12 From that time (5)
13 Tapers (7)
15 Fury (5)
18 Plural of is (3)
19 Dress (6)
21 Too old (7)
22 Speed (4)
23 Photograph (4)
24 Shortage (7)
26 Restrained (6)
29 Negative (3)
31 Slumber (5)
32 Soothe (7)
34 Extent (5)
35 Eon (3)
36 Keepsake (5)
37 Unit of weight (5)
38 Anaesthetic (5)

DOWN

1 Wild (5)
2 Corrupt (7)
4 Wartime alliance (4)
5 Find (6)
6 Exhausted (5)
7 Drain (5)
9 Tree (3)
12 Veered (7)
14 Mineral (3)
16 Titan (5)
17 Harvests (5)
19 Versus (7)
20 Narrative poems (5)
21 Yellow-orange (5)
23 Place (7)
24 Portray (6)
25 Lettuce (3)
27 Open sore (5)
28 Contradict (5)
30 Rep (5)
32 Assistant (4)
33 In the past (3)

38

ACROSS

1 Fiasco (5)
6 Shrill (5)
9 Avoided (7)
10 Hurry (5)
11 Looks lasciviously (5)
12 Symbol (5)
13 Sanctuary (7)
15 Donkey (3)
17 In this place (4)
18 Help (6)
19 Writing (5)
20 Commands (6)
22 Scheme (4)
24 Golf peg (3)
25 Assemble (7)
26 Fool (5)
27 Native New
Zealander (5)
28 Stately home (5)
29 Agrees (7)
30 Facade (5)
31 Taut (5)

DOWN

2 Red Indian (6)
3 Oxen (6)
4 Previous day (3)
5 Earlier (5)
6 Liberate (7)
7 Paradise (4)
8 Coercion (6)
12 Rips (5)
13 Fire (5)
14 Wear away (5)
15 Passage (5)
16 Feat of daring (5)
18 Race meeting (5)
19 Foretell (7)
21 Mend (6)
22 Gratify (6)
23 Thespians (6)
25 Enciphered (5)
26 Middle East country (4)
28 Encountered (3)

ACROSS

1 Distilled grape drink (6)
7 Street (8)
8 Couple (4)
10 Posture (6)
11 Not mentioned (6)
14 Regard (3)
16 Mends (5)
17 Insects (4)
19 Managed (5)
21 Afterwards (5)
22 Temptress (5)
23 Permits (4)
26 Foundation (5)
28 Expression of surprise (3)
29 Warns (6)
30 Submissive (6)
31 Dash (4)
32 Shrivelled (8)
33 From there (6)

DOWN

1 Japanese escort (6)
2 Aircraft (6)
3 Unit of land (4)
4 Apart (7)
5 Exclude (5)
6 Fasteners (5)
8 Over (4)
9 Frozen water (3)
12 Miserable (3)
13 Gold bar (5)
15 Inn (5)
18 Of birth (5)
19 Vehicle (3)
20 Enclosure (3)
21 Hearkens (7)
22 Term of respect (3)
23 Discover (6)
24 Ireland (4)
25 Record cover (6)
26 Type of wood (5)
27 Prophets (5)
28 Mountain pass (3)
30 Hollow (4)

40

ACROSS

4 Shows contempt for (6)
7 Censure (8)
8 Edible bulbs (6)
10 Supply (5)
13 Press (4)
14 Rational (4)
15 Insect (4)
16 Argument (3)
17 Duo (4)
19 Religious image (4)
21 Imposed punishment on (9)
23 Nuisance (4)
24 Spool (4)
26 Auction item (3)
27 Tear (4)
29 Circuits (4)
32 Sweet rolls (4)
33 Valuable item (5)
34 Tumbled (6)
35 Winning (8)
36 Climb (6)

DOWN

1 Stupid (5)
2 Cutlery item (5)
3 Toil (4)
4 Plant life (5)
5 Norse god (4)
6 Sinew (6)
9 Catch sight of (6)
11 Faucet (3)
12 Yields (5)
13 Incarcerates (7)
15 Obtain (3)
16 Staff (3)
18 False (6)
20 Prison rooms (5)
21 Ready (3)
22 Mesh (3)
23 Absorbent (6)
25 Mimic (3)
28 Finished (5)
30 Moving (5)
31 Performance area (5)
32 Colour (4)
33 On holiday (4)

ACROSS

3 Impel (5)
8 Frivolous (5)
10 Finished (5)
11 Meadow (3)
12 Principle (5)
13 Gleamed (7)
15 Disprove (5)
18 Bounder (3)
19 Scold (6)
21 Inferred (7)
22 Fat (4)
23 Counterfeit (4)
24 Partitioned enclosure (7)
26 Types (6)
29 Owing (3)
31 Alloy (5)
32 Iterates (7)
34 Foreign currency units (5)
35 Mine (3)
36 Dissuade (5)
37 Brimless cap (5)
38 Ancient stringed instruments (5)

DOWN

1 Tablets (5)
2 Looked briefly (7)
4 Regretted (4)
5 Changed direction (6)
6 Come in (5)
7 First public appearance (5)
9 Garland (3)
12 Boring (7)
14 Pitch (3)
16 Wash (5)
17 Sides (5)
19 Moreover (7)
20 Tires (5)
21 Male bee (5)
23 Railway carriage (7)
24 Vegetable (6)
25 Drinking vessel (3)
27 Anaesthetic (5)
28 Drive back (5)
30 Absolute (5)
32 Flower (4)
33 Tune (3)

42

ACROSS

1 Snares (5)
6 Old-fashioned (5)
9 Attire (7)
10 Each (5)
11 Garden tool (5)
12 Holds firmly (5)
13 Zones (7)
15 Serpent (3)
17 Askew (4)
18 Perceptive (6)
19 Backbone (5)
20 Deep valley (6)
22 Scorch (4)
24 Before (3)
25 Colony governor (7)
26 Comedian (5)
27 Eskimo boat (5)
28 Book of charts (5)
29 Full (7)
30 Writing material (5)
31 Strayed (5)

DOWN

2 Reconsider (6)
3 Equality (6)
4 Secret agent (3)
5 Couples (5)
6 Hold in contempt (7)
7 Mountains (4)
8 Most senior (6)
12 Small fruit (5)
13 Sword (5)
14 Desire (5)
15 Predict (5)
16 Small coin (5)
18 Caper (5)
19 Game (7)
21 Fleet (6)
22 Improved (6)
23 Turn (6)
25 Country residence (5)
26 Be concerned (4)
28 Consumed (3)

43

ACROSS

1 Sweet (6)
7 Obliquely (8)
8 Heroic narrative (4)
10 Adapt (6)
11 Courteous (6)
14 Domestic animal (3)
16 Ascended (5)
17 Survive (4)
19 Perch (5)
21 Telegram (5)
22 Evaluated (5)
23 Pace (4)
26 Temptress (5)
28 For every (3)
29 Believe (6)
30 Helping (6)
31 Jump (4)
32 Sick (8)
33 Feline (6)

DOWN

1 Of teeth (6)
2 Hut (6)
3 Russian ruler (4)
4 Regret (7)
5 Indian dresses (5)
6 Pale (5)
8 Drinks daintily (4)
9 Obtained (3)
12 Illuminated (3)
13 Anxious (5)
15 Loose garments (5)
18 Moving (5)
19 Rodent (3)
20 Elderly (3)
21 Teeth (7)
22 Colour (3)
23 Placid (6)
24 Journey (4)
25 Young swine (6)
26 Doughy cake (5)
27 Happen again (5)
28 Pastry dish (3)
30 Too (4)

44

ACROSS

4 Elevated (6)
7 Up until now (8)
8 Fragrances (6)
10 Defence of being elsewhere (5)
13 Just (4)
14 South American country (4)
15 Idealised man (4)
16 Frozen water (3)
17 Insect (4)
19 Heal (4)
21 Theatre (9)
23 Units of length (4)
24 Church recess (4)
26 Noise (3)
27 Shade (4)
29 Running event (4)
32 Yield (4)
33 Willow (5)
34 Temperament (6)
35 Horrified (8)
36 Disclose (6)

DOWN

1 Inexpensive (5)
2 Step (5)
3 Fairy (4)
4 Beaten contestant (5)
5 Run away (4)
6 Lure (6)
9 Flower (6)
11 Shelter (3)
12 Brass instrument (5)
13 Greenhouse gas (7)
15 Dried grass (3)
16 Anger (3)
18 Gossip (6)
20 Employers (5)
21 Writing implement (3)
22 Choose (3)
23 Closing sequence (6)
25 Expert (3)
28 Perfect (5)
30 Passage (5)
31 Wear away (5)
32 Appealing (4)
33 Elliptical (4)

45

ACROSS

3 Automaton (5)
8 Tumbles (5)
10 Wireless (5)
11 Zodiac sign (3)
12 Royal (5)
13 Bandage (7)
15 Pick-me-up (5)
18 Depressed (3)
19 Give (6)
21 Always (7)
22 Wander (4)
23 Spoken (4)
24 Dip (7)
26 Swamp (6)
29 Kernel (3)
31 Foundation (5)
32 Felines (7)
34 Urbane (5)
35 Stray (3)
36 Cotton fabric (5)
37 Snap (5)
38 Wear away (5)

DOWN

1 Decorative shrub (5)
2 Bloom (7)
4 Finished (4)
5 Public speaker (6)
6 Claw (5)
7 Extent (5)
9 Meadow (3)
12 Recovers (7)
14 Pitch (3)
16 Mother-of-pearl (5)
17 Prison rooms (5)
19 Protection (7)
20 Particle of bread (5)
21 Travelling
   entertainments (5)
23 Stablemen (7)
24 Publisher (6)
25 Regret (3)
27 Desert's fertile patch (5)
28 Church passage (5)
30 Thong (5)
32 Roman poet (4)
33 Mineral (3)

46

ACROSS

1   Body of men (5)
6   Taut (5)
9   Superior (7)
10 Frightening (5)
11 Magnanimous (5)
12 Pleats (5)
13 Projectile (7)
15 Single (3)
17 Woes (4)
18 Aviators (6)
19 Wallow (5)
20 Impede (6)
22 Greek letter (4)
24 Gratuity (3)
25 Vacation (7)
26 Wading bird (5)
27 Yearned (5)
28 Tale (5)
29 Daydream (7)
30 Urged (5)
31 Faith (5)

DOWN

2   Draw back (6)
3   Female monster (6)
4   Snoop (3)
5   Dugout (5)
6   Threadlike leaf (7)
7   Cupid (4)
8   Without sound (6)
12 Airman (5)
13 Power (5)
14 Sudden decline (5)
15 Seeped (5)
16 Treatise (5)
18 Evita's surname (5)
19 Ebbed (7)
21 Assisting (6)
22 Tart (6)
23 Zodiac sign (6)
25 Inn (5)
26 In this place (4)
28 Be seated (3)

47

ACROSS

1. Pure (6)
7. Suave (8)
8. Speed (4)
10. Fairy king (6)
11. Looks fixedly (6)
14. Plunder (3)
16. Disturbed (5)
17. Turn (4)
19. Matter (5)
21. Scandinavian (5)
22. Drop in standard (5)
23. Flightless bird (4)
26. Donkeys (5)
28. Garden tool (3)
29. Portray (6)
30. Shade of blue (6)
31. Revise (4)
32. Authorised (8)
33. Followed (6)

DOWN

1. Criminals (6)
2. Girl's name (6)
3. Paradise (4)
4. Luck (7)
5. Couples (5)
6. Ridge (5)
8. Fairy (4)
9. Male swan (3)
12. Suitable (3)
13. Creepy (5)
15. Type of code (5)
18. Lever (5)
19. Policeman (3)
20. Employ (3)
21. Being born (7)
22. Garland (3)
23. Small birds (6)
24. Warmth (4)
25. Be present (6)
26. Confuse (5)
27. Dot (5)
28. Brick-carrier (3)
30. Surrender (4)

48

ACROSS

4 Remarking (6)
7 Panic (8)
8 Aromas (6)
10 Elegance (5)
13 Unusual (4)
14 Every (4)
15 Story (4)
16 Young man (3)
17 Among (4)
19 So be it (4)
21 Very thin (9)
23 Finished (4)
24 Declare (4)
26 Anger (3)
27 Bird of prey (4)
29 Object of worship (4)
32 Lake (4)
33 Condition (5)
34 Dwell (6)
35 Fed (8)
36 Landed property (6)

DOWN

1 Form (5)
2 Savoury jelly (5)
3 Dried up (4)
4 Of the nose (5)
5 Large shrub (4)
6 Idea (6)
9 Invent (6)
11 Scull (3)
12 Disgrace (5)
13 Emit (7)
15 Spasm (3)
16 Cot (3)
18 Stained (6)
20 Deserve (5)
21 Previous day (3)
22 Greeting (3)
23 Commands (6)
25 Auction item (3)
28 Girl's name (5)
30 Milk-producing company (5)
31 Guides (5)
32 Isinglass (4)
33 Location (4)

ACROSS

3 Faith (5)
8 Afterwards (5)
10 Evidence (5)
11 Ruminant (3)
12 Conscious (5)
13 Edible crustaceans (7)
15 Come in (5)
18 Faucet (3)
19 Pungent root (6)
21 Abraded (7)
22 Reluctant (4)
23 Amaze (4)
24 Denies (7)
26 Spoken (6)
29 Peculiar (3)
31 Make an effort (5)
32 Allow (7)
34 Book of maps (5)
35 Nothing (3)
36 Satan (5)
37 Rashers (5)
38 Birds' homes (5)

DOWN

1 Hidden store (5)
2 Fascinate (7)
4 Tiers (4)
5 Extend (6)
6 Fashion (5)
7 Sharpens (5)
9 Hill (3)
12 Dress (7)
14 Spoil (3)
16 Shades (5)
17 Horned mammal (5)
19 Comes back (7)
20 Addict (5)
21 Stow (5)
23 Influential (7)
24 Baby's toy (6)
25 Sound of disappoval (3)
27 Drive out (5)
28 Cerebral organ (5)
30 Permit (5)
32 Compass point (4)
33 Spasm (3)

50

ACROSS

1 Proverb (5)
6 Contestant (5)
9 Told (7)
10 Enlist (5)
11 Implore (5)
12 Climb (5)
13 Having a will (7)
15 Belonging to him (3)
17 Catch sight of (4)
18 Brook (6)
19 Wash (5)
20 Gateway (6)
22 Elliptical (4)
24 Mineral (3)
25 Stern (7)
26 Feat of daring (5)
27 Forger's block (5)
28 Madagascan primate (5)
29 Conclusive game (7)
30 Yields (5)
31 Stage whisper (5)

DOWN

2 Fools (6)
3 Unattractive (6)
4 Slippery fish (3)
5 Jousting weapon (5)
6 Full (7)
7 Lazy (4)
8 Tropical tree (6)
12 Take unlawfully (5)
13 Musical time (5)
14 Steeple (5)
15 Lift with effort (5)
16 Grin (5)
18 Yell (5)
19 Fights (7)
21 Fruit (6)
22 Different people (6)
23 Rowed (6)
25 Caper (5)
26 Team (4)
28 Meadow (3)

ACROSS

1 Enticing (6)
7 Prolong (8)
8 Church recess (4)
10 Water down (6)
11 Dull (6)
14 Snoop (3)
16 Female relative (5)
17 Get up (4)
19 Minimum (5)
21 Send (5)
22 Royal (5)
23 Small bird (4)
26 Reverie (5)
28 Field (3)
29 Hire payment (6)
30 Harass (6)
31 Border (4)
32 Needles (8)
33 Ornamental tuft (6)

DOWN

1 Set of steps (6)
2 Sullied (6)
3 Merriment (4)
4 Versus (7)
5 Peal (5)
6 Fish (5)
8 Mountain range (4)
9 Pig-pen (3)
12 Be seated (3)
13 Sharp (5)
15 Beefcake (2-3)
18 Habituate (5)
19 Limb (3)
20 Afflict (3)
21 Stays (7)
22 Rodent (3)
23 Forces apart (6)
24 Anger (3)
25 Usual (6)
26 Attire (5)
27 Access (5)
28 Boy (3)
30 Supreme (4)

52

ACROSS

- 4 Awning (6)
- 7 Turn up again (8)
- 8 Forces (6)
- 10 Lustre (5)
- 13 Flightless birds (4)
- 14 Exchange for money (4)
- 15 Beers (4)
- 16 Beverage (3)
- 17 Dial (4)
- 19 Guide (4)
- 21 Conducting (9)
- 23 Metal (4)
- 24 Cans (4)
- 26 Lair (3)
- 27 Circular band (4)
- 29 Vases (4)
- 32 Close (4)
- 33 Scrubland (5)
- 34 Changes (6)
- 35 Annoy (8)
- 36 Rocks (6)

DOWN

- 1 Salad plant (5)
- 2 Auctioneer's hammer (5)
- 3 Honest (4)
- 4 Felony (5)
- 5 Pinches (4)
- 6 Drew (6)
- 9 Cotton fabric (6)
- 11 Chop (3)
- 12 Delicate and charming (5)
- 13 Voter (7)
- 15 Expert (3)
- 16 Label (3)
- 18 Bowman (6)
- 20 Follow (5)
- 21 Noise (3)
- 22 Hint (3)
- 23 Fanatic (6)
- 25 Insect (3)
- 28 Desert's fertile patch (5)
- 30 Navigation aid (5)
- 31 Narrow fragment (5)
- 32 Gas (4)
- 33 Greet (4)

53

ACROSS

3 Fire (5)
8 Backless chair (5)
10 Pitches tent (5)
11 Listening organ (3)
12 Slumber (5)
13 Umpire (7)
15 Loans (5)
18 Silent (3)
19 Sullen (6)
21 Furniture item (7)
22 Middle East country (4)
23 Applications (4)
24 Device (7)
26 Lumberjack (6)
29 Mineral (3)
31 Sabre (5)
32 Perfectly (7)
34 Revises (5)
35 Decay (3)
36 Drive back (5)
37 Absolute (5)
38 Judges (5)

DOWN

1 Alloy (5)
2 Supervisor (7)
4 Gap (4)
5 Large feline (6)
6 Narrow (5)
7 Potatoes (5)
9 Buffoon (3)
12 Lecture (7)
14 Chafe (3)
16 Hangman's rope (5)
17 Feeling (5)
19 Procedures (7)
20 Implements (5)
21 Freight (5)
23 Discover (7)
24 Interfere (6)
25 Anger (3)
27 Proprietor (5)
28 Avarice (5)
30 Change (5)
32 Detail (4)
33 Great quantity (3)

54

ACROSS

1 Food fish (5)
6 Uproars (5)
9 Takes small bites (7)
10 Grind (5)
11 Keyed instrument (5)
12 Power sources (5)
13 Tumbler (7)
15 Guided (3)
17 Back (4)
18 Look out for (6)
19 Berate (5)
20 Change (6)
22 Beers (4)
24 No matter which (3)
25 Contend (7)
26 Reverie (5)
27 Crouch (5)
28 Lukewarm (5)
29 Finery (7)
30 Celebrated (5)
31 Stupid (5)

DOWN

2 Royal son (6)
3 Mooring device (6)
4 Bind (3)
5 Concerning (5)
6 Answered (7)
7 Egyptian goddess (4)
8 Firewood (6)
12 Fiasco (5)
13 Scent (5)
14 Bad-tempered (5)
15 Large spoon (5)
16 Thick (5)
18 Blossom (5)
19 Began (7)
21 Unparalelled (6)
22 Seem (6)
23 Morals (6)
25 Gem's unit of weight (5)
26 Challenge (4)
28 Spasm (3)

ACROSS

1 Has faith (6)
7 Pervade (8)
8 Entreaty (4)
10 Trader (6)
11 Courteous (6)
14 Solidify (3)
16 Adam's ale (5)
17 So be it (4)
19 Managed (5)
21 Stratum (5)
22 Sacred book of Islam (5)
23 Merriment (4)
26 Shinbone (5)
28 Vegetable (3)
29 Corrects (6)
30 Sausage (6)
31 Painting, sculpture, etc (4)
32 Imperil (8)
33 Happenings (6)

DOWN

1 Treeless plain (6)
2 Sombre (6)
3 Practise boxing (4)
4 Authorise (7)
5 Custom (5)
6 Dissuade (5)
8 Errand-boy (4)
9 Slippery fish (3)
12 Boy (3)
13 Taut (5)
15 Regal (5)
18 Note value (5)
19 Vehicle (3)
20 Enclosure (3)
21 Burden (7)
22 Family (3)
23 Placid (6)
24 Falls behind (4)
25 Signs up (6)
26 Stories (5)
27 Stoops (5)
28 Equal (3)
30 Nude (4)

56

ACROSS

4 Iterate (6)
7 Demote (8)
8 Calls (6)
10 Join (5)
13 Ancient symbol (4)
14 Always (4)
15 Regimen (4)
16 Perform (3)
17 Amongst (4)
19 Every (4)
21 Ample supply (9)
23 Fog (4)
24 Outdoor swimming-pool (4)
26 Mountain pass (3)
27 Bound (4)
29 Tear (4)
32 Eye-glass (4)
33 Go in (5)
34 Stick together (6)
35 Large cats (8)
36 Seven-piece band (6)

DOWN

1 Misdemeanour (5)
2 Distress signal (5)
3 Leer (4)
4 Sketch show (5)
5 Sit (4)
6 Fasten (6)
9 Mean (6)
11 Previous day (3)
12 Snatches (5)
13 Puzzles (7)
15 Noise (3)
16 Expert (3)
18 Grumble (6)
20 Oak tree fruit (5)
21 Afflict (3)
22 Help (3)
23 Gloomy (6)
25 Single (3)
28 Awkward (5)
30 Anaesthetic (5)
31 Lock of hair (5)
32 Loaned (4)
33 Consumes (4)

57

ACROSS

3 Pamphlet (5)
8 Slum (5)
10 Hostlery (5)
11 Intelligence (3)
12 Ladle (5)
13 US city (7)
15 Gets up (5)
18 Garland (3)
19 Contort (6)
21 Loaners (7)
22 Garden tools (4)
23 Level (4)
24 Solve (7)
26 Pondering (6)
29 Bind (3)
31 Mix (5)
32 Protection (7)
34 Dignified (5)
35 Charged particle (3)
36 Middle East country (5)
37 Sluggish (5)
38 Prepared (5)

DOWN

1 Cringe (5)
2 Colonises (7)
4 Ready to eat (4)
5 Refrain (6)
6 Pick-me-up (5)
7 Insurgent (5)
9 By way of (3)
12 Slipping (7)
14 Number (3)
16 Ability (5)
17 Chairs (5)
19 Respire (7)
20 Manual digit (5)
21 Contract (5)
23 Sensation (7)
24 Loosened (6)
25 Contend (3)
27 Sore (5)
28 Archery ring (5)
30 Type (5)
32 Sleigh (4)
33 Pedal digit (3)

58

ACROSS

1 Hidden store (5)
6 Cord (5)
9 Cigarette-end receptacle (7)
10 Steep slope (5)
11 Feeling (5)
12 Aids in crime (5)
13 Inferiors (7)
15 Guided (3)
17 Serpents (4)
18 Next to (6)
19 Celebrations (5)
20 Musical embellishments (6)
22 Dimensions (4)
24 Group (3)
25 Window cover (7)
26 Grin (5)
27 Wireless (5)
28 Cooks in water (5)
29 Desirous (7)
30 Storey (5)
31 Laziness (5)

DOWN

2 Curved structures (6)
3 Torment (6)
4 Psychic intuition (3)
5 Counterfoils (5)
6 Rooks (7)
7 Yes votes (4)
8 Whipped (6)
12 Regions (5)
13 Endures (5)
14 Cleft (5)
15 Extent (5)
16 Dissuade (5)
18 Wash (5)
19 Allure (7)
21 Remember (6)
22 Saunter (6)
23 Fanatic (6)
25 Strips of wood (5)
26 Grain store (4)
28 Coach (3)

59

ACROSS

1 Sheepskin (6)
7 Multi-linguist (8)
8 French cheese (4)
10 Posture (6)
11 Smart (6)
14 Born (3)
16 Foggy (5)
17 European river (4)
19 Perspire (5)
21 Scorches (5)
22 Frighten (5)
23 Stone (4)
26 Long-snouted
   mammal (5)
28 Agent (3)
29 Unprincipled (6)
30 Recompensed (6)
31 Object of worship (4)
32 Burden excessively (8)
33 Oozed (6)

DOWN

1 Farce (6)
2 Paid worker (6)
3 Fencing sword (4)
4 Bedwear (7)
5 Slides (5)
6 Fable (5)
8 Cause of misery (4)
9 Frozen water (3)
12 Mine (3)
13 Principle (5)
15 Conscious (5)
18 Reverie (5)
19 Body of water (3)
20 Before (3)
21 Scribbles (7)
22 Term of respect (3)
23 Rest (6)
24 Gemstone (4)
25 Fooled (6)
26 Claw (5)
27 Might (5)
28 Colour (3)
30 Frees (4)

60

ACROSS

4 Encipher (6)
7 Army clergyman (8)
8 Large prawns (6)
10 Tender (5)
13 Terse (4)
14 Spool (4)
15 Clarified butter (4)
16 Tree (3)
17 Scandinavian (4)
19 Melody (4)
21 Loath (9)
23 Section (4)
24 Considerate (4)
26 Snoop (3)
27 Level (4)
29 Deserve (4)
32 Network (4)
33 Dried plum (5)
34 Most recent (6)
35 Clapping (8)
36 Hand tool (6)

DOWN

1 Performer (5)
2 Social blunder (5)
3 Insult (4)
4 Follow (5)
5 Informal talk (4)
6 Remove from office (6)
9 Greek islander (6)
11 Charge (3)
12 Senior (5)
13 Verified (7)
15 Wildebeest (3)
16 Insect (3)
18 Changes (6)
20 Beneath (5)
21 Beam (3)
22 Can (3)
23 Give moral instruction (6)
25 Vase (3)
28 Essential (5)
30 Predict (5)
31 At no time (5)
32 Sets (4)
33 Draw (4)

61

ACROSS

3 Characteristic (5)
8 Rashers (5)
10 Large house (5)
11 Hill (3)
12 Ruminant (5)
13 Merit (7)
15 Start (5)
18 Regard (3)
19 Flowers (6)
21 Whim (7)
22 Bow (4)
23 Finished (4)
24 Dispossess (7)
26 Diploma (6)
29 European Currency Unit (3)
31 Killed (5)
32 Ineffectual (7)
34 Urban areas (5)
35 Plural of is (3)
36 Principle (5)
37 Harsh (5)
38 Chairs (5)

DOWN

1 Loathed (5)
2 Predicted (7)
4 Garden tool (4)
5 Obtrude (6)
6 Tarnish (5)
7 Inferior (5)
9 Lettuce (3)
12 Supervise (7)
14 Agent (3)
16 Work for (5)
17 Russian rulers (5)
19 Performer (7)
20 Potatoes (5)
21 Latin American dance (5)
23 Produce eggs (7)
24 Designate (6)
25 Frozen water (3)
27 Senior (5)
28 Ceremonies (5)
30 Employers (5)
32 Item (4)
33 Before (3)

62

ACROSS

1 Remnant (5)
6 Conceit (5)
9 Disapproval (7)
10 Spanish coast (5)
11 Come in (5)
12 Animal (5)
13 Horse-drawn vehicle (7)
15 Era (3)
17 Permits (4)
18 Unfastened (6)
19 Break out (5)
20 Cooks in the oven (6)
22 Skin (4)
24 Donkey (3)
25 Rests (7)
26 Handle (5)
27 Wash (5)
28 Chews (5)
29 Furniture item (7)
30 Salivate (5)
31 Nurses (5)

DOWN

2 Dress (6)
3 Players (6)
4 Vegetable (3)
5 Valuable item (5)
6 Gift (7)
7 Tear (4)
8 Sprinkle (6)
12 Pigs (5)
13 Girl's name (5)
14 Book of maps (5)
15 Assistants (5)
16 Revises (5)
18 Disturbed (5)
19 Everlasting (7)
21 Stableman (6)
22 Civil (6)
23 Myth (6)
25 Fanatical (5)
26 Filled tortilla (4)
28 Wager (3)

ACROSS

1 Abscond (6)
7 Working clothes (8)
8 Strong wind (4)
10 Swiss lodge (6)
11 Purify (6)
14 Record (3)
16 Easily frightened (5)
17 Peruse (4)
19 Might (5)
21 Celebrated (5)
22 Sacred song (5)
23 Pour (4)
26 Curse (5)
28 Hint (3)
29 Card suit (6)
30 Obvious (6)
31 Competent (4)
32 Dusting (8)
33 Make beloved (6)

DOWN

1 Fools (6)
2 Arthurian resting place (6)
3 Bard (4)
4 Saluted (7)
5 Demand (5)
6 Enquired (5)
8 Festive occasion (4)
9 Limb (3)
12 Tree (3)
13 Relative (5)
15 Greek poet (5)
18 Cheshire town (5)
19 Affectionate tap (3)
20 Damp (3)
21 Luck (7)
22 Spoil (3)
23 Named (6)
24 Fencing sword (4)
25 Substance (6)
26 Hut (5)
27 Enthusiastic (5)
28 Identification flap (3)
30 Errand-boy (4)

64

ACROSS

4 Stop (6)
7 Uncorrupted (8)
8 Religious songs (6)
10 Clan (5)
13 Chinese cooking vessels (4)
14 Sparkling water (4)
15 Location (4)
16 Bad actor (3)
17 Filth (4)
19 Egyptian goddess (4)
21 Large mammals (9)
23 Pitcher (4)
24 Gaelic (4)
26 Chop (3)
27 Microorganism (4)
29 Paradise (4)
32 Eye-glass (4)
33 Malice (5)
34 Go to bed (6)
35 Accosted (8)
36 Fixed (6)

DOWN

1 Notices (5)
2 Stiff (5)
3 Eye inflammation (4)
4 Warehouse (5)
5 Bodies of water (4)
6 Brazilian dances (6)
9 Flocks of geese (6)
11 Argument (3)
12 Swiss city (5)
13 Shrivels (7)
15 Drink (3)
16 Of him (3)
18 Commercial combination (6)
20 Precipitous (5)
21 Sheep (3)
22 Weapon (3)
23 Await (6)
25 Obtain (3)
28 Foe (5)
30 The same (5)
31 Requirements (5)
32 Fruit (4)
33 Appear (4)

65

ACROSS

3 Labourers (5)
8 Term of respect (5)
10 Ceremonies (5)
11 Preserve (3)
12 Brimless cap (5)
13 Bulwark (7)
15 Predict (5)
18 Self-image (3)
19 Sovereignty (6)
21 Excuse (7)
22 Cupid (4)
23 Blackthorn (4)
24 Recluses (7)
26 Performer (6)
29 Non-amateur (3)
31 Indian instrument (5)
32 Clergymen (7)
34 Wash (5)
35 Car test (3)
36 Oar (5)
37 Principle (5)
38 Decree (5)

DOWN

1 Indian ruler (5)
2 Picnic baskets (7)
4 Aid in crime (4)
5 Imagined (6)
6 Become suddenly alert (3,2)
7 Reappear (5)
9 Weir (3)
12 Relative (7)
14 Era (3)
16 Young women (5)
17 Readjust (5)
19 Instance (7)
20 Loans (5)
21 Indicate (5)
23 Raged (7)
24 Messenger (6)
25 Anger (3)
27 Letter (5)
28 Wire (5)
30 Assumed a role (5)
32 Debonair (4)
33 Charged particle (3)

66

ACROSS

1 Capital of Ghana (5)
6 Relaxes (5)
9 Invigorate (7)
10 Crawled (5)
11 Nip (5)
12 Chinese secret society (5)
13 Finery (7)
15 Beer (3)
17 Friend (4)
18 Tested (6)
19 Couples (5)
20 Consecrate (6)
22 Sack (4)
24 Born (3)
25 Less large (7)
26 Myth (5)
27 Wanderer (5)
28 Melodies (5)
29 Include (7)
30 At no time (5)
31 Anaesthetic (5)

DOWN

2 Trust (6)
3 Further match (6)
4 Insect (3)
5 Jewelled headdress (5)
6 Mends (7)
7 Girl's name (4)
8 Confront (6)
12 Giant (5)
13 Textile fibre (5)
14 Clearing (5)
15 Use (5)
16 Come in (5)
18 Fundamental (5)
19 Bullfighter (7)
21 Take away (6)
22 Show off (6)
23 Ebb (6)
25 Roofing material (5)
26 Dial (4)
28 Bind (3)

67

ACROSS

1 Hot pepper (6)
7 Suave (8)
8 French name (4)
10 Small wave (6)
11 Morals (6)
14 Slippery fish (3)
16 Peers (5)
17 Sleigh (4)
19 Chess pieces (5)
21 Metal fastener (5)
22 Sharpened (5)
23 Hairstyle (4)
26 Antitoxin (5)
28 Equal (3)
29 Culmination (6)
30 Human being (6)
31 Speed (4)
32 Bedwear item (8)
33 Sings, Swiss-style (6)

DOWN

1 Duties (6)
2 Walked irregularly (6)
3 Lazy (4)
4 Omen (7)
5 Long-snouted mammal (5)
6 Scum (5)
8 Fencing sword (4)
9 Sick (3)
12 Owns (3)
13 Transparent (5)
15 Judge's hammer (5)
18 Tag (5)
19 Narrow brooch (3)
20 Marry (3)
21 E European country (7)
22 Low drone (3)
23 Divided (6)
24 Gaelic (4)
25 Note values (6)
26 Fragrance (5)
27 Telephones (5)
28 Vegetable (3)
30 Victim (4)

68

ACROSS

4 Faint (6)
7 Swiss language (8)
8 Insult (6)
10 Rush (5)
13 Young cow (4)
14 Fairy (4)
15 Sport (4)
16 Wager (3)
17 Lacerate (4)
19 Street (4)
21 Objection (9)
23 Religious leader (4)
24 Concludes (4)
26 Faucet (3)
27 Group (4)
29 Female sheep (4)
32 Trial (4)
33 Precipitous (5)
34 Musical sounds (6)
35 Climbed (8)
36 Bad-tempered (6)

DOWN

1 Understanding (5)
2 Bedaub (5)
3 On one occasion (4)
4 Group of fish (5)
5 Polish (4)
6 Pierced (6)
9 Excessively ornate (6)
11 Favourite (3)
12 Indonesian island (5)
13 Amass (7)
15 Young dog (3)
16 Racket (3)
18 Entertained (6)
20 Beginning (5)
21 Trophy (3)
22 Insect (3)
23 Assemble (6)
25 Shelter (3)
28 Treatise (5)
30 Unwanted plants (5)
31 Garden tool (5)
32 Spruce (4)
33 Ooze (4)

69

ACROSS

3 Pry (5)
8 Honour (5)
10 Nip (5)
11 Afflict (3)
12 Start (5)
13 Saluted (7)
15 At no time (5)
18 Free (3)
19 Dwell (6)
21 Came out (7)
22 Ring of light (4)
23 Hollow (4)
24 Male fowl (7)
26 Haphazard (6)
29 Not at home (3)
31 Bequeath (5)
32 Means (7)
34 Clock faces (5)
35 Food fish (3)
36 Rule (5)
37 Absolute (5)
38 Surrey town (5)

DOWN

1 Vital organ (5)
2 Sicilian capital (7)
4 Require (4)
5 Gave an opinion (6)
6 Yearns (5)
7 Felt pain (5)
9 Expire (3)
12 Boudoir (7)
14 Bind (3)
16 Adder (5)
17 Hires (5)
19 Grounds (7)
20 Ration (5)
21 Antelope (5)
23 Perceives (7)
24 Water sport (6)
25 Sound of disapproval (3)
27 Rage (5)
28 Evade (5)
30 Appended (5)
32 Former education authority (4)
33 Negative (3)

70

ACROSS

1 Composition (5)
6 Indicate (5)
9 Satire (7)
10 Red Indian trophy (5)
11 Tend (5)
12 Horse-drawn vehicles (5)
13 Grid (7)
15 Moose (3)
17 Strays (4)
18 Deteriorate (6)
19 Faint (5)
20 Blush (6)
22 Relax (4)
24 Prosecute (3)
25 Becomes more amenable (7)
26 Buffalo (5)
27 Riding display (5)
28 Intimidate (5)
29 Amorous (7)
30 Islands (5)
31 Hoard (5)

DOWN

2 Football (6)
3 Permits (6)
4 Yelp (3)
5 Talk (5)
6 Card game (7)
7 Responsibility (4)
8 Snuggle (6)
12 Royal headdress (5)
13 Approaches (5)
14 Deal (5)
15 German city (5)
16 Ties (5)
18 Females (5)
19 Grave (7)
21 Praising speech (6)
22 Conclusion (6)
23 Needle (6)
25 Beats conclusively (5)
26 Trouser support (4)
28 Coach (3)

ACROSS

1 Rubs (6)
7 Engineer (8)
8 Entreaty (4)
10 Bomb hole (6)
11 Coarse (6)
14 Set (3)
16 Sheets of glass (5)
17 Prophet (4)
19 Antic (5)
21 Phoneys (5)
22 Principle (5)
23 Refined (4)
26 Performer (5)
28 Vehicle (3)
29 Deprive of food (6)
30 Cleared out (6)
31 Gaelic (4)
32 Empty of people (8)
33 Small basket (6)

DOWN

1 Flower (6)
2 Hesitate (6)
3 Mark (4)
4 Bands (7)
5 Giant (5)
6 Loans (5)
8 Errand boy (4)
9 Slippery fish (3)
12 Exclude (3)
13 Prise (5)
15 Captured (5)
18 Upright (5)
19 Tin (3)
20 Favourite (3)
21 Zeal (7)
22 Hill (3)
23 Clergyman (6)
24 Desire (4)
25 Most senior (6)
26 Poplar (5)
27 Spanish snack (5)
28 Dog (3)
30 Look furtively (4)

72

ACROSS

4 Parcel (6)
7 Poise (8)
8 Talent-spotters (6)
10 Duty (5)
13 Cease (4)
14 Residence (4)
15 Particle (4)
16 Also (3)
17 Ashen (4)
19 Crooked (4)
21 Sorry (9)
23 Assist (4)
24 Quote (4)
26 Seed case (3)
27 Man's name (4)
29 Wise Men (4)
32 Follow (4)
33 Man-made material (5)
34 Account (6)
35 Mechanic (8)
36 Things of value (6)

DOWN

1 Instruct (5)
2 Broom (5)
3 Overdue (4)
4 Pasta sauce (5)
5 Harvest (4)
6 Range (6)
9 Battle (6)
11 Brick-carrier (3)
12 Drive back (5)
13 Design applicator (7)
15 Beer (3)
16 Insect (3)
18 Seem (6)
20 Foe (5)
21 Colour (3)
22 Spasm (3)
23 Inns (6)
25 In the past (3)
28 Ceremonies (5)
30 Change (5)
31 Sluggish (5)
32 Volume (4)
33 Tack (4)

73

ACROSS

3 Cornish town (5)
8 Deduce (5)
10 Of vision (5)
11 Slippery fish (3)
12 Swagger (5)
13 Subtracts (7)
15 Lukewarm (5)
18 Female deer (3)
19 Lessen (6)
21 Spanish currency units (7)
22 Scan (4)
23 Insult (4)
24 Furniture items (7)
26 Onto land (6)
29 Plural of is (3)
31 Princess of Wales (5)
32 Strew (7)
34 Orderly pile (5)
35 Droop (3)
36 Commotion (5)
37 Reason (5)
38 Clan (5)

DOWN

1 Scornful expression (5)
2 Deceived (7)
4 Rodents (4)
5 Journeys (6)
6 Chose (5)
7 Ape (5)
9 Given food (3)
12 Spire (7)
14 Lettuce (3)
16 Drags (5)
17 Denounce (5)
19 Plunder (7)
20 Wide (5)
21 Egyptian governor (5)
23 Texan hat (7)
24 Bomb hole (6)
25 Age (3)
27 Located (5)
28 Commencement (5)
30 Legal, commonly (5)
32 Blackleg (4)
33 Label (3)

74

ACROSS

1 Spoilt children (5)
6 Exceptionally good person (5)
9 Bag (7)
10 Pale (5)
11 Senior (5)
12 Hackneyed (5)
13 Pleasure (7)
15 Prepared (3)
17 Poems (4)
18 Ridicule (6)
19 Command (5)
20 Band (6)
22 Beers (4)
24 Age (3)
25 Harsh (7)
26 Talent (5)
27 Paddle boat (5)
28 Easily frightened (5)
29 Number (7)
30 Shed hair (5)
31 At no time (5)

DOWN

2 Hurried (6)
3 Dissertation (6)
4 Child (3)
5 Fool (5)
6 Thin (7)
7 Friend (4)
8 Required (6)
12 Duty (5)
13 Extinguish (5)
14 Gain knowledge (5)
15 Move sideways (5)
16 Anxious (5)
18 Object (5)
19 Rich (7)
21 Red fruit (6)
22 Dress (6)
23 Stoat fir (6)
25 Helped (5)
26 Thwart (4)
28 Number (3)

ACROSS

1 Tail (6)
7 Gymshoe (8)
8 Learning (4)
10 Irish accent (6)
11 Very sad (6)
14 Barrel (3)
16 Rows (5)
17 Level (4)
19 Narrow (5)
21 Conductor's stick (5)
22 Nine-piece band (5)
23 Type of grass (4)
26 Concentrated beam (5)
28 For each (3)
29 Changes (6)
30 Relating to cattle (6)
31 Biblical garden (4)
32 Famous (8)
33 Veer (6)

DOWN

1 Small stone (6)
2 Catch phrase (6)
3 Fencing sword (4)
4 Tidy (7)
5 Smithy (5)
6 Groups of countries (5)
8 Adore (4)
9 Furrow (3)
12 Tune (3)
13 Angry (5)
15 Satisfied (5)
18 Essential (5)
19 Brown (3)
20 Cooking vessel (3)
21 Takes temporarily (7)
22 Born (3)
23 Venerate (6)
24 Ireland (4)
25 Dig up (6)
26 Scottish landowner (5)
27 Unit of weight (5)
28 Seed case (3)
30 Cots (4)

ACROSS

4 Female monster (6)
7 Fungus (8)
8 At the back (6)
10 Riddle (5)
13 Flightless bird (4)
14 Detest (4)
15 Rig (4)
16 Possess (3)
17 S African currency unit (4)
19 Merit (4)
21 Toleration (9)
23 Elderly (4)
24 Always (4)
26 Fuss (3)
27 Mislay (4)
29 Son of Isaac (4)
32 Agents (4)
33 Russian rulers (5)
34 Shopping mall (6)
35 Invalidation (8)
36 Handsome youth (6)

DOWN

1 Destroy (5)
2 Thing of worth (5)
3 Liberate (4)
4 US city (5)
5 Schedule (4)
6 Scattered (6)
9 Calm (6)
11 Man's name (3)
12 French author (5)
13 Compensation (7)
15 Wildebeest (3)
16 Mineral (3)
18 Confused (6)
20 Units of land (5)
21 Self-image (3)
22 Salutation (3)
23 Loved (6)
25 Pitch (3)
28 Unwraps (5)
30 Material (5)
31 Employing (5)
32 Precipitation (4)
33 Type of duck (4)

77

ACROSS

3 Scold (5)
8 Wallow (5)
10 Each (5)
11 Afflict (3)
12 Impel (5)
13 Round of applause (7)
15 Commencement (5)
18 Solidify (3)
19 Useless (6)
21 Reconstructed (7)
22 Binds (4)
23 Blackthorn (4)
24 Fabric (7)
26 Accustomed (6)
29 Attempt (3)
31 Danger (5)
32 Adolescent (7)
34 Storey (5)
35 Stray (3)
36 Supple (5)
37 Inquired (5)
38 Wear away (5)

DOWN

1 Kingdom (5)
2 Floods (7)
4 Injure (4)
5 Deeply religious (6)
6 Happening (5)
7 Fish basket (5)
9 By way of (3)
12 Watered down (7)
14 Society girl (3)
16 Move sideways (5)
17 Principle (5)
19 Small wager (7)
20 Undress (5)
21 Reappear (5)
23 Cunning (7)
24 Cashier (6)
25 Anger (3)
27 Horse's cry (5)
28 Shotgun (5)
30 Concur (5)
32 Related (4)
33 Noah's vessel (3)

78

ACROSS

1 Vestige (5)
6 Couples (5)
9 Yearbook (7)
10 Beat (5)
11 Pancake (5)
12 Asphyxiate (5)
13 Swagger (7)
15 Employ (3)
17 Spoken (4)
18 Reps (6)
19 Elegance (5)
20 Safe (6)
22 Greek character (4)
24 Cathedral city (3)
25 Wed again (7)
26 Fencing swords (5)
27 Red Indian trophy (5)
28 Walks irregularly (5)
29 Egg white (7)
30 Rock (5)
31 Leers (5)

DOWN

2 Listen to again (6)
3 Informal (6)
4 Moose (3)
5 Hidden store (5)
6 Parcel (7)
7 Area of land (4)
8 Meal (6)
12 Duty (5)
13 Composure (5)
14 French city (5)
15 Beneath (5)
16 Treatise (5)
18 Pains (5)
19 Wrestle (7)
21 Evoke (6)
22 Founding (6)
23 Treble (6)
25 Refute (5)
26 Dash (4)
28 Zodiac sign (3)

ACROSS

1 Rob (6)
7 Titled widows (8)
8 Overdue (4)
10 Selected (6)
11 Tiny (6)
14 Body of water (3)
16 Musical sounds (5)
17 Sleigh (4)
19 Narrow (5)
21 Manufactures (5)
22 Beer (5)
23 Jetty (4)
26 Step (5)
28 Pitch (3)
29 Apathetic (6)
30 Angry speech (6)
31 Honest (4)
32 Maxims (8)
33 Model (6)

DOWN

1 Rails (6)
2 Rubbed out (6)
3 Paradise (4)
4 Fissures (7)
5 First public appearance (5)
6 Donkeys (5)
8 Mislay (4)
9 Beverage (3)
12 And not (3)
13 Anxious (5)
15 Garden tools (5)
18 Slowly, musically (5)
19 Label (3)
20 For every (3)
21 Seagoing troops (7)
22 Rim (3)
23 Mother or father (6)
24 Middle East country (4)
25 Hand-rolled cigarette (6)
26 Ceases (5)
27 Archer's missile (5)
28 Hint (3)
30 Throw (4)

80

ACROSS

4 Accost (6)
7 Assess (8)
8 Period of instruction (6)
10 Perspire (5)
13 Hollow (4)
14 Short-term worker (4)
15 Nobleman (4)
16 Wager (3)
17 Complain (4)
19 Sign (4)
21 Upset (9)
23 Flee (4)
24 Performs (4)
26 Moist (3)
27 Level (4)
29 Wise man (4)
32 Network (4)
33 Man-made fibre (5)
34 Most recent (6)
35 Switch on (8)
36 Stoat-like animal (6)

DOWN

1 Minimum (5)
2 Seraglio (5)
3 Terse (4)
4 Commotion (5)
5 In case (4)
6 Talked (6)
9 Clothe (6)
11 Marry (3)
12 Month (5)
13 Deceived (7)
15 Mine (3)
16 Cot (3)
18 Flowers (6)
20 Untidy (5)
21 Speck (3)
22 Boy's name (3)
23 Scold (6)
25 In the past (3)
28 Essential (5)
30 Church table (5)
31 Go in (5)
32 Obtains (4)
33 Tack (4)

ACROSS

3 Drive (5)
8 Wild (5)
10 Essential (5)
11 Barrier (3)
12 Note value (5)
13 Harmed (7)
15 Recess (5)
18 Failure (3)
19 Deed (6)
21 Command (7)
22 Complain (4)
23 Lake (4)
24 Waterproof boots (7)
26 Shaving implements (6)
29 Terrorist group (3)
31 In that place (5)
32 Polishing substance (7)
34 Bread maker (5)
35 Boy (3)
36 Understood (5)
37 Of the kidneys (5)
38 Prickle (5)

DOWN

1 Honour (5)
2 Muslim fast (7)
4 Servant girl (4)
5 Show clearly (6)
6 Extent (5)
7 Sumo tournament (5)
9 Aries (3)
12 Interferes (7)
14 Pistol (3)
16 Quotes (5)
17 Go in (5)
19 Artist's studio (7)
20 Tidy (5)
21 Sweetcorn (5)
23 Disease (7)
24 Garland (6)
25 Anger (3)
27 In front (5)
28 Circle (5)
30 Navigation aid (5)
32 Ale (4)
33 Pale (3)

82

ACROSS

1 Savoury jelly (5)
6 Graves (5)
9 Control (7)
10 Holds firmly (5)
11 Relaxes (5)
12 Plunders (5)
13 Furniture item (7)
15 Males (3)
17 Islamic chieftain (4)
18 Religious house (6)
19 Steeple (5)
20 Lamps (6)
22 Unaccompanied (4)
24 Single (3)
25 Pain-killer (7)
26 Lifting device (5)
27 Unit of gem weight (5)
28 Velocity (5)
29 Entourage (7)
30 Appended (5)
31 Addresses God (5)

DOWN

2 Yell (6)
3 Weaken (6)
4 Lettuce (3)
5 Aviator (5)
6 Torment (7)
7 Minerals (4)
8 Improve (6)
12 Jumps (5)
13 Stringed instrument (5)
14 Eating bout (5)
15 Engine (5)
16 Man-made fibre (5)
18 Lever (5)
19 Began (7)
21 Under control (2,4)
22 Smile coyly (6)
23 Probable (6)
25 Caper (5)
26 Be concerned (4)
28 Dine (3)

83

ACROSS

1 Weaving fibre (6)
7 Water closet (8)
8 Run away (4)
10 Swiss villa (6)
11 Bomb hole (6)
14 Mountain pass (3)
16 Religious song (5)
17 Casserole (4)
19 Aspires (5)
21 Commenced (5)
22 Primate (5)
23 Painful (4)
26 Flower (5)
28 Cot (3)
29 Human (6)
30 Doting (6)
31 Incline (4)
32 Sicken (8)
33 Reveries (6)

DOWN

1 Responds (6)
2 Pursue (6)
3 Aid in crime (4)
4 Hone (7)
5 Main artery (5)
6 Obsequious flattery (5)
8 Dial (4)
9 Slippery fish (3)
12 Donkey (3)
13 Senior (5)
15 Important person (5)
18 Trunk (5)
19 Border (3)
20 Equal (3)
21 Scolded (7)
22 Allow (3)
23 Governing body (6)
24 Norse god (4)
25 Occurrences (6)
26 Correct (5)
27 Fish (5)
28 Insect (3)
30 Sleigh (4)

84

ACROSS

4 Areas of land (6)
7 Vegetable (8)
8 About (6)
10 Helicopter blade (5)
13 Concoction (4)
14 Layer (4)
15 Close noisily (4)
16 Female deer (3)
17 Stare open-mouthed (4)
19 So be it (4)
21 Sailing vessel (9)
23 Rave (4)
24 Annoys (4)
26 Prohibit (3)
27 Compass point (4)
29 Merely (4)
32 Unit of length (4)
33 Garden ornament (5)
34 Coiffure (6)
35 Sane (8)
36 Period of instruction (6)

DOWN

1 Terminate (5)
2 Journey (5)
3 Wound's mark (4)
4 Jewelled headdress (5)
5 Promise (4)
6 Sinew (6)
9 Comment (6)
11 Lubricate (3)
12 Keyboard instrument (5)
13 Stain (7)
15 Resort (3)
16 Lair (3)
18 Be present (6)
20 Stone-worker (5)
21 Tin (3)
22 Painting, etc (3)
23 Damage (6)
25 Tree (3)
28 Oak fruit (5)
30 Parts of speech (5)
31 Shouts (5)
32 Flower (4)
33 Forbidding (4)

85

ACROSS

3 Put (5)
8 Of the nose (5)
10 Fish (5)
11 Pinch (3)
12 Begin (5)
13 Madmen (7)
15 Noblemen (5)
18 Bind (3)
19 Polecat (6)
21 Bulwark (7)
22 Implement (4)
23 Middle East port (4)
24 Assorted (7)
26 Supernatural (6)
29 Negative (3)
31 Prophets (5)
32 Location (7)
34 Deserves (5)
35 Writing fluid (3)
36 Change (5)
37 Appended (5)
38 Destroy (5)

DOWN

1 Man-made waterway (5)
2 Main city (7)
4 Auction items (4)
5 Floor covering (6)
6 Come in (5)
7 Distress signal (5)
9 Transgression (3)
12 Non-believer (7)
14 Target (3)
16 Wear away (5)
17 Rock (5)
19 Chums (7)
20 Stalks (5)
21 Excite (5)
23 Straddling (7)
24 Render harmless (6)
25 Staff (3)
27 Shouts (5)
28 Large shrubs (5)
30 Enquired (5)
32 Insects (4)
33 Conclude (3)

86

ACROSS

1 Conflict (5)
6 Occasions (5)
9 Model (7)
10 Employers (5)
11 Performed (5)
12 Roost (5)
13 Colonist (7)
15 Insect (3)
17 Vegetables (4)
18 Begrudge (6)
19 Yearned (5)
20 Re-experience (6)
22 Border (4)
24 Before (3)
25 Editor (7)
26 Characteristic (5)
27 Unit of a gem's weight (5)
28 Closes (5)
29 Young hare (7)
30 Lazed (5)
31 Flower (5)

DOWN

2 Tenant (6)
3 Fish (6)
4 Possesses (3)
5 Navigate (5)
6 Trailed (7)
7 Unit of length (4)
8 Cricket team (6)
12 Pennies (5)
13 Surplus (5)
14 List (5)
15 Stoops (5)
16 Anaesthetic (5)
18 Readjust (5)
19 Avoided (7)
21 Mission (6)
22 Rowing teams (6)
23 Tender (6)
25 Metal fastener (5)
26 Story (4)
28 Body of water (3)

ACROSS

1 Woollen fabric (6)
7 List of letters (8)
8 Observed (4)
10 Dodged (6)
11 Man's name (6)
14 Harden (3)
16 Fashion (5)
17 Russian ruler (4)
19 Turret (5)
21 Log (5)
22 Custom (5)
23 Foots the bill (4)
26 Aspires (5)
28 Deceive (3)
29 Warns (6)
30 Conductors' sticks (6)
31 Paradise (4)
32 Limits (8)
33 Giggle (6)

DOWN

1 Perceive (6)
2 Provider of food (6)
3 Alight (4)
4 Gossip (7)
5 Superior (5)
6 Get up (5)
8 Prose narrative (4)
9 Slippery fish (3)
12 Stray (3)
13 Foe (5)
15 Small bird (5)
18 Reel (5)
19 Label (3)
20 Moist (3)
21 Rooks (7)
22 That woman (3)
23 Powerful (6)
24 Soon (4)
25 Nurse (6)
26 Shelter (5)
27 Trivial (5)
28 Rotter (3)
30 Most excellent (4)

88

ACROSS

4 Log (6)
7 Coffee (8)
8 Rare (6)
10 Male duck (5)
13 Harvest (4)
14 Unaccompanied (4)
15 Not as much (4)
16 Miserable (3)
17 Genuine (4)
19 Peal (4)
21 Compulsory (9)
23 Breathing organ (4)
24 Nurse (4)
26 Insane (3)
27 Region (4)
29 Level (4)
32 Elderly (4)
33 Box (5)
34 Proverbs (6)
35 Herbivorous reptile (8)
36 Turning point (6)

DOWN

1 Loans (5)
2 Horrify (5)
3 Yield (4)
4 Flowers (5)
5 Applaud (4)
6 Ethic (6)
9 Start knitting (4,2)
11 Tier (3)
12 Muslim holy book (5)
13 Told (7)
15 Boy (3)
16 Cunning (3)
18 Hire (6)
20 Command (5)
21 Slime (3)
22 Beverage (3)
23 Set of steps (6)
25 Wager (3)
28 Relaxes (5)
30 Sound (5)
31 At no time (5)
32 A long time (4)
33 Felines (4)

ACROSS

3 Oar (5)
8 Muslim holy book (5)
10 Desert's fertile patches (5)
11 Vehicle (3)
12 Sedate (5)
13 Fruit (7)
15 Anxious (5)
18 Vigour (3)
19 Principles (6)
21 More cheerful (7)
22 Paradise (4)
23 Operatic song (4)
24 Portrays (7)
26 Boxes (6)
29 Not at home (3)
31 Sharpens (5)
32 Epidermis (7)
34 Fibbers (5)
35 Decay (3)
36 Senses (5)
37 Award (5)
38 Stores (5)

DOWN

1 Pub (5)
2 Camping trailer (7)
4 Beds (4)
5 Linger (6)
6 Loaded (5)
7 Minimum (5)
9 Managed (3)
12 Tastes (7)
14 Pinch (3)
16 Approaches (5)
17 Treatise (5)
19 Boring (7)
20 Roost (5)
21 Muscular male (2-3)
23 Dressed (7)
24 Cease (6)
25 Sever (3)
27 Flowers (5)
28 Relates (5)
30 Church table (5)
32 Black bird (4)
33 Fish (3)

90

ACROSS

1 Crystal (5)
6 Excite (5)
9 Breed of dog (7)
10 In operation (5)
11 Wed (5)
12 Reel (5)
13 Cargo (7)
15 Couple (3)
17 Among (4)
18 Aid (6)
19 Smithy (5)
20 Detests (6)
22 Gaelic (4)
24 Auction item (3)
25 Pirate (7)
26 Under (5)
27 Hood (5)
28 Dance (5)
29 Continuous (7)
30 Seraglio (5)
31 At no time (5)

DOWN

2 Change (6)
3 Unemotional (6)
4 Encountered (3)
5 Crawled (5)
6 Compassion (7)
7 Spoken (4)
8 Drinking tubes (6)
12 Drives away (5)
13 Deadly (5)
14 Rowing team (5)
15 Jewelled headdress (5)
16 Different (5)
18 Brilliant (5)
19 Liberty (7)
21 Former Yugoslav region (6)
22 Flee (6)
23 One (6)
25 Shore (5)
26 Skeleton part (4)
28 Unit of weight (3)

ACROSS

1 Breed of dog (6)
7 Curb (8)
8 Large bush (4)
10 Reach a destination (6)
11 Tiny (6)
14 Frozen water (3)
16 Prongs (5)
17 Serpents (4)
19 Essential (5)
21 Ship of the desert (5)
22 Rotten (5)
23 Fodder (4)
26 Accepted (5)
28 Hill (3)
29 Reps (6)
30 Steamy (6)
31 Mimics (4)
32 Appropriate (8)
33 Colonise (6)

DOWN

1 N American country (6)
2 Song words (6)
3 Fencing sword (4)
4 Public performance (7)
5 Started (5)
6 Pig-pens (5)
8 Journey (4)
9 Previous day (3)
12 Zero (3)
13 Curt (5)
15 Extent (5)
18 Cut of mutton (5)
19 Barrel (3)
20 Rock 'n' roller (3)
21 French coin (7)
22 Marshland (3)
23 Wooded area (6)
24 Strays (4)
25 Swindle (6)
26 Type of cat (5)
27 Sailing vessel (5)
28 Summit (3)
30 Labels (4)

92

ACROSS

4 Designates (6)
7 Lingerer (8)
8 Feels (6)
10 Serious (5)
13 Footwear item (4)
14 Storage unit (4)
15 Hollow (4)
16 Favourite (3)
17 Girl's name (4)
19 State (4)
21 Fan (9)
23 Pace (4)
24 Swerve (4)
26 Cunning (3)
27 Told an untruth (4)
29 Rescue (4)
32 Transmit (4)
33 Flower part (5)
34 Adulterate (6)
35 Make-believe (8)
36 View (6)

DOWN

1 Banners (5)
2 Opponent (5)
3 Yield (4)
4 Gas (5)
5 Plunder (4)
6 Wobble (6)
9 Spin (6)
11 Chest bone (3)
12 Fashion (5)
13 Enamoured (7)
15 Immerse (3)
16 For every (3)
18 Fruit (6)
20 Poetry (5)
21 Enclosure (3)
22 Colour (3)
23 Slumbers (6)
25 Eggs (3)
28 Awkward (5)
30 Make amends (5)
31 Senior (5)
32 Identical (4)
33 Mines (4)

ACROSS

3 Celebrities (5)
8 Placates (5)
10 Fruit (5)
11 Chest bone (3)
12 Box (5)
13 Inhalations (7)
15 Sluggish (5)
18 Meadow (3)
19 Spin (6)
21 Tidy (7)
22 Decays (4)
23 Endure (4)
24 Ogre (7)
26 Road (6)
29 Scull (3)
31 Fashion (5)
32 Affianced (7)
34 Seasons (5)
35 Number (3)
36 Cancel (5)
37 Gauge (5)
38 Treatise (5)

DOWN

1 Delay (5)
2 Preserves (7)
4 Hills (4)
5 Share (6)
6 Exhausted (5)
7 Aware (5)
9 Untruth (3)
12 Horse-drawn vehicle (7)
14 Beverage (3)
16 Keen (5)
17 Rips (5)
19 Grounds (7)
20 Faith (5)
21 Stow (5)
23 Scolded (7)
24 Honours (6)
25 Label (3)
27 Torso (5)
28 Follow (5)
30 Principle (5)
32 Sicilian volcano (4)
33 Obtain (3)

94

ACROSS

1 Performing area (5)
6 Criminal (5)
9 Return (7)
10 Deadly (5)
11 Poplar (5)
12 Ridge (5)
13 Cold-blooded creature (7)
15 Zodiac sign (3)
17 Minerals (4)
18 Account (6)
19 Got up (5)
20 Detective (6)
22 Yield (4)
24 Listening organ (3)
25 Accumulator (7)
26 Handle (5)
27 Step (5)
28 Artists' stand (5)
29 Recommence (7)
30 Appended (5)
31 Peruses (5)

DOWN

2 Dealer (6)
3 Allows (6)
4 Slippery fish (3)
5 Look fixedly (5)
6 Collided (7)
7 Repose (4)
8 First batsman (6)
12 Material (5)
13 Excite (5)
14 Dwindle (5)
15 Adored (5)
16 Different (5)
18 Automaton (5)
19 Featured (7)
21 Survived (6)
22 Invent (6)
23 Protect (6)
25 Rush (5)
26 Weary (4)
28 Stray (3)

ACROSS

1 Shuts (6)
7 Slash (8)
8 Sheet of glass (4)
10 Joined (6)
11 Heart, commonly (6)
14 Favourite (3)
16 Flowers (5)
17 Outbuilding (4)
19 Mislays (5)
21 Decaying (5)
22 Afterwards (5)
23 Rushed (4)
26 Backless seat (5)
28 Body of water (3)
29 Talkative (6)
30 Lampoon (6)
31 Object of worship (4)
32 Persuaded (8)
33 Embrace (6)

DOWN

1 Hits (6)
2 Sitting (6)
3 Sleigh (4)
4 Wanted (7)
5 Fires (5)
6 Prophets (5)
8 Duct (4)
9 Mesh (3)
12 Lettuce (3)
13 Creepy (5)
15 Inn (5)
18 Open land (5)
19 Permit (3)
20 Term of respect (3)
21 Hesitates (7)
22 Auction item (3)
23 Depart (3,3)
24 Bucket (4)
25 Considered (6)
26 Metal fastener (5)
27 Vows (5)
28 Miserable (3)
30 Team (4)

96

ACROSS

4 Nurse (6)
7 Assess (8)
8 Corrects (6)
10 Rigid (5)
13 Fall (4)
14 Cash register (4)
15 Compass point (4)
16 Bread roll (3)
17 Experts (4)
19 Pitcher (4)
21 Defended (9)
23 Jetty (4)
24 Stratagem (4)
26 Chasm (3)
27 Badger's home (4)
29 Bird (4)
32 Eyeglass (4)
33 Normal (5)
34 Characteristics (6)
35 Disturb (8)
36 Figure (6)

DOWN

1 Creature (5)
2 Herb (5)
3 Polish (4)
4 Prophets (5)
5 Ooze (4)
6 Make beloved (6)
9 Religious songs (6)
11 End (3)
12 Distress signal (5)
13 Abandons (7)
15 Damp (3)
16 Cot (3)
18 Foundation garment (6)
20 Widow's clothes (5)
21 Seed (3)
22 Sever (3)
23 Tropical bird (6)
25 Eggs (3)
28 Follow (5)
30 Evicts (5)
31 Senior (5)
32 Table (4)
33 Second-hand (4)

ACROSS

3 Spoilt children (5)
8 Stringed instruments (5)
10 Make amends (5)
11 Dog (3)
12 Jewelled headdress (5)
13 Amusing (7)
15 Allow (5)
18 Bed (3)
19 Improve (6)
21 Twist (7)
22 Idle talk (4)
23 Quick (4)
24 Bomb holes (7)
26 Engines (6)
29 Golf support (3)
31 Steeple (5)
32 Suggested (7)
34 Art form (5)
35 Fastener (3)
36 Salute (5)
37 Principle (5)
38 Insurgent (5)

DOWN

1 Mexican snacks (5)
2 Fruit (7)
4 Track (4)
5 Aim (6)
6 Commence (5)
7 Senseless (5)
9 Peculiar (3)
12 Shreds (7)
14 Deceive (3)
16 Book of maps (5)
17 Hackneyed (5)
19 Fragile (7)
20 Swindles (5)
21 Prickly plants (5)
23 Cold storage unit (7)
24 Invent (6)
25 Slippery fish (3)
27 Musical drama (5)
28 Command (5)
30 Drive back (5)
32 Pain (4)
33 Trap (3)

98

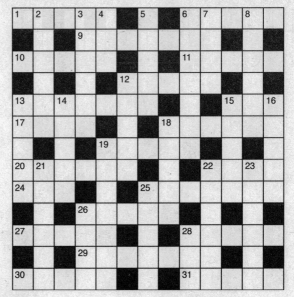

ACROSS

1 Thong (5)
6 Managed (5)
9 Tea urn (7)
10 Simple song (5)
11 Hesitate (5)
12 Month (5)
13 Terrors (7)
15 Favourite (3)
17 Paradise (4)
18 Procession (6)
19 Wall painting (5)
20 Save (6)
22 Move (4)
24 Expire (3)
25 Recovers (7)
26 Log (5)
27 Yell (5)
28 Tree (5)
29 Material (7)
30 Wept (5)
31 Lazed (5)

DOWN

2 Camera stand (6)
3 At the back (6)
4 Remunerate (3)
5 Cavorts (5)
6 Money (7)
7 Spoken (4)
8 Followed (6)
12 Row (5)
13 Listened (5)
14 Re-employ (5)
15 Glue (5)
16 Rips (5)
18 Writing material (5)
19 Changed (7)
21 Any of two (6)
22 Felt (6)
23 Hinder (6)
25 Relaxes (5)
26 Appealing (4)
28 Man's name (3)

ACROSS

1 Set up tent (6)
7 Forefather (8)
8 Achievement (4)
10 Fold (6)
11 Matures (6)
14 Supernatural intuition (3)
16 Teams (5)
17 Otherwise (4)
19 Shelter (5)
21 Satisfied (5)
22 Disturbed (5)
23 Untidy state (4)
26 In that place (5)
28 Colour (3)
29 Posture (6)
30 Tooth (6)
31 Give out (4)
32 Orbital route (4,4)
33 Cream cake (6)

DOWN

1 Day nursery (6)
2 Gratify (6)
3 Fruit (4)
4 Concocted (7)
5 War-horse (5)
6 Angry (5)
8 Charges (4)
9 Snake (3)
12 Metal fastener (3)
13 Approaches (5)
15 Provide food (5)
18 Lamp (5)
19 Owns (3)
20 Animal doctor (3)
21 Ghoul (7)
22 Vase (3)
23 Servile (6)
24 Revise (4)
25 Searcher (6)
26 Russian rulers (5)
27 Deserves (5)
28 Aries (3)
30 Surrender (4)

100

ACROSS

4 Cold dishes (6)
7 Broadcast (8)
8 Decrees (6)
10 Nationality (5)
13 Equal (4)
14 Country (4)
15 Microorganism (4)
16 Lubricant (3)
17 German river (4)
19 Nobleman (4)
21 Excite (9)
23 Stalk (4)
24 Remitted (4)
26 Cunning (3)
27 Encounter (4)
29 Religious image (4)
32 Turn (4)
33 Range (5)
34 Account (6)
35 Poise (8)
36 Someone owing (6)

DOWN

1 Undress (5)
2 Navigation aid (5)
3 Sparkling wine (4)
4 Bullock (5)
5 Den (4)
6 Item (6)
9 Debase (6)
11 Agent (3)
12 Cite (3)
13 Scanned (7)
15 Jewel (3)
16 Mineral (3)
18 Less bright (6)
20 Garret (5)
21 Pig-pen (3)
22 Permit (3)
23 Record cover (6)
25 Jump (3)
28 Go in (5)
30 Matter (5)
31 At no time (5)
32 Sailing vessel (4)
33 Droops (4)

ACROSS

3 Feel (5)
8 Yielded (5)
10 Angry (5)
11 Farm animal (3)
12 Sound loudly (5)
13 Competent (7)
15 Pains (5)
18 Zodiac sign (3)
19 Affirm (6)
21 Condemn (7)
22 That woman's (4)
23 Level (4)
24 Join (7)
26 Haphazard (6)
29 Sick (3)
31 Reverie (5)
32 Earnings (7)
34 Gain knowledge (5)
35 By way of (3)
36 Managed (5)
37 Assists (5)
38 Graceful girl (5)

DOWN

1 Flower part (5)
2 Amuses (7)
4 Theatrical part (4)
5 Corsair (6)
6 Build (5)
7 Pig-pens (5)
9 Immerse (3)
12 Bloom (7)
14 Scottish mountain peak (3)
16 Lift with effort (5)
17 Get up (5)
19 Middle Eastern (7)
20 Broken fragment (5)
21 Wading bird (5)
23 Invigorate (7)
24 Comic play (6)
25 Kind (3)
27 Missile (5)
28 Valleys (5)
30 Open-mouthed (5)
32 Snare (4)
33 Zero (3)

102

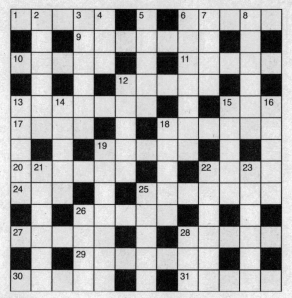

ACROSS

1 Doomed (5)
6 Circular (5)
9 Perceived (7)
10 Hurry (5)
11 Aviator (5)
12 Giant (5)
13 Elation (7)
15 Beer (3)
17 Object of worship (4)
18 Bomb-hole (6)
19 Entrances (5)
20 Inexperienced (6)
22 Story (4)
24 Secret agent (3)
25 Edited (7)
26 Satisfied (5)
27 Armada (5)
28 Hesitate (5)
29 Stopped working (7)
30 Enquired (5)
31 Flower (5)

DOWN

2 Astounded (6)
3 Impose (6)
4 Female deer (3)
5 Extent (5)
6 Mends (7)
7 Norse god (4)
8 Pasta strip (6)
12 Toss (5)
13 Records (5)
14 Money, commonly (5)
15 Book of maps (5)
16 Strayed (5)
18 System of beliefs (5)
19 Gave (7)
21 Fruit (6)
22 Angry outburst (6)
23 Decrease (6)
25 Send (5)
26 Arid (4)
28 Vigour (3)

ACROSS

1 Short-sightedness (6)
7 Fungus (8)
8 Homework, in brief (4)
10 Pinafores (6)
11 Shopping street (6)
14 Peculiar (3)
16 Ideal (5)
17 Catch sight of (4)
19 Sheets of glass (5)
21 Narrow (5)
22 Principle (5)
23 Victim (4)
26 Cold dish (5)
28 Shout of disapproval (3)
29 Line of latitude (6)
30 Particular (6)
31 Elderly (4)
32 Supported (8)
33 Be present (6)

DOWN

1 Desert image (6)
2 Satire (6)
3 Units of current (4)
4 Attractive person (7)
5 Wanderer (5)
6 Force (5)
8 Rugby player (4)
9 Conclude (3)
12 Lettuce (3)
13 Thick (5)
15 Writing material (5)
18 Curse (5)
19 Cooking vessel (3)
20 Mesh (3)
21 Boring (7)
22 Knock (3)
23 Powerful (6)
24 Street (4)
25 Shouted (6)
26 Reek (5)
27 Juggernaut (5)
28 Implore (3)
30 Baby word for father (4)

104

ACROSS

4 Fireworks (6)
7 Exceed one's credit (8)
8 Feline (6)
10 Hackneyed (5)
13 Extended voyage (4)
14 Prophet (4)
15 Tear (4)
16 Taxi (3)
17 Paradise (4)
19 Dull (4)
21 Waterproof fabric (9)
23 Greek character (4)
24 Reared (4)
26 Information (3)
27 Oven (4)
29 Merriment (4)
32 Just (4)
33 Inclined (5)
34 Travelling case (6)
35 Toxic liquid (8)
36 Calm (6)

DOWN

1 Plunders (5)
2 Creepy (5)
3 Border (4)
4 Faint (5)
5 Employer (4)
6 African tree (6)
9 Hug (6)
11 Colour (3)
12 Handle (5)
13 Defensible (7)
15 Agent (3)
16 Tin (3)
18 Male ducks (6)
20 Crest (5)
21 Number (3)
22 Vase (3)
23 Scold (6)
25 Domestic fowl (3)
28 Girl's name (5)
30 Dead language (5)
31 Anaesthetic (5)
32 Rodents (4)
33 Regard (4)

ACROSS

3 Knife edge (5)
8 Cowls (5)
10 Go in (5)
11 Peculiar (3)
12 Deadens (5)
13 Lured (7)
15 Predict (5)
18 Fabled bird (3)
19 Fold (6)
21 Residence (7)
22 Stagger (4)
23 Surrender (4)
24 Public performance (7)
26 Gate (6)
29 Pitch (3)
31 Located (5)
32 Light (7)
34 Opponent (5)
35 Scull (3)
36 Joins (5)
37 Enlist (5)
38 Absolute (5)

DOWN

1 Hackneyed (5)
2 Naval officer (7)
4 Guide (4)
5 Leave (6)
6 Follow (5)
7 Planet (5)
9 Not at home (3)
12 Unit of sound (7)
14 Male swan (3)
16 Judge's hammer (5)
17 Wallow (5)
19 Chief city (7)
20 Lets fall (5)
21 Vital organ (5)
23 Boxes (7)
24 Pungent root (6)
25 Brown (3)
27 Lubricated (5)
28 Conditions (5)
30 Mistake (5)
32 Feeble (4)
33 Listening organ (3)

106

ACROSS

1 Roughly (5)
6 Wading bird (5)
9 Pause (7)
10 Delete (5)
11 Holy messenger (5)
12 Toy (5)
13 Assembly (7)
15 Group (3)
17 Get up (4)
18 Next to (6)
19 Broken fragment (5)
20 Severe (6)
22 Just (4)
24 Declare (3)
25 Furniture item (7)
26 Small boat (5)
27 Scatter (5)
28 Money bag (5)
29 Implore (7)
30 Aspic (5)
31 Inclined (5)

DOWN

2 Breed of dog (6)
3 Bear-like (6)
4 Golf peg (3)
5 Upset (5)
6 Began (7)
7 Canvas shelter (4)
8 Stank (6)
12 Battle (5)
13 Stupid (5)
14 Money-lending (5)
15 Temptress (5)
16 Principle (5)
18 Snap (5)
19 Meagre (7)
21 Gossip (6)
22 Tiny (6)
23 Ground (6)
25 Bear (5)
26 Capsize (4)
28 Friend (3)

ACROSS

1 Floats (6)
7 Worker (8)
8 Clean (4)
10 Tolled (6)
11 Vipers (6)
14 Agent (3)
16 Fertile patch (5)
17 Fine shingle (4)
19 Small bird (5)
21 Drain (5)
22 Trainee officer (5)
23 Ooze (4)
26 Stringed instrument (5)
28 Bad actor (3)
29 Hypnotic state (6)
30 Narrow valley (6)
31 Revise (4)
32 Solitary (8)
33 Determined (6)

DOWN

1 Hangs (6)
2 Unsuccessful (6)
3 Sleigh (4)
4 Bedroom (7)
5 Attempts (5)
6 Attire (5)
8 Admonish (4)
9 Vigour (3)
12 Karate expert (3)
13 Wash out (5)
15 Cringe (5)
18 Moving (5)
19 Colour (3)
20 Wager (3)
21 Irony (7)
22 Tin (3)
23 Rescuing (6)
24 Give out (4)
25 Looked furtively (6)
26 Musty (5)
27 Tarnish (5)
28 Owned (3)
30 Rush (4)

108

ACROSS

4 Banquets (6)
7 Choke (8)
8 Band of flowers (6)
10 Make happy (5)
13 Tidy (4)
14 Schedule (4)
15 Indian dress (4)
16 Implore (3)
17 Lure (4)
19 Uttered (4)
21 Calculating (9)
23 Harvest (4)
24 Telephone (4)
26 Month (3)
27 Dash (4)
29 Gaelic (4)
32 Spoken (4)
33 System of beliefs (5)
34 Unwrapped (6)
35 Delirious (8)
36 Remain (4,2)

DOWN

1 Navigate (5)
2 Handle (5)
3 Eye inflammation (4)
4 Smaller number (5)
5 Aid in crime (4)
6 Sounded disapproving (6)
9 Dried grape (6)
11 Auction item (3)
12 Forbidden (5)
13 Unaffected (7)
15 Drink daintily (3)
16 Large (3)
18 Unit of current (6)
20 Rage (5)
21 Weep (3)
22 Metal (3)
23 Floor covering (6)
25 Employ (3)
28 Loaded (5)
30 Tears (5)
31 Decree (5)
32 Just (4)
33 Appealing (4)

ACROSS

3 Couples (5)
8 Greets (5)
10 Foe (5)
11 Also (3)
12 French river (5)
13 Wailing spirit (7)
15 Rips (5)
18 Transgress (3)
19 Equality (6)
21 Optimistic (7)
22 First man (4)
23 Profound (4)
24 Chewed up (7)
26 Cunning (6)
29 Listening organ (3)
31 Item of bedlinen (5)
32 Affianced (7)
34 Tarnish (5)
35 Novel (3)
36 Unilluminated (5)
37 Leers (5)
38 Thick (5)

DOWN

1 Of birth (5)
2 Bloom (7)
4 Pain (4)
5 Charge (6)
6 Scornful expression (5)
7 Clever (5)
9 Charged particle (3)
12 Renovation (7)
14 Joint (3)
16 Ventilated (5)
17 Graceful girl (5)
19 Caustic (7)
20 Spanish snacks (5)
21 Hurry (5)
23 Drive mad (7)
24 Change (6)
25 Hang back (3)
27 Horned mammal (5)
28 Rotten (5)
30 Drain (5)
32 Concludes (4)
33 Solidify (3)

110

ACROSS

1 Encouraged (5)
6 Denounce (5)
9 Called (7)
10 Naive (5)
11 Intends (5)
12 Devil (5)
13 Lamp (7)
15 Favourite (3)
17 Burden (4)
18 Dwell (6)
19 Velocity (5)
20 Amuse (6)
22 Audacious (4)
24 Previous day (3)
25 Scolds (7)
26 Rage (5)
27 Decree (5)
28 Condition (5)
29 Denial (7)
30 Enquired (5)
31 Periods of time (5)

DOWN

2 European (6)
3 Happenings (6)
4 Noise (3)
5 Temptress (5)
6 Relegated (7)
7 Paradise (4)
8 Raved (6)
12 Hang (5)
13 French river (5)
14 Push gently (5)
15 Aviator (5)
16 Inclines (5)
18 Allude (5)
19 At an angle (7)
21 Dodges (6)
22 Struggle (6)
23 Character (6)
25 Started (5)
26 Unit of land (4)
28 Declare (3)

111

ACROSS

1 Inexperienced (6)
7 Practise (8)
8 Jason's ship (4)
10 Loosens (6)
11 Coarse (6)
14 Honour (3)
16 Friends (5)
17 Identical (4)
19 Affected (5)
21 Shelter (5)
22 Principle (5)
23 Rush (4)
26 Stringed instrument (5)
28 Enclosure (3)
29 Pancakes (6)
30 Fame (6)
31 Metal (4)
32 Breathes (8)
33 Cricket team (6)

DOWN

1 Hits (6)
2 Writer (6)
3 Cupid (4)
4 Diet (7)
5 Handle (5)
6 Guides (5)
8 Particle (4)
9 Expression of surprise (3)
12 Wicked (3)
13 Madagascan primate (5)
15 Adores (5)
18 Moving (5)
19 Male (3)
20 Animal doctor (3)
21 Unorthodox thinker (7)
22 Faucet (3)
23 Designate (6)
24 Soon (4)
25 Sinew (6)
26 Frighten (5)
27 Anxious (5)
28 For every (3)
30 Get up (4)

112

ACROSS

4 Microscopic creature (6)
7 Cruel (8)
8 Gratify (6)
10 Journeys (5)
13 Expensive (4)
14 Champion (4)
15 US coin (4)
16 Expert (3)
17 Celebrity (4)
19 Shade (4)
21 Relevant (9)
23 Fairy (4)
24 Challenge (4)
26 Female pig (3)
27 Look furtively (4)
29 Fury (4)
32 Hills (4)
33 Absolute (5)
34 Decipher (6)
35 Principal cities (8)
36 Road (6)

DOWN

1 Veracity (5)
2 Step (5)
3 Beers (4)
4 Poplar (5)
5 Finished (4)
6 Halve (6)
9 Last mentioned (6)
11 Colour (3)
12 Riddle (5)
13 Mocks (7)
15 Feline (3)
16 Insect (3)
18 Camera stand (6)
20 Sluggish (5)
21 Church seat (3)
22 Short sleep (3)
23 Powerful (6)
25 Era (3)
28 Build (5)
30 Book of maps (5)
31 Delete (5)
32 Volume (4)
33 Item (4)

113

ACROSS

3 Gush (5)
8 Mother-of-pearl (5)
10 Mistake (5)
11 Snake (3)
12 Cease-fire (5)
13 Recommence (7)
15 Come in (5)
18 Man's name (3)
19 Suffer (6)
21 Dense (7)
22 Tribe (4)
23 Quote (4)
24 Long-serving soldier (7)
26 Rouse (6)
29 Rim (3)
31 Bullock (5)
32 Local (7)
34 Fabric (5)
35 Brown (3)
36 Creature (5)
37 Deadly (5)
38 Noise (5)

DOWN

1 Log (5)
2 Speech (7)
4 Harbour (4)
5 Modern (6)
6 Fashion (5)
7 Riddle (5)
9 Lettuce (3)
12 Hunter (7)
14 Weapon (3)
16 Italian city (5)
17 Insurgent (5)
19 Level of command (7)
20 Blacklegs (5)
21 Motive (5)
23 Money (7)
24 Shrew (6)
25 Tear (3)
27 Anaesthetic (5)
28 Aquatic birds (5)
30 Commonplace (5)
32 Urban area (4)
33 Feline (3)

114

ACROSS

1 Portly (5)
6 Flowing garments (5)
9 Walker (7)
10 Middle (5)
11 Skins (5)
12 Chairs (5)
13 Altered (7)
15 Curve (3)
17 Stringed instrument (4)
18 Jacket (6)
19 Contradict (5)
20 Catch-phrase (6)
22 Increased (4)
24 Use a needle (3)
25 Cattle tender (7)
26 Stone-worker (5)
27 Blemish (5)
28 Moral (5)
29 Furniture item (7)
30 Encourages (5)
31 Yearns (5)

DOWN

2 Rubbishy (6)
3 Bear-like (6)
4 Ragged article (3)
5 Receded (5)
6 Cold-blooded creature (7)
7 Minerals (4)
8 Whole (6)
12 Lucky number (5)
13 Form (5)
14 Missile (5)
15 Shade of blue (5)
16 Throng (5)
18 Buffalo (5)
19 Fruit (7)
21 Character (6)
22 Slum (6)
23 Straying (6)
25 Amusing (5)
26 Rodents (4)
28 Slippery fish (3)

ACROSS

1 Accuses (6)
7 Fortify (8)
8 Soon (4)
10 Feel remorse (6)
11 Front (6)
14 Before (3)
16 Entire range (5)
17 Girl (4)
19 Antic (5)
21 Engine (5)
22 Religious song (5)
23 Pitcher (4)
26 Piece for nine players (5)
28 Woman's undergarment (3)
29 Amorous (6)
30 Calling (6)
31 Item (4)
32 Stretched (8)
33 Happenings (6)

DOWN

1 Keg (6)
2 Colliers (6)
3 Broadcast (4)
4 Director (7)
5 Vapour (5)
6 Principle (5)
8 Mimics (4)
9 Single (3)
12 Vehicle (3)
13 Fool (5)
15 Adam's ale (5)
18 Detest (5)
19 Bed (3)
20 Kitty (3)
21 Movements (7)
22 Encountered (3)
23 Fur (6)
24 Serve (4)
25 Claims (6)
26 At no time (5)
27 Compass point (5)
28 Prohibit (3)
30 Naked (4)

116

ACROSS

4 Preserve (6)
7 Brass instrument (8)
8 Mission (6)
10 Mark (5)
13 Harvest (4)
14 Relaxation (4)
15 Mislaid (4)
16 Wager (3)
17 Manner (4)
19 Among (4)
21 Induced (9)
23 Food fish (4)
24 Female sheep (4)
26 Guided (3)
27 Knowledge (4)
29 Wise man (4)
32 Herb (4)
33 Electricity support (5)
34 Pick-me-ups (6)
35 All people (8)
36 Climb (6)

DOWN

1 Performing area (5)
2 Schedules (5)
3 Competent (4)
4 Equals (5)
5 Nag (4)
6 Touched down (6)
9 Turn (6)
11 Knock (3)
12 Devil (5)
13 Change over (7)
15 Garland (3)
16 Tender (3)
18 Slanted letter (6)
20 Untidy (5)
21 Slime (3)
22 Wonder (3)
23 Singers (6)
25 In the past (3)
28 Beginning (5)
30 Permit (5)
31 Concluded (5)
32 Unit of distance (4)
33 Section (4)

ACROSS

3 Map (5)
8 Tropical bird (5)
10 Speak in public (5)
11 Short sleep (3)
12 Clan (5)
13 Home (7)
15 Loosen (5)
18 Small child (3)
19 At the back (6)
21 Twist (7)
22 Indifferent (4)
23 Small drink (4)
24 Reaches a destination (7)
26 Wanderers (6)
29 Miserable (3)
31 Garbage (5)
32 Acclimatised (7)
34 Feeling (5)
35 Trophy (3)
36 At no time (5)
37 Absolute (5)
38 Anxious (5)

DOWN

1 Man-made waterway (5)
2 Statehouse (7)
4 Injure (4)
5 Sturdy (6)
6 English river (5)
7 Step (5)
9 Taxi (3)
12 Rags (7)
14 Weight (3)
16 Rips (5)
17 Foe (5)
19 Performer (7)
20 Limited (5)
21 Punctuation mark (5)
23 Subtracts (7)
24 Stick (6)
25 Barrel (3)
27 Command (5)
28 Thing of value (5)
30 Drive back (5)
32 Inquires (4)
33 Kernel (3)

118

ACROSS

1 Hidden store (5)
6 Long seat (5)
9 Protective garment (7)
10 Malice (5)
11 Treatise (5)
12 Senseless (5)
13 Introduction (7)
15 Enclosure (3)
17 Slippery fish (4)
18 Determine (6)
19 Cold dish (5)
20 Draw back (6)
22 River crossing (4)
24 Was seated (3)
25 Discusses (7)
26 Yearned (5)
27 Rock (5)
28 In front (5)
29 Speak badly of (7)
30 Delete (5)
31 Style (5)

DOWN

2 Hope (6)
3 Inns (6)
4 Previous day (3)
5 Salt water (5)
6 Mixed (7)
7 Otherwise (4)
8 Pursued (6)
12 Perfect (5)
13 Equals (5)
14 Choose (5)
15 Aviator (5)
16 Requires (5)
18 Old-fashioned (5)
19 Genuine (7)
21 Religious festival (6)
22 Relative (6)
23 Stay (6)
25 Actions (5)
26 Insects (4)
28 Perform (3)

119

ACROSS

1 Gossip (6)
7 Practise (8)
8 Lubricates (4)
10 Sofa (6)
11 Part (6)
14 Frozen water (3)
16 Devil (5)
17 Engrave (4)
19 Mature (5)
21 Afterwards (5)
22 Principle (5)
23 Remainder (4)
26 Sound of misery (5)
28 Set (3)
29 Long-eared mammal (6)
30 Find (6)
31 Paradise (4)
32 Curiosity (8)
33 Colonise (6)

DOWN

1 Struggle (6)
2 Spasm (6)
3 Gaelic (4)
4 Inventor (7)
5 Characteristic (5)
6 Lucky number (5)
8 Of the ear (4)
9 Shelter (3)
12 Vehicle (3)
13 Fruit (5)
15 Rituals (5)
18 Jewelled headdress (5)
19 Managed (3)
20 Favourite (3)
21 Tolerant (7)
22 Label (3)
23 Modern (6)
24 Dash (4)
25 From there (6)
26 Magnificent (5)
27 Fat (5)
28 Deity (3)
30 Not as much (4)

120

ACROSS

4 Scattered (6)
7 Infantile (8)
8 Vigour (6)
10 Illumination (5)
13 Swerve (4)
14 Mislay (4)
15 Crooked (4)
16 Prohibit (3)
17 Spoil (4)
19 Type of duck (4)
21 Land mass (9)
23 Deceives (4)
24 Sparkling water (4)
26 Staff (3)
27 Affirm (4)
29 Black bird (4)
32 Manner (4)
33 Look fixedly (5)
34 Plaits (6)
35 Expressing gratitude (8)
36 Religious songs (6)

DOWN

1 Oar (5)
2 Telephones (5)
3 Revise (4)
4 Lustre (5)
5 State (4)
6 Sign (6)
9 Trapped (6)
11 Charged particle (3)
12 Wading bird (5)
13 Deer meat (7)
15 Part (3)
16 Racket (3)
18 Tacit (6)
20 Decree (5)
21 Food fish (3)
22 At this time (3)
23 Snakes (6)
25 On behalf of (3)
28 Undergarments (5)
30 Quick (5)
31 Jam (5)
32 Grind (4)
33 Transmit (4)

ACROSS

3 Supple (5)
8 Cheerful (5)
10 Irritate (5)
11 Central Intelligence Agency (3)
12 Scottish landowner (5)
13 Cigar (7)
15 Subtract (5)
18 Piece of cloth (3)
19 Decrease (6)
21 Refrain (7)
22 Affirm (4)
23 Elderly (4)
24 Contend (7)
26 Observation (6)
29 At the stern (3)
31 Follow (5)
32 Craftsman (7)
34 Entire range (5)
35 Managed (3)
36 Extra payment (5)
37 Honour (5)
38 Hires (5)

DOWN

1 Hidden store (5)
2 Small bird (7)
4 Insect (4)
5 Pantry (6)
6 Concluded (5)
7 Comedian (5)
9 Pastry dish (3)
12 Registration document (7)
14 Scull (3)
16 Protuberance (5)
17 Inclines (5)
19 Embankment (7)
20 Mother-of-pearl (5)
21 Shapes (5)
23 Dressed (7)
24 Fold (6)
25 Newt (3)
27 Bequeath (5)
28 Predict (5)
30 Trite (5)
32 Relative (4)
33 Miserable (3)

122

ACROSS

1 Scope (5)
6 Young sheep (5)
9 Crossbreed (7)
10 Shoot from cover (5)
11 Untidy (5)
12 Sides (5)
13 Accomplish an aim (7)
15 Poem (3)
17 Carriage (4)
18 Traps (6)
19 Creature (5)
20 Iterate (6)
22 Sparkling water (4)
24 Before (3)
25 Nonsense (7)
26 Teller, for instance (5)
27 Forbidden (5)
28 Destined (5)
29 Controversy (7)
30 Port (5)
31 Canvas shelters (5)

DOWN

2 Italian city (6)
3 Collision (6)
4 Digit (3)
5 Leered (5)
6 Rodent (7)
7 Beers (4)
8 Next to (6)
12 Principle (5)
13 Frighten (5)
14 Pancake (5)
15 Constellation (5)
16 Treatise (5)
18 Move furtively (5)
19 Party decoration (7)
21 Mistakes (6)
22 Comfort (6)
23 Perceive (6)
25 Rear (5)
26 Manage (4)
28 Suitable (3)

ACROSS

1 Chiefs (6)
7 Fellow player (8)
8 Assistant (4)
10 Loan (6)
11 Furrow (6)
14 Man's name (3)
16 Missile (5)
17 Spoken (4)
19 Tale (5)
21 Assessed (5)
22 Student officer (5)
23 Fibbed (4)
26 Cold dish (5)
28 Exclude (3)
29 Foreign (6)
30 Go to bed (6)
31 A long time (4)
32 Unknown person (8)
33 Involve (6)

DOWN

1 Tropical grass (6)
2 Helix (6)
3 Casserole (4)
4 Gemstone (7)
5 Large house (5)
6 Renovate (5)
8 Operatic song (4)
9 Professor (3)
12 Mineral (3)
13 Fashion (5)
15 Detests (5)
18 Take rest (5)
19 Craze (3)
20 Wager (3)
21 Glowing (7)
22 Feline (3)
23 Dormant (6)
24 Part of the eye (4)
25 Fuel (6)
26 Feeling (5)
27 Juggernaut (5)
28 Implore (3)
30 Unusual (4)

124

ACROSS

4 Gratify (6)
7 Cross (8)
8 Xmas decoration (6)
10 Run off to marry (5)
13 Glass (4)
14 Exchange for money (4)
15 Sets (4)
16 Eggs (3)
17 State (4)
19 Melody (4)
21 Excite (9)
23 Prophet (4)
24 Seasoning (4)
26 Consumed (3)
27 Frozen (4)
29 Border (4)
32 Pleased (4)
33 Salivate (5)
34 Shown mercy (6)
35 Dissent (8)
36 Foamy (6)

DOWN

1 Pig-pens (5)
2 Xmas song (5)
3 Just (4)
4 Flower part (5)
5 Sea eagle (4)
6 Veer (6)
9 Place in position (6)
11 Allow (3)
12 Crockery item (5)
13 Scanned (7)
15 Jewel (3)
16 Single (3)
18 Manly (6)
20 Absolute (5)
21 Regard (3)
22 Boy (3)
23 Unconsciousness (6)
25 In the past (3)
28 Golfer's attendant (5)
30 Entrances (5)
31 Senior (5)
32 Gravel (4)
33 Expensive (4)

125

ACROSS

3 Step (5)
8 Rituals (5)
10 Full range (5)
11 Delve (3)
12 Deadly (5)
13 Public performance (7)
15 Lukewarm (5)
18 Spoil (3)
19 Dwell (6)
21 Discusses (7)
22 Lean (4)
23 Stir (4)
24 Bulwark (7)
26 Liberally (6)
29 Can (3)
31 Smithy (5)
32 Salad vegetable (7)
34 Quick (5)
35 Anger (3)
36 Mountain range (5)
37 Metric weight (5)
38 Canvas shelters (5)

DOWN

1 Teams (5)
2 Diet (7)
4 Genuine (4)
5 Gemstones (6)
6 Valleys (5)
7 Sensational (5)
9 Twitch (3)
12 Distant (7)
14 Label (3)
16 Aviator (5)
17 Dissuade (5)
19 Of the same family (7)
20 Rod (5)
21 Frogman (5)
23 Touch upon (7)
24 Gratify (6)
25 Mine (3)
27 Circular (5)
28 Wading bird (5)
30 Aroma (5)
32 Table (4)
33 Vase (3)

126

ACROSS

1 Coarse (5)
6 The same (5)
9 Takes away (7)
10 Backless chair (5)
11 Frivolous (5)
12 Revises (5)
13 Recovers (7)
15 Nourished (3)
17 Cupid (4)
18 Spanish dance (6)
19 Tale (5)
20 Dialect (6)
22 Experts (4)
24 Pig-pen (3)
25 See (7)
26 Fragment (5)
27 Extent (5)
28 Tree (5)
29 Anxiety (7)
30 Yielded (5)
31 Hidden store (5)

DOWN

2 Cad (6)
3 Crowds (6)
4 Slippery fish (3)
5 Noblemen (5)
6 Smash (7)
7 Egyptian goddess (4)
8 Cashier (6)
12 Gives out (5)
13 Harvests (5)
14 Crazy (5)
15 Wooden barrier (5)
16 Extinguish (5)
18 Plait (5)
19 Spotted (7)
21 Dress (6)
22 Stress (6)
23 Treatises (6)
25 Scum (5)
26 Location (4)
28 Lettuce (3)

ACROSS

1 Writing implement (6)
7 Unsafe (8)
8 Foreign currency unit (4)
10 Melted (6)
11 Shrew (6)
14 Consume (3)
16 Postpone (5)
17 Peruse (4)
19 Detested (5)
21 Skinflint (5)
22 Glue (5)
23 Overdue (4)
26 Thing of value (5)
28 Border (3)
29 Intones (6)
30 Large cats (6)
31 Norse god (4)
32 Teaching (8)
33 Vocalist (6)

DOWN

1 Feathers (6)
2 Greek islander (6)
3 One of a pride (4)
4 Final game (7)
5 Wall painting (5)
6 Lure (5)
8 Entreaty (4)
9 Ready (3)
12 Colour (3)
13 Haggard (5)
15 Hurry (5)
18 Collide (5)
19 Belonging to him (3)
20 Golf peg (3)
21 Affairs (7)
22 Enclosure (3)
23 Military unit (6)
24 So be it (4)
25 Religious festival (6)
26 Sharp (5)
27 Fried in little fat (5)
28 Concealed (3)
30 Digits (4)

128

ACROSS

4 Be able to pay (6)
7 Torments (8)
8 Reproductions (6)
10 Jousting weapon (5)
13 Look intently (4)
14 Always (4)
15 Writing implements (3)
16 Rig (3)
17 State (4)
19 On top of (4)
21 Defeats (9)
23 Layer (4)
24 Shades (4)
26 Set (3)
27 Let it stand (4)
29 Journey (4)
32 Guide (4)
33 Stage whisper (5)
34 Coercion (6)
35 Herb (8)
36 Water-boiler (6)

DOWN

1 Musty (5)
2 Wading bird (5)
3 Certain (4)
4 Tree (5)
5 Just (4)
6 Keep (6)
9 Summary (6)
11 Greeting (3)
12 Desire (5)
13 Roosted (7)
15 For every (3)
16 Greek island (3)
18 Lines of poetry (6)
20 Nuisances (5)
21 Lubricant (3)
22 Not at home (3)
23 Terms of office (6)
25 Free (3)
28 Sample (5)
30 Crest (5)
31 Coin (5)
32 Abandoned (4)
33 Ventilates (4)

129

ACROSS

3 Garden tool (5)
8 Drive back (5)
10 Surplus (5)
11 Glue (3)
12 Incline (5)
13 Furniture item (7)
15 Mistake (5)
18 Intestine (3)
19 Whole (6)
21 Vie (7)
22 Regretted (4)
23 Hint (4)
24 Entourage (7)
26 Dealer (6)
29 Animal doctor (3)
31 Long-eared mammals (5)
32 Antennae (7)
34 Italian city (5)
35 Beer (3)
36 Seraglio (5)
37 Willow (5)
38 Prepared (5)

DOWN

1 Royal (5)
2 Minor deity (7)
4 Hide (4)
5 Rely (6)
6 Make an effort (5)
7 Clergyman (5)
9 Tavern (3)
12 Colonist (7)
14 Devout woman (3)
16 Shotgun (5)
17 Insurgent (5)
19 Invigorate (7)
20 Veracity (5)
21 Tree (5)
23 Sword (7)
24 Summary (6)
25 Born (3)
27 Navigation aid (5)
28 Dissuade (5)
30 System of beliefs (5)
32 Discover (4)
33 Prophet (3)

130

ACROSS

1 Hidden store (5)
6 Hollows (5)
9 Sited (7)
10 Heaped (5)
11 Musical instrument (5)
12 Start (5)
13 Arrogant (7)
15 Lair (3)
17 Minerals (4)
18 Safe (6)
19 Month (5)
20 Goes over again (6)
22 Missile (4)
24 Cunning (3)
25 Soup dishes (7)
26 Assesses (5)
27 Thighbone (5)
28 Cheerful (5)
29 Inhabitant (7)
30 Alloy (5)
31 Principle (5)

DOWN

2 Clothes-maker (6)
3 Slumbers (6)
4 Brick-carrier (3)
5 Pals (5)
6 Unit of sound (7)
7 Paradise (4)
8 Cashier (6)
12 Knocks (5)
13 Teems (5)
14 Clemency (5)
15 Fool (5)
16 Requirements (5)
18 Bodily cavity (5)
19 Attire (7)
21 Most senior (6)
22 Calm (6)
23 False (6)
25 Lukewarm (5)
26 Impolite (4)
28 Encountered (3)

ACROSS

1 Achieve (6)
7 Man-made object (8)
8 Defect (4)
10 Keepsakes (6)
11 Draw back (6)
14 Insect (3)
16 Flowers (5)
17 Day (4)
19 Managed (5)
21 Satisfied (5)
22 Large house (5)
23 Mimics (4)
26 Reverie (5)
28 Wildebeest (3)
29 Reviser (6)
30 Sign (6)
31 Singles (4)
32 Raised (8)
33 Reply (6)

DOWN

1 Dreaded (6)
2 Cat-like (6)
3 Decrees (4)
4 Respected (7)
5 Country roads (5)
6 Pig-pens (5)
8 Level (4)
9 Perform (3)
12 Fish (3)
13 Thick (5)
15 Helicopter blade (5)
18 Prize (5)
19 Tin (3)
20 For every (3)
21 Tea urn (7)
22 Floor covering (3)
23 Holy messengers (6)
24 Plays on words (4)
25 Vendor (6)
26 Postpone (5)
27 Type of duck (5)
28 Trap (3)
30 Sparkling water (4)

132

ACROSS

4	Appoint (6)
7	Hunters (8)
8	Religious songs (6)
10	Contract (5)
13	Swerve (4)
14	Whip (4)
15	Stoop (4)
16	Intelligence (3)
17	Norse god (4)
19	Aid in crime (4)
21	Foretold (9)
23	Schedule (4)
24	Prosecutes (4)
26	Wager (3)
27	Plunder (4)
29	Sculls (4)
32	Aquatic bird (4)
33	Force (5)
34	Disc (6)
35	Praised (8)
36	Furnace-tender (6)

DOWN

1	Yet (5)
2	Spanish snack (5)
3	Church recess (4)
4	Poplar (5)
5	Celebrity (4)
6	Opening move (6)
9	Steady (6)
11	Listening organ (3)
12	Brief (5)
13	Deer meat (7)
15	Offer (3)
16	Marry (3)
18	Trader (6)
20	Broom (5)
21	Cooking vessel (3)
22	Sever (3)
23	Modern (6)
25	Anger (3)
28	Command (5)
30	Fruit (5)
31	Slip (5)
32	Accepted (4)
33	Metal (4)

133

ACROSS

3 Lights (5)
8 Prestige (5)
10 Leading (5)
11 Kernel (3)
12 Jewelled headdress (5)
13 Makes beloved (7)
15 Sphere (5)
18 Non-amateur (3)
19 Washes (6)
21 Relating to touch (7)
22 Cooking fat (4)
23 Couple (4)
24 Denial (7)
26 Steering device (6)
29 Weight (3)
31 Semi-frozen rain (5)
32 Discussed (7)
34 Easily frightened (5)
35 Male swan (3)
36 Prise (5)
37 Yell (5)
38 Answer (5)

DOWN

1 Amusing (5)
2 Writing block (7)
4 Line of rotation (4)
5 Conditional release (6)
6 Ration (5)
7 Ship's room (5)
9 Failure (3)
12 Pig's foot (7)
14 Curve (3)
16 Trite (5)
17 Russian rulers (5)
19 Struck (7)
20 Insults (5)
21 Deal (5)
23 Swagger (7)
24 Go to bed (6)
25 Weep (3)
27 Painful complaint (5)
28 Dissuade (5)
30 First public performance (5)
32 Herb (4)
33 Also (3)

134

ACROSS

1 Homeless children (5)
6 Ruin (5)
9 Pause (7)
10 Intertwine (5)
11 Mistake (5)
12 Piece for nine players (5)
13 Aquatic bird (7)
15 Permit (3)
17 Mimicked (4)
18 Refer (6)
19 Canal boat (5)
20 Gloomy (6)
22 Drinks daintily (4)
24 Insect (3)
25 Rod (7)
26 Felony (5)
27 Hidden store (5)
28 Take unlawfully (5)
29 Springy (7)
30 Stores (5)
31 Number (5)

DOWN

2 Slumbering (6)
3 Cold (6)
4 Ready (3)
5 Pinafore (5)
6 Spire (7)
7 Saucy (4)
8 Pressed (6)
12 Of birth (5)
13 Bearlike mammal (5)
14 Minimum (5)
15 Sensational (5)
16 Anxious (5)
18 Open-mouthed (5)
19 Kegs (7)
21 Unbroken (6)
22 Grab (6)
23 Gratify (6)
25 Destroy (5)
26 Gnaw (4)
28 Be seated (3)

ACROSS

1 Knife-edges (6)
7 Permissive (8)
8 Fairy (4)
10 Hidden gunman (6)
11 Injury (6)
14 Guided (3)
16 Stories (5)
17 Type of gun (4)
19 Drugged (5)
21 Manages (5)
22 Bet (5)
23 Level (4)
26 Cut (5)
28 Chopper (3)
29 Islander (6)
30 Giants (6)
31 Hero (4)
32 Fragrant (8)
33 Water-boiler (6)

DOWN

1 Brutes (6)
2 Become more intense (6)
3 Move (4)
4 Tells (7)
5 Deadly (5)
6 Pig-pens (5)
8 Heap (4)
9 Colour (3)
12 Demented (3)
13 Type (5)
15 Aspirations (5)
18 Turret (5)
19 Follow (3)
20 For every (3)
21 Portable holiday home (7)
22 Moist (3)
23 Secure by violence (6)
24 Calf's meat (4)
25 Snuggle (6)
26 Abandon (5)
27 Poison (5)
28 Help (3)
30 Clock's sound (4)

136

ACROSS

4 Sight (6)
7 Unravel (8)
8 Talk (6)
10 Big (5)
13 Cease (4)
14 Row (4)
15 Informal conversation (4)
16 Everything (3)
17 Fever (4)
19 Compass point (4)
21 Small birds (9)
23 Nobleman (4)
24 Elect (4)
26 Meadow (3)
27 So be it (4)
29 Close (4)
32 A long time (4)
33 Musty (5)
34 Murderer (6)
35 Moon-shape (8)
36 Particular (6)

DOWN

1 Erected (5)
2 Look fixedly (5)
3 On one occasion (4)
4 Match (5)
5 Ooze (4)
6 Supernatural (6)
9 Powerful (6)
11 Afflict (3)
12 Fireplace (5)
13 Postpones (7)
15 Dog (3)
16 Donkey (3)
18 Car shed (6)
20 Rep (5)
21 Body of water (3)
22 Charged particle (3)
23 Die (6)
25 Friend (3)
28 Clemency (5)
30 Keen (5)
31 Relaxes (5)
32 As well (4)
33 Average (2-2)

ACROSS

3 Started (5)
8 Hidden store (5)
10 Regretful (5)
11 Definite article (3)
12 Airs (5)
13 More aggressive (7)
15 Respond (5)
18 Male (3)
19 Teacher (6)
21 Money (7)
22 Tumble (4)
23 Secure (4)
24 Pampers (7)
26 Effort (6)
29 Garden tool (3)
31 Coach (5)
32 Zealot (7)
34 Demon (5)
35 Rim (3)
36 Seraglio (5)
37 Alloy (5)
38 Old-fashioned (5)

DOWN

1 Dead language (5)
2 Of heat (7)
4 Always (4)
5 Of the stars (6)
6 Snoops (5)
7 Vestige (5)
9 Revolutionary's fore-name (3)
12 Deer meat (7)
14 Headwear item (3)
16 Book of maps (5)
17 Attempts (5)
19 Officer (7)
20 Ridge (5)
21 Girl's name (5)
23 Secrecy (7)
24 Film theatre (6)
25 Age (3)
27 Step (5)
28 Helped (5)
30 Two-legged creature (5)
32 Penalty (4)
33 Bind (3)

138

ACROSS

1 Malice (5)
6 Extinguish (5)
9 Turned aside (7)
10 Pancake (5)
11 Quotes (5)
12 Blemish (5)
13 Dream (7)
15 Eggs (3)
17 Second-hand (4)
18 Wrote (6)
19 Fragment (5)
20 Breaks out (6)
22 Office worker (4)
24 Distress signal (3)
25 String group (7)
26 For all to hear (5)
27 Pamphlet (5)
28 Supercilious (5)
29 Blasphemer (7)
30 Appended (5)
31 Principle (5)

DOWN

2 Money bags (6)
3 Knocked (6)
4 Previous day (3)
5 Box (5)
6 Determined (7)
7 Norse god (4)
8 Postpone (6)
12 Exhales audibly (5)
13 Ancient symbols (5)
14 Planet (5)
15 Beginning (5)
16 Skilful (5)
18 Conceited (5)
19 Bombastic (7)
21 Bellowed (6)
22 Hypnotic state (6)
23 Interfere (6)
25 Calm (5)
26 Pain (4)
28 Be seated (3)

ACROSS

1 Ramblers (6)
7 Data processor (8)
8 Schedule (4)
10 Noisier (6)
11 Front (6)
14 Devout woman (3)
16 Quick (5)
17 Bulk (4)
19 Black bird (5)
21 Hostelry (5)
22 Chinese region (5)
23 Girl (4)
26 Locations (5)
28 Bad actor (3)
29 Handles (6)
30 Building material (6)
31 Sign (4)
32 Abandoned (8)
33 Whole (6)

DOWN

1 Manhattan area (6)
2 Departure (6)
3 Mark (4)
4 Attire (7)
5 Thong (5)
6 Avarice (5)
8 Sprints (4)
9 Number (3)
12 Tin (3)
13 Eats (5)
15 Afterwards (5)
18 Moving (5)
19 Thieve (3)
20 Animal doctor (3)
21 Record (7)
22 Beverage (3)
23 Dirge (6)
24 So be it (4)
25 Colonise (6)
26 Den (5)
27 Anxious (5)
28 Border (3)
30 Cipher (4)

140

ACROSS

4 Opening move (6)
7 Lose energy (8)
8 From one side to the other (6)
10 Month (5)
13 Item (4)
14 Entreaty (4)
15 Insect (4)
16 Peculiar (3)
17 Stink (4)
19 Unusual (4)
21 Escapade (9)
23 Church recess (4)
24 English river (4)
26 Employ (3)
27 Amphibian (4)
29 Help in crime (4)
32 Boy's name (4)
33 Stage whisper (5)
34 Coercion (6)
35 Huge (8)
36 Hire charge (6)

DOWN

1 Collapse (5)
2 Trap (5)
3 Luxuriant (4)
4 African country (5)
5 Market (4)
6 Within (6)
9 Type of fruit (6)
11 Mountain (3)
12 Characters (5)
13 Not famous (7)
15 Expression of surprise (3)
16 Mineral (3)
18 Occurrences (6)
20 Regions (5)
21 Mimic (3)
22 Sound of disapproval (3)
23 Perceptive (6)
25 Marry (3)
28 Artist's stand (5)
30 Buffalo (5)
31 Curt (5)
32 Transmitted (4)
33 Ventilates (4)

141

ACROSS

3 Angry (5)
8 Steal, commonly (5)
10 Sharp (5)
11 Meadow (3)
12 Cord (5)
13 Cheese (7)
15 Sluggish (5)
18 Barrier (3)
19 Anxiety (6)
21 Scent (7)
22 Cooking fat (4)
23 Breed (4)
24 Transporting vehicle (7)
26 Account (6)
29 Agent (3)
31 Follow (5)
32 Keeps behind (7)
34 Spanish snack (5)
35 Annoy (3)
36 Facial hair (5)
37 Spoken exams (5)
38 Treatise (5)

DOWN

1 Scottish skirts (5)
2 Singed (7)
4 Chestnut (4)
5 Salty (6)
6 Place of action(5)
7 Celebrities (5)
9 Garland (3)
12 Luxury (7)
14 Pitch (3)
16 Keen (5)
17 Rips (5)
19 Referees (7)
20 Distress signal (5)
21 Supports (5)
23 Mends (7)
24 Steps (6)
25 Allow (3)
27 Go in (5)
28 Extravagant (5)
30 Leg joint (5)
32 Art movement (4)
33 Man's name (3)

142

ACROSS

1 Residence (5)
6 Thick (5)
9 Genteel (7)
10 Written slander (5)
11 Long seat (5)
12 Wash (5)
13 Quantity (7)
15 Anger (3)
17 Friend (4)
18 More expensive (6)
19 Yielded (5)
20 Embrace (6)
22 Eye inflammation (4)
24 Rodent (3)
25 Achieve an aim (7)
26 Anything (5)
27 Pamphlet (5)
28 Interrogate (5)
29 Blasphemer (7)
30 Possessed (5)
31 Requirements (5)

DOWN

2 Ring-shaped roll (6)
3 Elegant (6)
4 Slippery fish (3)
5 Shotgun (5)
6 Discussed (7)
7 Paradise (4)
8 Safe (6)
12 Belief (5)
13 Manufacturer (5)
14 In the air (5)
15 Angry (5)
16 Strayed (5)
18 First public performance (5)
19 Hit (7)
21 Restricted (6)
22 Rare (6)
23 Shouted (6)
25 Lustre (5)
26 Pain (4)
28 Trap (3)

143

ACROSS

1 Pure (6)
7 Waterproof garment (8)
8 Cupid (4)
10 Sedate (6)
11 Payment (6)
14 Frozen water (3)
16 Type (5)
17 Day (4)
19 Assessed (5)
21 Engine (5)
22 Small bird (5)
23 Corrosion (4)
26 Aviator (5)
28 Prohibit (3)
29 Amorous (6)
30 Open-mouthed (6)
31 Revise (4)
32 Resounding (8)
33 Arranged (6)

DOWN

1 Scolded (6)
2 Tree (6)
3 Gaelic (4)
4 Number (7)
5 Ancient Italian (5)
6 Metal fasteners (5)
8 Give out (4)
9 Mineral (3)
12 Marry (3)
13 Ancient symbols (5)
15 Dead language (5)
18 Moving (5)
19 Thieve (3)
20 Weight (3)
21 Gestures (7)
22 Decay (3)
23 Sword (6)
24 Item (4)
25 Labelled (6)
26 Fruit (5)
27 Bloodsucking insect (5)
28 Wicked (3)
30 Obtains (4)

144

ACROSS

4 Turn (6)
7 Proof (8)
8 Peals (6)
10 Baffle (5)
13 Spoil (4)
14 Garden implement (4)
15 Deer (4)
16 Expert (3)
17 Attack (4)
19 Pit (4)
21 Beggar (9)
23 Untidy state (4)
24 Bamboo stem (4)
26 Racket (3)
27 Question (4)
29 Remunerated (4)
32 Spool (4)
33 Absolute (5)
34 Lampoon (6)
35 Hanging (8)
36 Niche (6)

DOWN

1 Lead (5)
2 Less (5)
3 Retain (4)
4 Happen again (5)
5 Slender (4)
6 From there (6)
9 Hired assassin (3,3)
11 Summit (3)
12 Lakes (5)
13 Fundamental (7)
15 Concealed (3)
16 Insect (3)
18 Respond (6)
20 Awkward (5)
21 Encountered (3)
22 Feline (3)
23 Run (6)
25 Fasten (3)
28 Pays attention (5)
30 Garret (5)
31 Pulls (5)
32 Mature (4)
33 Encourage (4)

145

ACROSS

3 Clearing (5)
8 Tropical bird (5)
10 Finished (5)
11 Faucet (3)
12 Knocks (5)
13 Natural home (7)
15 Predict (5)
18 Pitch (3)
19 Invent (6)
21 Twist (7)
22 Cash register (4)
23 Elderly (4)
24 Syrup (7)
26 Small fruit (6)
29 Weep (3)
31 Creepy (5)
32 Scanned (7)
34 Celebrities (5)
35 Encountered (3)
36 Condition (5)
37 Choppers (5)
38 Wear away (5)

DOWN

1 Deadly (5)
2 Statehouse (7)
4 Hooligan (4)
5 Leave (6)
6 Follow (5)
7 First public performance (5)
9 Taxi (3)
12 Haggles (7)
14 Brown (3)
16 Meter (5)
17 Prepared (5)
19 Folds (7)
20 Performing area (5)
21 Transparent (5)
23 Egg white (7)
24 Wobble (6)
25 Expression of surprise (3)
27 Relaxes (5)
28 Ski-slope (5)
30 Trivial (5)
32 Poke (4)
33 Diocese (3)

146

ACROSS

1. Open-mouthed (5)
6. Boisterous (5)
9. Responded (7)
10. Force (5)
11. Percussion instrument (5)
12. Cutlery item (5)
13. Moulding (7)
15. Allow (3)
17. Beers (4)
18. Dress (6)
19. Black birds (5)
20. Gaol (6)
22. Drinks daintily (4)
24. Group (3)
25. Fragile (7)
26. Look fixedly (5)
27. Commotion (5)
28. Opponent (5)
29. Surround (7)
30. Inclination (5)
31. Principle (5)

DOWN

2. Frolic (6)
3. Primps (6)
4. Slippery fish (3)
5. Range (5)
6. Accounts (7)
7. Norse god (4)
8. Meal (6)
12. Derision (5)
13. Pitches tent (5)
14. Send (5)
15. Extent (5)
16. Anxious (5)
18. Conscious (5)
19. Satisfied (7)
21. Disclose (6)
22. Band (6)
23. Gratify (6)
25. Rear (5)
26. Regarded (4)
28. Decay (3)

ACROSS

1 Photographic device (6)
7 Bitterness (8)
8 Sparkling water (4)
10 Dealer in fabrics (6)
11 Happen to (6)
14 Information (3)
16 Strong winds (5)
17 Female deer (4)
19 Bounded (5)
21 Prise (5)
22 Adam's ale (5)
23 Sleigh (4)
26 Devil (5)
28 Untruth (3)
29 Fashions (6)
30 Tell (6)
31 Middle East port (4)
32 Memory-jogger (8)
33 Landed property (6)

DOWN

1 Frank (6)
2 Runs away to marry (6)
3 Slightly open (4)
4 Whole number (7)
5 Essential (5)
6 Aquatic mammals (5)
8 Herb (4)
9 Lair (3)
12 Craze (3)
13 Contract (5)
15 Stirred (5)
18 Film award (5)
19 Permit (3)
20 For every (3)
21 Alighting (7)
22 Pale (3)
23 Without sound (6)
24 Slender (4)
25 Drag (6)
26 Begin (5)
27 Pours (5)
28 Guided (3)
30 Unusual (4)

148

ACROSS

4 Metal (6)
7 Geometric shape (8)
8 Mock (6)
10 Build (5)
13 Breathe heavily (4)
14 Schedule (4)
15 Terse (4)
16 Undergarment (3)
17 Tribe (4)
19 Fencing sword (4)
21 Talked idly (9)
23 Regrets (4)
24 Gaelic (4)
26 Agent (3)
27 Weary (4)
29 Attack (4)
32 Writers (4)
33 Stage whisper (5)
34 Ebb (6)
35 Treatise (8)
36 Severe (6)

DOWN

1 Navigate (5)
2 Metal fastener (5)
3 Item (4)
4 Tree (5)
5 Saucy (4)
6 Suffer (6)
9 Goes in (6)
11 Tier (3)
12 Hidden store (5)
13 Customers (7)
15 Feline (3)
16 Cot (3)
18 Survived (6)
20 Equals (5)
21 Trophy (3)
22 Before (3)
23 Begrudge (6)
25 Offer (3)
28 Awkward (5)
30 Passage (5)
31 Hollows (5)
32 Fairy (4)
33 Mountains (4)

ACROSS

3 Middle (5)
8 Strong winds (5)
10 Mistake (5)
11 Set (3)
12 In that place (5)
13 Flop (7)
15 Come in (5)
18 Undergarment (3)
19 Suffer (6)
21 Restrict (7)
22 Implore (4)
23 Trade (4)
24 Corsairs (7)
26 Sensual (6)
29 Jewel (3)
31 Keepsake (5)
32 Signifies (7)
34 Mountain range (5)
35 Horse (3)
36 New Zealand native (5)
37 Note (5)
38 Sharp (5)

DOWN

1 Heathen (5)
2 Page (7)
4 Pain (4)
5 Calm (6)
6 Fashion (5)
7 Might (5)
9 Garland (3)
12 Transportation (7)
14 Vase (3)
16 Melodies (5)
17 Staggers (5)
19 Hires (7)
20 Superior (5)
21 Christmas song (5)
23 Satanic (7)
24 Outdoor meal (6)
25 Number (3)
27 Transmit (5)
28 Jewelled headdress (5)
30 Start (5)
32 Hollow (4)
33 Brown (3)

150

ACROSS

1 Cutlery item (5)
6 Code (5)
9 Overdue (7)
10 Principle (5)
11 Approaches (5)
12 Canvas shelters (5)
13 Takes away (7)
15 Favourite (3)
17 Norse god (4)
18 Courteous (6)
19 Backless sofa (5)
20 Oozed (6)
22 Weeps (4)
24 Conclude (3)
25 Easily broken (7)
26 Lakes (5)
27 Child (5)
28 Concerning (5)
29 In general (7)
30 Senseless (5)
31 Even (5)

DOWN

2 Skinned (6)
3 Fairy king (6)
4 Mesh (3)
5 Earnings (5)
6 Say in passing (7)
7 Poems (4)
8 Road (6)
12 Lukewarm (5)
13 Excite (5)
14 Acted silently (5)
15 Aviator (5)
16 Anxious (5)
18 Couples (5)
19 Merit (7)
21 Naval flag (6)
22 Steady (6)
23 Female garment (6)
25 Ales (5)
26 Satellite (4)
28 Everybody (3)

151

ACROSS

1 Floor covering (6)
7 Artillery fragments (8)
8 Schedule (4)
10 Herdsman (6)
11 Claws (6)
14 Cot (3)
16 Type (5)
17 Gun (4)
19 Ranted (5)
21 Aspirations (5)
22 Understood (5)
23 Mail (4)
26 Undress (5)
28 Barrier (3)
29 Punches (6)
30 Optical illusion (6)
31 So be it (4)
32 Memory-jogger (8)
33 Whole (6)

DOWN

1 Scolds (6)
2 Shown to be true (6)
3 Russian ruler (4)
4 Injures (7)
5 Edible bulb (5)
6 Form (5)
8 Flowing dress (4)
9 Abbreviated name (3)
12 Guided (3)
13 Deadens (5)
15 Quick (5)
18 Veracity (5)
19 Fabled bird (3)
20 Obtain (3)
21 Occurs (7)
22 Boy's name (3)
23 Mother or father (6)
24 M East country (4)
25 From there (6)
26 Supply (5)
27 Card game (5)
28 Dull (3)
30 Female horse (4)

152

ACROSS

4 Informal gathering (6)
7 Cruel (8)
8 Twist (6)
10 Cords (5)
13 Profound (4)
14 Summit (4)
15 Hair treatment (4)
16 Single (3)
17 Ache (4)
19 Appends (4)
21 Enlarged (9)
23 Greek character (4)
24 Region (4)
26 Wager (3)
27 Layer (4)
29 Extra (4)
32 Fronded plant (4)
33 Flower (5)
34 Snake-haired woman (6)
35 Neatness (8)
36 Stick (6)

DOWN

1 Jewelled headdress (5)
2 Form (5)
3 Units of current (4)
4 Drain (5)
5 Potato strip (4)
6 Greek capital (6)
9 Stay (6)
11 Choose (3)
12 Immigrant (2-3)
13 Inhabitant (7)
15 Metal fastener (3)
16 Peculiar (3)
18 Gemstones (6)
20 Considers (5)
21 Encountered (3)
22 In favour (3)
23 Decapitate (6)
25 Mineral (3)
28 Angry (5)
30 Different (5)
31 Delete (5)
32 Rage (4)
33 Among (4)

153

ACROSS

3 Alloy (5)
8 Ringlets (5)
10 Fanatical (5)
11 Shelter (3)
12 Church council (5)
13 Feels remorse (7)
15 Devil (5)
18 Vehicle (3)
19 Term of office (6)
21 Discussed (7)
22 Attack (4)
23 Slippery fish (4)
24 Hidden gunmen (7)
26 Gaps (6)
29 Organ of hearing (3)
31 Temptress (5)
32 Variable (7)
34 Extent (5)
35 Twitch (3)
36 Oar (5)
37 Broaden (5)
38 Feeling (5)

DOWN

1 Laws (5)
2 Swindled (7)
4 Playthings (4)
5 Wore away (6)
6 Loaded (5)
7 Lesser (5)
9 Agent (3)
12 Tunes (7)
14 Arrest, commonly (3)
16 Beasts of burden (5)
17 Scottish monster (5)
19 Storm (7)
20 Stupid (5)
21 Foreign monetary unit (5)
23 Irregular (7)
24 Doting (6)
25 Consume (3)
27 Nip (5)
28 Prison rooms (5)
30 Painful complaint (5)
32 Afflicts (4)
33 Offer (3)

154

ACROSS

1 System of belief (5)
6 Prepared (5)
9 Transport network (7)
10 Cutlery item (5)
11 Engine (5)
12 Principle (5)
13 Furniture item (7)
15 Zodiac sign (3)
17 Of the ears (4)
18 Deprive (6)
19 Poplar (5)
20 Deceive (6)
22 Team (4)
24 Utter (3)
25 Stammer (7)
26 Badgers' homes (5)
27 Skinflint (5)
28 More senior (5)
29 Attribute (7)
30 Gemstone (5)
31 Go in (5)

DOWN

2 Iterate (6)
3 Sensual (6)
4 Karate expert (3)
5 Semi-frozen rain (5)
6 Savoury dish (7)
7 River island (4)
8 Herds (6)
12 Anxious (5)
13 Ropes (5)
14 Male goat (5)
15 Legal, commonly (5)
16 Freshwater mammal (5)
18 Hollows (5)
19 Hostile (7)
21 Dining (6)
22 Taken unlawfully (6)
23 Cross out (6)
25 Commence (5)
26 Chair (4)
28 Honour (3)

155

ACROSS

1 Outhouse (6)
7 Decry (8)
8 Pallid (4)
10 Greek islander (6)
11 Widely scattered (6)
14 Colour (3)
16 Flower (5)
17 Move (4)
19 US farm (5)
21 Suggest (5)
22 Slumber (5)
23 Stratagem (4)
26 Boat (5)
28 Noise (3)
29 Line of equal pressure (6)
30 Spiritualist (6)
31 Aid in crime (4)
32 Fearless (8)
33 Ascertain (6)

DOWN

1 Cuts (6)
2 Straw hat (6)
3 Paradise (4)
4 Dense (7)
5 Sound of contempt (5)
6 Drain (5)
8 Fairy (4)
9 Boy (3)
12 Tree (3)
13 Scorches (5)
15 Concentrated beam (5)
18 Spanish snacks (5)
19 Fish eggs (3)
20 Pinch (3)
21 Contented (7)
22 Weep (3)
23 Horsemen (6)
24 One (4)
25 Fur (6)
26 Polite (5)
27 Compass point (5)
28 Debutante (3)
30 Manufactured (4)

156

ACROSS

4	Cattle leather (6)
7	Cooperation (8)
8	Skilful (6)
10	M East inhabitants (5)
13	Raced (4)
14	Girl's name (4)
15	Black-marketeer (4)
16	Elderly (3)
17	Drive away (4)
19	Sculls (4)
21	Thankfulness (9)
23	Jump (4)
24	Animal fat (4)
26	Professor (3)
27	Quick look (4)
29	Gaelic (4)
32	Stoop (4)
33	Colour (5)
34	Steep valley (6)
35	Dampness (8)
36	Salad plant (6)

DOWN

1	Weasel-like animal (5)
2	Heathen (5)
3	Is indebted to (4)
4	Ruminant mammal (5)
5	Difficult (4)
6	Exercises (6)
9	Eat (6)
11	Tear (3)
12	M East port (5)
13	Ruined (7)
15	Drunkard (3)
16	Mineral (3)
18	Occur (6)
20	Viper (5)
21	Knowledge (3)
22	Knock (3)
23	Find (6)
25	Employ (3)
28	Foe (5)
30	Reappear (5)
31	Concluded (5)
32	Chew (4)
33	Point (4)

ACROSS

3 Christmas song (5)
8 Backless sofa (5)
10 Corrodes (5)
11 Trap (3)
12 Tooth (5)
13 Sketch (7)
15 Prongs (5)
18 Male (3)
19 Felt hat (6)
21 Bartered (7)
22 Metal (4)
23 Peel (4)
24 Six-piece ensembles (7)
26 Drew breath sharply (6)
29 Anger (3)
31 Sugary (5)
32 Implored (7)
34 Musty (5)
35 Rim (3)
36 Salivate (5)
37 Precipitous (5)
38 Chairs (5)

DOWN

1 Stiff (5)
2 Executioner (7)
4 Particle (4)
5 Spoke in public (6)
6 Sensational (5)
7 Navigate (5)
9 By way of (3)
12 Crushed (7)
14 Scrap of material (3)
16 Recesses (5)
17 Canonised person (5)
19 Prolific (7)
20 Circles (5)
21 Quadruped (5)
23 Secrecy (7)
24 Colonise (6)
25 Before (3)
27 Conscious (5)
28 Mexican currency units (5)
30 Drive back (5)
32 Scheme (4)
33 Expire (3)

158

ACROSS

1 Secrete (5)
6 Ales (5)
9 Baffled (7)
10 Follow (5)
11 Feel (5)
12 Coach (5)
13 Stern (7)
15 Poem (3)
17 Permits (4)
18 Improved (6)
19 Entrances (5)
20 Bisects (6)
22 Lake (4)
24 Consumed (3)
25 Obtained (7)
26 Foul (5)
27 Trite (5)
28 Black bird (5)
29 Pride (7)
30 Ovine animal (5)
31 Hides (5)

DOWN

2 Language (6)
3 Gushes (6)
4 Colour (3)
5 Shade of blue (5)
6 Moreover (7)
7 Paradise (4)
8 Dwell (6)
12 Three-man bands (5)
13 Greek letter (5)
14 Took illegally (5)
15 Freshwater mammal (5)
16 Strayed (5)
18 Propagate (5)
19 Unfold (7)
21 Fasten (6)
22 Evolve (6)
23 Modern (6)
25 Because (5)
26 Countenance (4)
28 Tear (3)

ACROSS

1 BBC nickname (6)
7 Adorn (8)
8 Boast (4)
10 Option (6)
11 Procession (6)
14 Frozen water (3)
16 Drying cloth (5)
17 Competent (4)
19 Wandered (5)
21 Lifeless (5)
22 Symbol (5)
23 Window frame (4)
26 Polite (5)
28 Agent (3)
29 Outbuilding (4-2)
30 Certainly (6)
31 Dregs (4)
32 Demote (8)
33 Every seven days (6)

DOWN

1 Shrub (6)
2 Three times (6)
3 Border (4)
4 Turned (7)
5 Tropical bird (5)
6 Wallow (5)
8 Cook in water (4)
9 Expert (3)
12 Staff (3)
13 Writing tables (5)
15 Manages (5)
18 Contradict (5)
19 Rodent (3)
20 Vigour (3)
21 Electricity (7)
22 Can (3)
23 Calm (6)
24 Mimics (4)
25 Prime (6)
26 Teller (5)
27 Arched cellar (5)
28 Regret (3)
30 Killed (4)

160

ACROSS

4 Explosions (6)
7 Snake (8)
8 Cutlery items (6)
10 Harvests (5)
13 Forehead (4)
14 Exchange for cash (4)
15 Rig (4)
16 Globe (3)
17 Applications (4)
19 Sculls (4)
21 Abundance (9)
23 Layer (4)
24 Amount of medicine (4)
26 Insane (3)
27 Pitcher (4)
29 Rind (4)
32 Automobiles (4)
33 Alloy (5)
34 Determine (6)
35 Sun-room (8)
36 View (6)

DOWN

1 Couples (5)
2 Deadly (5)
3 Throw (4)
4 Iraqi port (5)
5 Affirm (4)
6 Singers (6)
9 Absorbent (6)
11 Slippery fish (3)
12 Feather (5)
13 Moreover (7)
15 Solidify (3)
16 Mineral (3)
18 Extend (6)
20 Skilful (5)
21 Assist (3)
22 Hill (3)
23 Narrows (6)
25 Sheltered side (3)
28 Seize forcibly (5)
30 Creepy (5)
31 Beast of burden (5)
32 Quote (4)
33 Celebrity (4)

161

ACROSS

3 Feel (5)
8 Cheerful (5)
10 Attempted (5)
11 Pinch (3)
12 Clean (5)
13 Under (7)
15 Prodded (5)
18 Beer (3)
19 Manly (6)
21 Asserted (7)
22 Concludes (4)
23 Eye inflammation (4)
24 Thickness (7)
26 Tended (6)
29 Before (3)
31 Unwraps (5)
32 Hatchet (7)
34 Assistants (5)
35 Males (3)
36 Carries (5)
37 Unit of length (5)
38 Anaesthetic (5)

DOWN

1 Becomes smaller (5)
2 Requests for aid (7)
4 Every (4)
5 Silly (6)
6 Mistake (5)
7 Wallow (5)
9 Metal fastener (3)
12 Navigated (7)
14 Everything (3)
16 Fund (5)
17 Dissuade (5)
19 Containers (7)
20 Party (5)
21 Love (5)
23 Ship (7)
24 Refrain (6)
25 Anger (3)
27 Disturbed (5)
28 Trap (5)
30 Kind (5)
32 Yield (4)
33 Animal doctor (3)

162

ACROSS

1 Desires (5)
6 Lotto (5)
9 Edited (7)
10 Milk delivery vehicle (5)
11 Killed (5)
12 Hackneyed (5)
13 Repair (7)
15 Eggs (3)
17 Mimics (4)
18 Bisects (6)
19 Last (5)
20 Polish composer (6)
22 Encourage (4)
24 That woman (3)
25 Less sharp (7)
26 Hell (5)
27 Track (5)
28 Custom (5)
29 Satanic (7)
30 Units of heredity (5)
31 Coiled length of yarn (5)

DOWN

2 Slumbering (6)
3 Characteristics (6)
4 Ready (3)
5 Liquid measure (5)
6 Savage (7)
7 Lazy (4)
8 Mourn (6)
12 Coach (5)
13 US farm (5)
14 Spanish gentleman (5)
15 Observable (5)
16 Flower (5)
18 Greets (5)
19 Closing sections (7)
21 Coffin-bearing vehicle (6)
22 Empty a suitcase (6)
23 Zodiac sign (6)
25 Broom (5)
26 Conceal (4)
28 Belonging to him (3)

ACROSS

1 Refuge (6)
7 Clapping (8)
8 Inquires (4)
10 Curved structures (6)
11 Hypnotic state (6)
14 Domestic fowl (3)
16 Edition (5)
17 Elderly (4)
19 Blood-sucking creature (5)
21 Footwear items (5)
22 Musical composition (5)
23 Cipher (4)
26 Month (5)
28 Jewel (3)
29 Cheerful (6)
30 Photographic device (6)
31 Honest (4)
32 Statements of homage (8)
33 Gossip (6)

DOWN

1 Fleet (6)
2 Whipped (6)
3 Large amount (4)
4 Clergymen (7)
5 Scorches (5)
6 Brawl (5)
8 Pain (4)
9 Knowledge (3)
12 Charred residue (3)
13 Eros (5)
15 Happen again (5)
18 Mathematical chart (5)
19 Record (3)
20 Stretch (3)
21 Yellow element (7)
22 Tree (3)
23 Building material (6)
24 Sign (4)
25 Empower (6)
26 Sharp (5)
27 Stiff (5)
28 Chasm (3)
30 Expense (4)

164

ACROSS

4 Large cats (6)
7 Harem (8)
8 Coaches (6)
10 Rub out (5)
13 Action (4)
14 Tear (4)
15 Play boisterously (4)
16 Female pig (3)
17 Norse god (4)
19 Particle (4)
21 Cartoon (9)
23 Mimics (4)
24 Neat (4)
26 Perform (3)
27 Manner (4)
29 Level (4)
32 Magic stick (4)
33 Love (5)
34 Relating to old age (6)
35 Firm (8)
36 Affirm (6)

DOWN

1 Flower (5)
2 Keyboard instrument (5)
3 Leer (4)
4 Symbol (5)
5 Pleased (4)
6 Haphazard (6)
9 Recompensed (6)
11 Agent (3)
12 Rock (5)
13 Given (7)
15 Edge (3)
16 Child (3)
18 Gloomy (6)
20 Played (5)
21 Suitable (3)
22 Can (3)
23 Brogue (6)
25 For every (3)
28 Sluggish (5)
30 Fashion (5)
31 At no time (5)
32 Sapient (4)
33 County (4)

165

ACROSS

3 Spoilt children (5)
8 Adam's ale (5)
10 Creepy (5)
11 Lettuce (3)
12 Postage sticker (5)
13 Drives forward (7)
15 Hesitate (5)
18 Anger (3)
19 Cashier (6)
21 Footballer (7)
22 Ancient symbol (4)
23 Roman emperor (4)
24 Tremble (7)
26 Insult (6)
29 Regret (3)
31 Of the sun (5)
32 Violinist (7)
34 Board (5)
35 Rule (3)
36 Number (5)
37 Drive back (5)
38 Ability (5)

DOWN

1 Mother-of-pearl (5)
2 Interval of rest (7)
4 Decays (4)
5 Mood (6)
6 Flower part (5)
7 Wash out (5)
9 Also (3)
12 Dexterity (7)
14 Stray (3)
16 Painful complaint (5)
17 Mistake (5)
19 Climbing plant part (7)
20 Scum (5)
21 Edible mollusc (5)
23 Sewing implements (7)
24 Decreased in size (6)
25 Failure (3)
27 Adores (5)
28 Yawns (5)
30 Drain (5)
32 Sense (4)
33 Circuit (3)

166

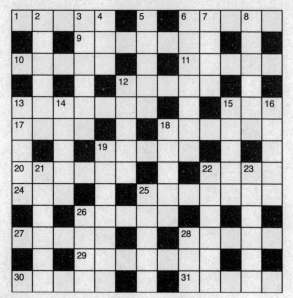

ACROSS

1 Ecstasy (5)
6 Fiasco (5)
9 Drinker (7)
10 Commence (5)
11 Aroma (5)
12 Soup (5)
13 Fair-haired women (7)
15 Lair (3)
17 Tear (4)
18 Religious house (6)
19 Type of music (5)
20 Floor (6)
22 Sport (4)
24 Transgress (3)
25 Loser (4-3)
26 Corrosive substances (5)
27 Roost (5)
28 Helped (5)
29 Esteem (7)
30 Ancient Greek instruments (5)
31 Canvas shelters (5)

DOWN

2 Small (6)
3 Desert (6)
4 Be seated (3)
5 Practises boxing (5)
6 Rots (7)
7 Curved structure (4)
8 Horse's gait (6)
12 Stomach (5)
13 Alloy (5)
14 Edible bulb (5)
15 Giver (5)
16 Man-made fibre (5)
18 Tolls (5)
19 Long seats (7)
21 Opportune (6)
22 Well-mannered (6)
23 Dirge (6)
25 Skilful (5)
26 Area of land (4)
28 Deed (3)

ACROSS

1 Blood ingredient (6)
7 Pertinent (8)
8 Leave out (4)
10 Song words (6)
11 Substance (6)
14 Consumed (3)
16 Layers (5)
17 Competent (4)
19 Indian monetary unit (5)
21 Cords (5)
22 Not as many (5)
23 Quarry (4)
26 Fire (5)
28 Meadow (3)
29 Prises (6)
30 Next to (6)
31 Paradise (4)
32 Threatening (8)
33 Forms (6)

DOWN

1 Spanish dish (6)
2 Jew or Arab (6)
3 Painting, sculpture, etc. (4)
4 Scolds (7)
5 Speed (5)
6 Heavenly bodies (5)
8 Spoken (4)
9 Frozen water (3)
12 Draw (3)
13 Wear away (5)
15 Deceives (5)
18 Wash (5)
19 Argument (3)
20 For every (3)
21 Take back (7)
22 Enemy (3)
23 Spanish monetary unit (6)
24 Precipitation (4)
25 Succumbs (6)
26 Collapse (5)
27 Sheep-like (5)
28 Guided (3)
30 Implores (4)

168

ACROSS

4 Hire (6)
7 Large pot (8)
8 Rations (6)
10 Big (5)
13 Regretted (4)
14 Jetty (4)
15 Look intently (4)
16 Agent (3)
17 Of heroic proportions (4)
19 Poems (4)
21 Endorsed (9)
23 Cipher (4)
24 Diplomacy (4)
26 Marry (3)
27 Nourish (4)
29 Level (4)
32 Eyeglass (4)
33 Greek island (5)
34 Account (6)
35 Revelation (8)
36 Unconsciousness (6)

DOWN

1 Red Indian trophy (5)
2 Money (5)
3 Border (4)
4 Follow (5)
5 Pleased (4)
6 Aquatic birds (6)
9 Courageous (6)
11 Afflict (3)
12 Avarice (5)
13 Intones (7)
15 Mine (3)
16 Colour (3)
18 Favour (6)
20 Dissuade (5)
21 Food fish (3)
22 Trend (3)
23 Building material (6)
25 Moist (3)
28 Go in (5)
30 Planet (5)
31 At no time (5)
32 Curve (4)
33 Hew (4)

ACROSS

3 Recreation (5)
8 Bed-time drink (5)
10 Keyboard instrument (5)
11 Adhesive (3)
12 Hackneyed (5)
13 Bear (7)
15 Mountain range (5)
18 Wonder (3)
19 Affirm (6)
21 Syrup (7)
22 Pain (4)
23 State (4)
24 Love affair (7)
26 Secure (6)
29 Born (3)
31 Alloy (5)
32 Customers (7)
34 Sudden fear (5)
35 Large (3)
36 Custom (5)
37 Dossiers (5)
38 Thick (5)

DOWN

1 Counterfeit (5)
2 Liken (7)
4 Section (4)
5 Turn (6)
6 English river (5)
7 Breakers (5)
9 Drinking vessel (3)
12 Treachery (7)
14 Be indebted to (3)
16 Dig (5)
17 Stores (5)
19 Calendar (7)
20 Homeless children (5)
21 Not these (5)
23 Bitter (7)
24 Narrate (6)
25 Mesh (3)
27 Book of maps (5)
28 Lukewarm (5)
30 Fury (5)
32 Swine (4)
33 Lubricate (3)

170

ACROSS

1 Ridge (5)
6 Adored (5)
9 Loomed (7)
10 Following (5)
11 Taut (5)
12 Notices (5)
13 Roars (7)
15 Use needle and thread (3)
17 Line of rotation (4)
18 Foolish (6)
19 Entity (5)
20 Sharp reply (6)
22 State (4)
24 Donkey (3)
25 Splinters (7)
26 Fence post (5)
27 Warehouse (5)
28 Easily frightened (5)
29 Trifled (7)
30 Strike heavily (5)
31 Poplar (5)

DOWN

2 Involuntary response (6)
3 Takes illegally (6)
4 Hill (3)
5 Assists (5)
6 Permitting (7)
7 Poems (4)
8 Follows (6)
12 Sugary (5)
13 Iraqi port (5)
14 Tables (5)
15 Strain (5)
16 Erodes (5)
18 Relative (5)
19 Fragile (7)
21 Respect (6)
22 Evades (6)
23 Northern stoat (6)
25 Item of clothing (5)
26 Gentle (4)
28 Beverage (3)

ACROSS

1 Treeless plain (6)
7 Throttle (8)
8 Look for (4)
10 Marine molluscs (6)
11 Breakfast fish (6)
14 Beer (3)
16 Requires (5)
17 Auction items (4)
19 Writing material (5)
21 Bad habits (5)
22 Sacred vocal piece (5)
23 Satisfy (4)
26 Reel (5)
28 Biblical prophet (3)
29 Rain-bearing cloud (6)
30 Eluded (6)
31 Ensnares (4)
32 Meditated (8)
33 Nurse (6)

DOWN

1 Hand tool (6)
2 Resides (6)
3 Inquires (4)
4 Deep valleys (7)
5 Open-mouthed (5)
6 Prophets (5)
8 Chair (4)
9 Stretch (3)
12 For every (3)
13 Decree (5)
15 Shoe fasteners (5)
18 African ruminant (5)
19 Mine (3)
20 Domestic animal (3)
21 Books (7)
22 Crowd (3)
23 Roofing tiles (6)
24 Helps (4)
25 Cause to be loved (6)
26 Shoot from cover (5)
27 Signs (5)
28 Previous day (3)
30 Concludes (4)

172

ACROSS

4 Most secure (6)
7 Rebuke (8)
8 Reviser (6)
10 Backless chair (5)
13 Swerve (4)
14 Cash register (4)
15 Isn't, commonly (4)
16 Wager (3)
17 Woes (4)
19 Pitcher (4)
21 Fall of snow (9)
23 Worry (4)
24 Entrance (4)
26 Spasm (3)
27 Paradise (4)
29 Moos (4)
32 Responsibility (4)
33 Ability (5)
34 Former gold coins (6)
35 Booms (8)
36 Whips (6)

DOWN

1 Faith (5)
2 Reel (5)
3 Implement (4)
4 Lustre (5)
5 Just (4)
6 Downpour (6)
9 Perceive (6)
11 Can (3)
12 Oily fruit (5)
13 Faces (7)
15 Everything (3)
16 Insect (3)
18 Dormant (6)
20 Mollusc (5)
21 Curve (3)
22 Granny (3)
23 Leg bone (6)
25 Night bird (3)
28 Cleans (5)
30 Lubricated (5)
31 Hack (5)
32 Vow (4)
33 Transmit (4)

173

ACROSS

3 Falls (5)
8 Insurgent (5)
10 Pinafore (5)
11 Club (3)
12 Sword (5)
13 Fundamental (7)
15 Mountain range (5)
18 Mythical bird (3)
19 Most peculiar (6)
21 Reform (7)
22 Regrets (4)
23 Herb (4)
24 Tool (7)
26 Fastens securely (6)
29 Tune (3)
31 Spanish snacks (5)
32 Freedom (7)
34 At no time (5)
35 Dog (3)
36 Dull (5)
37 State (5)
38 Stage whisper (5)

DOWN

1 Exclude (5)
2 Goes to bed (7)
4 Genuine (4)
5 Procession (6)
6 Use money (5)
7 Aspires (5)
9 Wicked (3)
12 Packets (7)
14 Lettuce (3)
16 Satan (5)
17 Yet (5)
19 Outdoors (4-3)
20 Pamphlet (5)
21 Summarise (5)
23 Leads (7)
24 Disturbs (6)
25 Thus (3)
27 Large spoon (5)
28 Divine food (5)
30 Fastening pin (5)
32 Metal (4)
33 Kernel (3)

174

ACROSS

1 Desire (5)
6 Prepared (5)
9 Avoided (7)
10 Boulder (5)
11 US coins (5)
12 Start (5)
13 Zones (7)
15 Transgress (3)
17 Beg (4)
18 Easy (6)
19 Ultimate (5)
20 Cave (6)
22 Mark (4)
24 Before (3)
25 Occurs (7)
26 Invalidate (5)
27 Prosecuting (5)
28 Church passage (5)
29 Ignore (7)
30 Notions (5)
31 Rips (5)

DOWN

2 Cad (6)
3 Conceit (6)
4 Previous day (3)
5 Attempts (5)
6 Performance (7)
7 Paradise (4)
8 Particular (6)
12 Thinking organ (5)
13 Room (5)
14 Etch (5)
15 Because (5)
16 Approaches (5)
18 Deadly (5)
19 Outskirts (7)
21 In the vicinity (6)
22 Spirit (6)
23 Deer's horn (6)
25 Throws (5)
26 Indian coin (4)
28 Deed (3)

175

ACROSS

1 Inclines (6)
7 Imagined (8)
8 Entreaty (4)
10 Antenna (6)
11 Prairie wolf (6)
14 Solidify (3)
16 Madagascan primate (5)
17 Endure (4)
19 Informs (5)
21 Cords (5)
22 Send (5)
23 State of untidiness (4)
26 Reverie (5)
28 Food fish (3)
29 Reviser (6)
30 Swellings (6)
31 Fencing sword (4)
32 Bones (8)
33 Tarry (6)

DOWN

1 Immoral (6)
2 Imitation bullet (6)
3 Practise boxing (4)
4 Saunters (7)
5 Horse's attendant (5)
6 Viper (5)
8 Washing fasteners (4)
9 Slippery fish (3)
12 Affirmative (3)
13 Rotates (5)
15 Lukewarm (5)
18 Trophy (5)
19 Male cat (3)
20 Permit (3)
21 Taken away (7)
22 Rodent (3)
23 Accost (6)
24 Rim (4)
25 Nurse (6)
26 Thick (5)
27 Type of duck (5)
28 Drinking vessel (3)
30 Curve (4)

176

ACROSS

4 Painter (8)
7 Series of tunnels (8)
8 Jargon (6)
10 Sweets (5)
13 Dress (4)
14 Way (4)
15 Schedule (4)
16 Suitable (3)
17 Revise (4)
19 Urban area (4)
21 Too early (9)
23 Appear (4)
24 Mission (4)
26 Choose (3)
27 Employer (4)
29 Border (4)
32 Minerals (4)
33 Perfect (5)
34 Infertile (6)
35 Gemstone (8)
36 Unstick (6)

DOWN

1 Rascal (5)
2 Feat of daring (5)
3 Experts (4)
4 Abbey head (5)
5 Melody (4)
6 Drowsy (6)
9 Counting frame (6)
11 Man's name (3)
12 In that place (5)
13 Turns (7)
15 Lip (3)
16 Consumed (3)
18 Reserved (6)
20 Annoyed (5)
21 Favourite (3)
22 Pitch (3)
23 Wrench (6)
25 Turkish ruler (3)
28 Feel (5)
30 Subtract (5)
31 Senior (5)
32 Spoken (4)
33 Mischievous sprites (4)

ACROSS

3 Solitary person (5)
8 Amusing (5)
10 Creature (5)
11 Blend (3)
12 Investigate (5)
13 Swords (7)
15 Lazes (5)
18 Mineral (3)
19 Within (6)
21 Swearing (7)
22 Belonging to that woman (4)
23 Clock face (4)
24 Respected (7)
26 Knocked (6)
29 Solidify (3)
31 Sat (5)
32 Boring (7)
34 Drain (5)
35 Revolver (3)
36 Utter (5)
37 Small mammal (5)
38 Clever (5)

DOWN

1 Of mankind (5)
2 Worried (7)
4 Sculls (4)
5 Receding (6)
6 Rushes (5)
7 Inquired (5)
9 Pinch (3)
12 Ironed (7)
14 Stray (3)
16 Furious (5)
17 Exchanges for money (5)
19 Rational number (7)
20 Acute (5)
21 Cuts very short (5)
23 Elation (7)
24 Regain (6)
25 Colour (3)
27 Main artery (5)
28 Nuisances (5)
30 Ancient symbols (5)
32 Rip (4)
33 Belonging to us (3)

178

ACROSS

1. Performing area (5)
6. Prison rooms (5)
9. Muslim fast (7)
10. Scornful expression (5)
11. Musical instrument (5)
12. Easily frightened (5)
13. Examiners (7)
15. Domestic fowl (3)
17. Mischievous sprites (4)
18. Security (6)
19. Reel (5)
20. Narrate (6)
22. Unaccompanied (4)
24. Insect (3)
25. Widen (7)
26. Really (5)
27. Lowest point (5)
28. Ties (5)
29. Mends (7)
30. Yielded (5)
31. Make amends (5)

DOWN

2. Two-seater bicycle (6)
3. Welcomes (6)
4. Listening organ (3)
5. Indian dresses (5)
6. Wealth (7)
7. Woman's name (4)
8. Brownish finch (6)
12. Nonsense (5)
13. Jewelled headdress (5)
14. Upset (5)
15. Biblical king (5)
16. Man-made fibre (5)
18. Regretful (5)
19. Moved (7)
21. Hire (6)
22. Cruel person (6)
23. Heavy (6)
25. Desolate (5)
26. Grow weary (4)
28. Woman's undergarment (3)

ACROSS

1 Writing implement (6)
7 Breed of terrier (8)
8 Painting, sculpture, etc (4)
10 Marine gastropod (6)
11 Turn (6)
14 Enclosure (3)
16 Worth (5)
17 Corrosion (4)
19 Turret (5)
21 Elector (5)
22 Assessed (5)
23 Unusual (4)
26 Flower part (5)
28 Jewel (3)
29 Amorous (6)
30 Ramshackle dwelling places (6)
31 Paradise (4)
32 Unravel (8)
33 Cross out (6)

DOWN

1 Lack of colour (6)
2 Floor covering (6)
3 Final (4)
4 Regain health (7)
5 Deadly (5)
6 Commotion (5)
8 Units of current (4)
9 Number (3)
12 Pitch (3)
13 Teacher (5)
15 Sacred song (5)
18 Total (5)
19 Small child (3)
20 Marry (3)
21 Brave (7)
22 Rodent (3)
23 Disclose (6)
24 So be it (4)
25 Make certain (6)
26 Blood ingredient (5)
27 Mails (5)
28 Deity (3)
30 Pay attention to (4)

180

ACROSS

- 4 Dwindles (6)
- 7 Demote (8)
- 8 Allow (6)
- 10 Room (5)
- 13 Increase (4)
- 14 Italian city (4)
- 15 Nuisance (4)
- 16 Enquire (3)
- 17 Genuine (4)
- 19 Irritation (4)
- 21 Snowfall (9)
- 23 Mimics (4)
- 24 Layer (4)
- 26 Perform (3)
- 27 Follow (4)
- 29 Honest (4)
- 32 Fronded plant (4)
- 33 Pigs (5)
- 34 Teeth (6)
- 35 Subdue (8)
- 36 At the back (6)

DOWN

- 1 Potato snack (5)
- 2 Entreaties (5)
- 3 Fever (4)
- 4 Equals (5)
- 5 Melt (4)
- 6 Enjoy (6)
- 9 Espy (6)
- 11 Mine (3)
- 12 Engrave (5)
- 13 Setting agent (7)
- 15 Friend (3)
- 16 Expert (3)
- 18 Religious festival (6)
- 20 Toss (5)
- 21 Suitable (3)
- 22 Zero (3)
- 23 Laterally (6)
- 25 Enclosure (3)
- 28 Fire-raising (5)
- 30 Aviator (5)
- 31 At no time (5)
- 32 Destiny (4)
- 33 Type (4)

181

ACROSS

3 Fireplace (5)
8 Group of witches (5)
10 Go in (5)
11 Twitch (3)
12 Placates (5)
13 Amusing (7)
15 Stiff paste (5)
18 Hill (3)
19 Gratify (6)
21 Breathe (7)
22 Declare (4)
23 Inform (4)
24 Bands (7)
26 Accustoms (6)
29 Sprint (3)
31 Warning device (5)
32 Be seated (3,4)
34 Grind up (5)
35 Tavern (3)
36 Delicate (5)
37 Scornful remark (5)
38 Rips (5)

DOWN

1 Helicopter blade (5)
2 Narrator (7)
4 Genuine (4)
5 Place of worship (6)
6 Follow (5)
7 Chairs (5)
9 Vigour (3)
12 Floor coverings (7)
14 Lettuce (3)
16 Accepts (5)
17 Shouts (5)
19 Grassy plain (7)
20 Foundation (5)
21 Happen again (5)
23 Caring for (7)
24 Doting (6)
25 Place (3)
27 Gunpowder ingredient (5)
28 Send (5)
30 Possessed (5)
32 Mark (4)
33 Single (3)

182

ACROSS

1 Mistreat (5)
6 Wireless (5)
9 Difficulty (7)
10 Look fixedly (5)
11 Essential (5)
12 Sensational (5)
13 Railing (7)
15 Tree (3)
17 Woman's name (4)
18 Make smaller (6)
19 Evade (5)
20 Invent (6)
22 Yield (4)
24 Consume (3)
25 Stronghold (7)
26 Facial hair (5)
27 Contempt (5)
28 Hand tool (5)
29 Unshakable (7)
30 Revises (5)
31 Canvas shelters (5)

DOWN

2 Superhero (6)
3 Extend (6)
4 Before (3)
5 Concerning (5)
6 Spoke badly of (7)
7 Among (4)
8 Slanted letter (6)
12 Depart (5)
13 Pennies (5)
14 Metal fastener (5)
15 Joined (5)
16 Wallow (5)
18 Stiff (5)
19 Is present (7)
21 Rank (6)
22 Danish king of England (6)
23 Fault (6)
25 Felony (5)
26 Spoilt child (4)
28 Insect (3)

ACROSS

1 Positioned (6)
7 Coming into being (8)
8 Run away (4)
10 Climbed (6)
11 Water down (6)
14 Mountain pass (3)
16 Utter (5)
17 Casserole (4)
19 Principle (5)
21 Cringe (5)
22 Shooting star (5)
23 Worry (4)
26 Indian instrument (5)
28 Snake (3)
29 Box (6)
30 Border (6)
31 Encourage (4)
32 Esteems (8)
33 Giggle (6)

DOWN

1 Levers (6)
2 Inexperienced (6)
3 Action (4)
4 Judge (7)
5 Refute (5)
6 Alloy (5)
8 Countenance (4)
9 Slippery fish (3)
12 Auction item (3)
13 List (5)
15 Less (5)
18 Shinbone (5)
19 Male cat (3)
20 Mesh (3)
21 Small crown (7)
22 Feline (3)
23 Neglect (6)
24 Fury (4)
25 Sensitive (6)
26 Frighten (5)
27 Faith (5)
28 Cafe (3)
30 Has to (4)

184

ACROSS

4 Occur (6)
7 Insect (8)
8 Summary (6)
10 Handle (5)
13 Stink (4)
14 Ages (4)
15 Minus (4)
16 Expert (3)
17 Frozen rain (4)
19 Island (4)
21 Four-sided figure (9)
23 Metal (4)
24 Sound quality (4)
26 Entreat (3)
27 At any time (4)
29 Border (4)
32 Singles (4)
33 Reel (5)
34 Apportions (6)
35 Brass instrument (8)
36 Strain (6)

DOWN

1 Strike heavily (5)
2 Poplar (5)
3 Break (4)
4 Aspirations (5)
5 Furtive glance (4)
6 Show clearly (6)
9 Give up a job (6)
11 Argument (3)
12 Pale (5)
13 Narrates (7)
15 Illuminated (3)
16 Beer (3)
18 Emphasis (6)
20 Slumber (5)
21 Manipulate
fraudulently (3)
22 And not (3)
23 Fanatic (6)
25 In the past (3)
28 Singlets (5)
30 Giver (5)
31 Senior (5)
32 Seep (4)
33 Identical (4)

ACROSS

3 Gardening tool (5)
8 Race meeting (5)
10 Goes out (5)
11 Male cat (3)
12 Clan (5)
13 Breathe (7)
15 Weapon-bearing (5)
18 Before (3)
19 Dress (6)
21 Foot lever (7)
22 Unusual (4)
23 Closed (4)
24 Small crown (7)
26 Sinew (6)
29 Colour (3)
31 Senior (5)
32 Liquid containers (7)
34 Smith's block (5)
35 That woman (3)
36 Fashion (5)
37 Sill (5)
38 Company of soldiers (5)

DOWN

1 Flower (5)
2 Master of ceremonies (7)
4 Unadulterated (4)
5 Discuss (6)
6 Make an effort (5)
7 Freshwater mammal (5)
9 Lettuce (3)
12 Treachery (7)
14 Anger (3)
16 Power (5)
17 Hollows (5)
19 Ethanol (7)
20 Hackneyed (5)
21 Fashion (5)
23 Fumed (7)
24 Angle (6)
25 Kernel (3)
27 Delight (5)
28 Traded (5)
30 Material (5)
32 Ballpoint pen (4)
33 Guided (3)

186

ACROSS

1 Slander (5)
6 Cursed (5)
9 Fascinate (7)
10 Fear (5)
11 Follow (5)
12 Inclined (5)
13 Refers (7)
15 Screen (3)
17 Dregs (4)
18 Mock (6)
19 Helicopter blade (5)
20 Occur (6)
22 Vegetables (4)
24 Donkey (3)
25 Opposite (7)
26 Punctuation mark (5)
27 Communion table (5)
28 Garish (5)
29 Bands (7)
30 Leaves out (5)
31 Wigwams (5)

DOWN

2 Confidence (6)
3 Counting frame (6)
4 Colour (3)
5 Regulations (5)
6 Thin (7)
7 Departed (4)
8 Excited (6)
12 Fruit (5)
13 Greek letter (5)
14 Jumps (5)
15 Adder (5)
16 Taut (5)
18 Twelve (5)
19 Accounts (7)
21 Shelter (6)
22 Study (6)
23 Aid (6)
25 Small bird (5)
26 Theatre company (4)
28 Allow (3)

ACROSS

1 Pamper (6)
7 Stationery item (8)
8 Is seated (4)
10 Fanatic (6)
11 Feel bitter at (6)
14 Obtained (3)
16 Ascends (5)
17 Celebrity (4)
19 At no time (5)
21 Located (5)
22 Spiral (5)
23 Pour (4)
26 Sugary (5)
28 Tier (3)
29 Factories (6)
30 Coercion (6)
31 Agents (4)
32 Light musical drama (8)
33 Device (6)

DOWN

1 Fads (6)
2 Seaman (6)
3 Trial (4)
4 Esteemed (7)
5 Manages (5)
6 Achievements (5)
8 Heroic narrative (4)
9 Small child (3)
12 Title (3)
13 Courage (5)
15 Stinking (5)
18 Fish (5)
19 Nothing (3)
20 Annoy (3)
21 Arranged (7)
22 Domestic fowl (3)
23 Apathetic (6)
24 Female sheep (4)
25 Lucky charm (6)
26 Reel (5)
27 Keen (5)
28 Regret (3)
30 Pull (4)

188

ACROSS

4 Named (6)
7 Irregular fighter (8)
8 Thin (6)
10 Turn (5)
13 Gown (4)
14 Every (4)
15 Ale (4)
16 Eggs (3)
17 Honest (4)
19 Competent (4)
21 Made believe (9)
23 Decays (4)
24 Leaves (4)
26 Strike (3)
27 Fastened (4)
29 Sign (4)
32 Trees (4)
33 Grin (5)
34 Maintenance (6)
35 Lift (8)
36 Container (6)

DOWN

1 Gemstone (5)
2 Keepsake (5)
3 Itemised record (4)
4 Paddled boat (5)
5 Entice (4)
6 Develop (6)
9 Scrape (6)
11 Pale (3)
12 Brief (5)
13 Goes back (7)
15 Wager (3)
16 Elderly (3)
18 Grinding implement (6)
20 Broom (5)
21 Cooking container (3)
22 Show assent (3)
23 Small wave (6)
25 Solidify (3)
28 Force (5)
30 Foggy (5)
31 Approaches (5)
32 Slippery fish (4)
33 Rescue (4)

ACROSS

3 Perform (5)
8 Insurgent (5)
10 Fire-raising (5)
11 Animal's coat (3)
12 Pigs (5)
13 Stops (7)
15 Liking (5)
18 By way of (3)
19 Bind (6)
21 Colonist (7)
22 Wagers (4)
23 Potato (4)
24 Barren (7)
26 Decadent (6)
29 Beer (3)
31 Postpone (5)
32 Citizen soldiery (7)
34 Got up (5)
35 Trap (3)
36 Savoury jelly (5)
37 Merriment (5)
38 Anaesthetic (5)

DOWN

1 Allude (5)
2 Deduces (7)
4 Tidings (4)
5 Horse's gait (6)
6 Handle (5)
7 Journey (5)
9 Coach (3)
12 Rule (7)
14 Pose (3)
16 Form (5)
17 Wear away (5)
19 Ground (7)
20 Receded (5)
21 Rod (5)
23 Sleds (7)
24 Severe (6)
25 Sick (3)
27 Banquet (5)
28 Creepy (5)
30 Penalises (5)
32 Lake (4)
33 Fasten (3)

190

ACROSS

1 Man-eating monsters (5)
6 Hide (5)
9 Soccer forward (7)
10 Whim (5)
11 Realign (5)
12 Attend (5)
13 Tidy up (7)
15 Thus (3)
17 Compass point (4)
18 Grab (6)
19 Rep (5)
20 Tree-lined street (6)
22 Join (4)
24 Can (3)
25 Wrestle (7)
26 Grin (5)
27 Roofing tile (5)
28 Buffalo (5)
29 Occupy (7)
30 Noise of contempt (5)
31 Nurses (5)

DOWN

2 Unit of mass (6)
3 Accompany (6)
4 Pig-pen (3)
5 Warning device (5)
6 Attendant (7)
7 Large shrub (4)
8 Picturesque (6)
12 Material (5)
13 Perspire (5)
14 Pale (5)
15 Precipitous (5)
16 Ring (5)
18 Trap (5)
19 Increase (7)
21 Stringed instrument (6)
22 Spirit (6)
23 Nut (6)
25 Sparkle (5)
26 Move (4)
28 Section (3)

191

ACROSS

1 Fold (6)
7 Retract (8)
8 Clean (4)
10 Turning points (6)
11 Promise (6)
14 Group (3)
16 Fashion (5)
17 Biblical garden (4)
19 Bet (5)
21 Float (5)
22 Nine-piece band (5)
23 Pain (4)
26 Navigate (5)
28 Everything (3)
29 Powerful (6)
30 Coarse (6)
31 So be it (4)
32 Tarnishing (8)
33 Whole (6)

DOWN

1 Section of theatre seats (6)
2 Originated (6)
3 Female sheep (4)
4 Lee (7)
5 Impure (5)
6 Possessed (5)
8 Sagacious (4)
9 Domestic animal (3)
12 Stray (3)
13 Grind (5)
15 Rescued (5)
18 Aforementioned (5)
19 Came first (3)
20 Obtain (3)
21 Wasps (7)
22 Born (3)
23 Watch-chain (6)
24 Tribe (4)
25 Last (6)
26 Malice (5)
27 Moral (5)
28 Goal (3)
30 Fury (4)

192

ACROSS

4 Listed (6)
7 Easy win (8)
8 Apprehend (6)
10 Cut (5)
13 Expired (4)
14 Canvas shelter (4)
15 Sensed (4)
16 Allow (3)
17 Gemstone (4)
19 Overwhelmed (4)
21 Elucidated (9)
23 Active person (4)
24 Departed (4)
26 Cot (3)
27 Pain (4)
29 Dull (4)
32 Revise (4)
33 Stage whisper (5)
34 Tower (6)
35 Airy (8)
36 Divides (6)

DOWN

1 Turn (5)
2 Wash (5)
3 Insect (4)
4 Track (5)
5 Poet (4)
6 Followed (6)
9 Keep (6)
11 Meadow (3)
12 Purloined (5)
13 Elation (7)
15 Distant (3)
16 Guided (3)
18 Procession (6)
20 Widow's outfit (5)
21 Fish (3)
22 Enemy (3)
23 Deceive (6)
25 Boy (3)
28 Quotes (5)
30 Angered (5)
31 Stomach (5)
32 Gaelic (5)
33 Terminated (4)

ACROSS

3 Cutting edge (5)
8 Scoundrel (5)
10 Chief minister of a synagogue (5)
11 Taxi (3)
12 Weasel-like mammal (5)
13 Badge (7)
15 Web-footed birds (5)
18 Meadow (3)
19 Hat (6)
21 Great joy (7)
22 Notion (4)
23 Unaccompanied (4)
24 Type of bacon (7)
26 Smother (6)
29 Arid (3)
31 In that place (5)
32 Mix (7)
34 Hatred (5)
35 Record (3)
36 Maturing (5)
37 Ridges of sand (5)
38 Rot (5)

DOWN

1 Bedtime drink (5)
2 German measles (7)
4 Tardy (4)
5 Mythical monster (6)
6 Consumed (5)
7 Maltreat (5)
9 Vapour (3)
12 Law (7)
14 Beverage (3)
16 Diplomat (5)
17 Distinctive character (5)
19 Tedium (7)
20 Prime (5)
21 Weird (5)
23 Azure (3,4)
24 Sleigh (6)
25 Equip (3)
27 Part of the leg (5)
28 Leaf of a fern (5)
30 Divine messenger (5)
32 Island in the West Indies (4)
33 Charged particle (3)

194

ACROSS

1 Tumbler (5)
6 Throw (5)
9 Notice (7)
10 Rush (5)
11 Blood vessel (5)
12 Up to (5)
13 Versus (7)
15 Public vehicle (3)
17 Check (4)
18 End (6)
19 Nimble (5)
20 Claim (6)
22 Dull pain (4)
24 Observe (3)
25 Soft juicy fruits (7)
26 Guide (5)
27 Country house (5)
28 Of the ear (5)
29 Reaches (7)
30 Join together (5)
31 Inclines (5)

DOWN

2 Sitting room (6)
3 Slight injury (6)
4 Cunning (3)
5 Perfume (5)
6 Treeless plain (7)
7 Object of worship (4)
8 Genus of fruit trees (6)
12 Custom (5)
13 Regions (5)
14 Gangway (5)
15 Type of tree (5)
16 Items of footwear (5)
18 Pilot (5)
19 Stir up (7)
21 Injury or wound (6)
22 Impute blame (6)
23 Harbinger (6)
25 Flower part (5)
26 Strip of wood (4)
28 Insect (3)

ACROSS

1 Occult (6)
7 Chord with notes played in succession (8)
8 Italian wine (4)
10 Individual (6)
11 Long flag (6)
14 Drinking vessel (3)
16 Stiff (5)
17 Pain (4)
19 Take illegally (5)
21 Essential (5)
22 Escapade (5)
23 Sleeping places (4)
26 Cut off (5)
28 Given food (3)
29 Allow (6)
30 Penalise (6)
31 Single entity (4)
32 Breed of dog (8)
33 Bicycle for two (6)

DOWN

1 Short-sightedness (6)
2 Paper handkerchief (6)
3 Brother of Abel (4)
4 Many (7)
5 Getting old (5)
6 Small hill (5)
8 Curved structure (4)
9 Summit (3)
12 Nought (3)
13 Lubricated (5)
15 Speak (5)
18 Hidden store (5)
19 Drink daintily (3)
20 Organ of hearing (3)
21 Diversity (7)
22 English river (3)
23 Genial (6)
24 Prepare for publication (4)
25 Split (6)
26 Lance (5)
27 Rub out (5)
28 Amusement (3)
30 Flat-bottomed boat (4)

196

ACROSS

4 Catchphrase (6)
7 Broadcast (8)
8 Feline mammal (6)
10 Chosen (5)
13 Relative, commonly (4)
14 Fairy (4)
15 Body of men (4)
16 Serpent (3)
17 Greek letter (4)
19 Unit of distance (4)
21 Fete (9)
23 Rabbit-like animal (4)
24 Skeleton part (4)
26 Equal (3)
27 Ship's company (4)
29 Scent (4)
32 Metal fastener (4)
33 Poplar (5)
34 Cruelty (6)
35 Memory aid (8)
36 Mimicry (6)

DOWN

1 Precipitous (5)
2 Long-snouted mammal (5)
3 Island (4)
4 Tempest (5)
5 Kiln (4)
6 Excite (6)
9 Caribbean islands (6)
11 Allow (3)
12 Roman river (5)
13 Snatched (7)
15 Consumed (3)
16 Beer (3)
18 Votes (6)
20 Units (5)
21 Vehicle (3)
22 Argue (3)
23 Cuban capital (6)
25 Employ (3)
28 Card game (5)
30 Upset (5)
31 Rap (5)
32 Storage tower (4)
33 Targets (4)

ACROSS

3 Economic decline (5)
8 Bellybutton (5)
10 Passageway (5)
11 Can (3)
12 Thrashes (5)
13 Talk idly (7)
15 Speak (5)
18 Tier (3)
19 Make (6)
21 Exhaustion (7)
22 Main body of a vessel (4)
23 Small case (4)
24 Accomplish (7)
26 Gaudy (6)
29 Mineral (3)
31 Gave out money (5)
32 Intensely hot chamber (7)
34 Melodies (5)
35 Anger (3)
36 Trainee officer (5)
37 Peruvian Indians (5)
38 Make merry (5)

DOWN

1 Turning device (5)
2 London tube line (7)
4 Suggestive look (4)
5 Ripe (6)
6 Ski slope (5)
7 Frozen rain (5)
9 By way of (3)
12 Enchant (7)
14 Youngster (3)
16 Sample (5)
17 Send (5)
19 Inquisitive (7)
20 Ruffians (5)
21 Burst of light (5)
23 Part of the day (7)
24 Shrewd (6)
25 Stray (3)
27 Dismay (5)
28 Bury (5)
30 Large sea (5)
32 Bazaar (4)
33 Curve (3)

198

ACROSS

1 Pale (5)
6 Apple drink (5)
9 Puzzles (7)
10 Plant used to make string (5)
11 Stiff (5)
12 Unruly children (5)
13 Wing flap (7)
15 Unit of electricity (3)
17 Move (4)
18 Ceremony (6)
19 Poplar (5)
20 Evoke (6)
22 Set of clothes (4)
24 Rodent (3)
25 Best wishes (7)
26 Urge (5)
27 Barrier (5)
28 Narrow-minded person (5)
29 Burdensome (7)
30 Be miserly (5)
31 Store secretly (5)

DOWN

2 Ghost (6)
3 Rubber (6)
4 Zero (3)
5 Decorate (5)
6 Sure (7)
7 Goddess (4)
8 Mystery (6)
12 Brag (5)
13 Flower (5)
14 Legal (5)
15 Presage (5)
16 Intrigues (5)
18 Drive off (5)
19 Sickness (7)
21 Mourn (6)
22 One who enjoys cruelty (6)
23 Fools (6)
25 Breeds (5)
26 Religious image (4)
28 Public vehicle (3)

ACROSS

1 Large scissors (6)
7 Unseemly (8)
8 Level (4)
10 Sea trip (6)
11 Mark of social disgrace (6)
14 Agent (3)
16 Cancel (5)
17 Beams of light (4)
19 Mischievous trick (5)
21 Face (5)
22 In a normal voice (5)
23 Unopened flowers (4)
26 Writing not in verse (5)
28 Play on words (3)
29 Respiratory disorder (6)
30 Food store (6)
31 In addition (4)
32 Repugnance (8)
33 Merited (6)

DOWN

1 Association football (6)
2 Friends (6)
3 Piece of land (4)
4 Navigational instrument (7)
5 Rule (5)
6 Take unlawfully (5)
8 Rage (4)
9 Snake (3)
12 Writing fluid (3)
13 Made silent (5)
15 Haughty (5)
18 States (5)
19 In favour (3)
20 Also (3)
21 One of Belgium's official languages (7)
22 Fire residue (3)
23 University official (6)
24 Release (4)
25 Rushed suddenly (6)
26 Heathen (5)
27 Mammal (5)
28 Comrade (3)
30 Narrow way (4)

200

ACROSS

4 Embedded (6)
7 Pasta tubes (8)
8 Unit of learning (6)
10 Furze (5)
13 Cloth or paper bag (4)
14 Region (4)
15 Measure of length (4)
16 Era (3)
17 Office note, in short (4)
19 Cry of pain (4)
21 Part (9)
23 Stinging insect (4)
24 Piquancy (4)
26 Colour (3)
27 German song (4)
29 Press (4)
32 Person in charge (4)
33 Near (5)
34 Ever (6)
35 Last (8)
36 Alter (6)

DOWN

1 Greek letter (5)
2 Cut (5)
3 Liberate (4)
4 Fragrant shrub (5)
5 Twilight (4)
6 Sufficient (6)
9 Resounds (6)
11 Sphere (3)
12 Island in the Aegean Sea (5)
13 Naps (7)
15 Little devil (3)
16 Perform (3)
18 Use (6)
20 Up to (5)
21 Bounder (3)
22 Diminutive of Edward (3)
23 Riches (6)
25 Type of lettuce (3)
28 Edition (5)
30 Regal (5)
31 At no time (5)
32 Farm building (4)
33 Cut off (4)

ACROSS

3 Savage (5)
8 Smudge (5)
10 Satisfied (5)
11 Stray (3)
12 Sumptuous meal (5)
13 Climb with difficulty (7)
15 Weird (5)
18 Supporter (3)
19 Leisurely walk (6)
21 Hugs (7)
22 Genuine (4)
23 Prefix meaning 'half' (4)
24 Pried (7)
26 Exposing (6)
29 Born (3)
31 Char (5)
32 Unyielding (7)
34 Inclines (5)
35 Anger (3)
36 Singing voice (5)
37 Access (5)
38 Willow (5)

DOWN

1 Odour (5)
2 Injurious (7)
4 Always (4)
5 Advantages (6)
6 Afterwards (5)
7 Demon (5)
9 Age (3)
12 Providing support, etc. (7)
14 Not good (3)
16 Wandered (5)
17 Mr Presley (5)
19 Moments (7)
20 Cots (5)
21 Mound of stones (5)
23 Appearing (7)
24 Shows contempt (6)
25 Seed eaten as a vegetable (3)
27 Assisted (5)
28 Eskimo dwelling (5)
30 Still (5)
32 Bet (4)
33 Skill (3)

202

ACROSS

1 Culinary plant (5)
6 Emblem (5)
9 White fur (7)
10 Range (5)
11 Greek letter (5)
12 Greenfly (5)
13 Heads (7)
15 Beer (3)
17 Desire (4)
18 Concurred (6)
19 Untrue (5)
20 Goes in (6)
22 Ascend (4)
24 Observe (3)
25 Saves (7)
26 Start (5)
27 Operatic songs (5)
28 Dizzy (5)
29 Word for word (7)
30 Play (5)
31 Leader of the 12 Apostles (5)

DOWN

2 Bowman (6)
3 Hinder (6)
4 Untruth (3)
5 Delicate strands (5)
6 Hem in (7)
7 Dry (4)
8 Play for money (6)
12 Regions (5)
13 Stringed instruments (5)
14 Semi-precious stone (5)
15 Eagle's nest (5)
16 Borders (5)
18 Poplar (5)
19 Fragrant flower (7)
21 Closer (6)
22 Abuse (6)
23 Smear (6)
25 Large stream (5)
26 Aromatic substance (4)
28 Opening (3)

203

ACROSS

1 Morally wrong (6)
7 Made up (8)
8 'Slippery' fish (4)
10 Throat (6)
11 Generous (6)
14 Area of water (3)
16 Spirit (5)
17 Maple genus (4)
19 Dim (5)
21 Northern moors (5)
22 Wooden peg (5)
23 Felines (4)
26 Shoe part (5)
28 Mentally dull (3)
29 Public way (6)
30 Cheap American restaurants (6)
31 Overt (4)
32 Showing unwillingness (8)
33 Rubber (6)

DOWN

1 Mark of social disgrace (6)
2 Antenna (6)
3 Item-by-item record (4)
4 Steps down (7)
5 Blemish (5)
6 Saying (5)
8 Otherwise (4)
9 Meadow (3)
12 Screen (3)
13 Period of darkness (5)
15 Stories (5)
18 Vault (5)
19 Not many (3)
20 Unwell (3)
21 Alien (7)
22 Name of rivers in Scotland, England and Wales (3)
23 Place where films are shown (6)
24 So be it (4)
25 Female relative (6)
26 Custom (5)
27 Haughty (5)
28 Dunk (3)
30 Formerly, a chief magistrate in Venice (4)

204

ACROSS

4 Tainted (6)
7 Unnecessary (8)
8 Muslim leader (6)
10 Lively (5)
13 Female relative (4)
14 Unaccompanied (4)
15 Worry (4)
16 Summit (3)
17 Bellow (4)
19 Press (4)
21 Man who serves drinks (9)
23 Food fish (4)
24 States (4)
26 Vessel (3)
27 Large town (4)
29 Foot digits (4)
32 Trees (4)
33 Savoury jelly (5)
34 Part of the foot (6)
35 Practice or drill (8)
36 Servile (6)

DOWN

1 Breaks suddenly (5)
2 Gem from an oyster (5)
3 Slaughter (4)
4 Edition (5)
5 Animal skin (4)
6 Cause (6)
9 Messy (6)
11 Age (3)
12 Sacred book of Islam (5)
13 Apprehends (7)
15 Obese (3)
16 Rocky hill (3)
18 Agency of divine revelation (6)
20 Pauses (5)
21 Small cake (3)
22 No (3)
23 Hypnotic state (6)
25 Flower garland (3)
28 Force (5)
30 Drinks dispenser (5)
31 Threaded fastener (5)
32 Small case (4)
33 Simple tunes (4)

ACROSS

3 Deliberate deception (5)
8 Draw off liquid (5)
10 Refute (5)
11 Lubricate (3)
12 Herb (5)
13 Ennui (7)
15 Uncertainty (5)
18 Sister (3)
19 Leading singer in a synagogue (6)
21 Natural landscape features (7)
22 Stack (4)
23 Tidy (4)
24 Stutter (7)
26 Spring flower (6)
29 Observe (3)
31 Outstanding (5)
32 Joining together (7)
34 Devil (5)
35 Auction item (3)
36 Tag (5)
37 Hard-wearing fabric (5)
38 Perishing (5)

DOWN

1 Ponder morbidly (5)
2 Lack of noise (7)
4 Rich soil (4)
5 Weekday (6)
6 Criminal (5)
7 Extra large (5)
9 Simple tune (3)
12 Hats (7)
14 Owing (3)
16 Speak (5)
17 Veracity (5)
19 Shade of red (7)
20 Glasses, informally (5)
21 Sailing vessel (5)
23 Sewing implements (7)
24 Certainly (6)
25 Males (3)
27 Of the country (5)
28 Gave up (5)
30 Unfasten (5)
32 Blessing (4)
33 Charged particle (3)

206

ACROSS

1 Salad plant (5)
6 Not fresh (5)
9 Goblet (7)
10 Wander (5)
11 Irate (5)
12 Grown-up (5)
13 Go before (7)
15 English river (3)
17 In this place (4)
18 Tell (6)
19 Flower-part (5)
20 Wobble (6)
22 Tolerate (4)
24 Aged (3)
25 Break-up of marriage (7)
26 Furious (5)
27 Drink dispenser (5)
28 Capital of France (5)
29 Long-tailed, furry mammal (7)
30 Portable chair (5)
31 Fastening (5)

DOWN

2 Withdraw (6)
3 In short supply (6)
4 Reserved (3)
5 Cutting edge (5)
6 Surgical instrument (7)
7 Canvas shelter (4)
8 Lasso (6)
12 Viper (5)
13 Snapshot, in short (5)
14 Strayed (5)
15 Provide food, services, etc. (5)
16 Unit of length (5)
18 Swift (5)
19 Aquatic bird (7)
21 Run out (6)
22 Study of plants (6)
23 Movement (6)
25 Narrow channel (5)
26 Italian unit of currency (4)
28 Cooking vessel (3)

ACROSS

1 Sly (6)
7 Flood (8)
8 Thick cord (4)
10 On a ship, train, etc. (6)
11 Corsair (6)
14 Pig pen (3)
16 Card game (5)
17 Foot digits (4)
19 Stiff (5)
21 Rescued (5)
22 Garden flower (5)
23 Abound (4)
26 Bay window (5)
28 Automobile (3)
29 Soundness of mind (6)
30 Spring bulbs (6)
31 Overt (4)
32 Infinite time (8)
33 Put in order (6)

DOWN

1 Overcome with amazement (6)
2 Festival vehicles (6)
3 German song (4)
4 Unpalatable (7)
5 Eskimo canoe (5)
6 At no time (5)
8 Ascended (4)
9 Snoop (3)
12 Staff (3)
13 Taut (5)
15 Polite (5)
18 Musical work (5)
19 Knock (3)
20 Information (3)
21 Dried grape (7)
22 Flower-garland (3)
23 Gift (6)
24 Old name for Ireland (4)
25 Muslim place of worship (6)
26 Willow (5)
27 Bury (5)
28 Drinking vessel (3)
30 Playthings (4)

208

ACROSS

4 Wet and sticky (6)
7 Observer (8)
8 Landed property (6)
10 Make corrections (5)
13 Italian wine (4)
14 Distinctive air (4)
15 Singing voice (4)
16 Unwell (3)
17 Group of actors (4)
19 Contest of speed (4)
21 Chief adversary (9)
23 Worry (4)
24 Went by car, etc. (4)
26 Favourite (3)
27 Chilled (4)
29 Common sense (4)
32 Keen (4)
33 Worship (5)
34 Overjoyed (6)
35 Nervousness (8)
36 Quake (6)

DOWN

1 Black tea (5)
2 More senior (5)
3 Cowl (4)
4 Badge (5)
5 Against (4)
6 Courage (6)
9 Set aside for future use (6)
11 Drinking vessel (3)
12 Mother-of-pearl (5)
13 Changed (7)
15 Tree (3)
16 Freezing (3)
18 Lively (6)
20 Alter (5)
21 Skill (3)
22 Show agreement (3)
23 Antenna (6)
25 Animal coat (3)
28 Apple drink (5)
30 Seeped (5)
31 Be aware of (5)
32 Very small particle (4)
33 Corrosive substance (4)

209

ACROSS

3 Vexed (5)
8 Catkin-bearing tree (5)
10 Fruit (5)
11 Pair (3)
12 Courageous (5)
13 Base (7)
15 Piece of cast metal (5)
18 Foot digit (3)
19 Buries (6)
21 Significance (7)
22 Listen to (4)
23 Raise (4)
24 Goes back (7)
26 Expelled (6)
29 Staff (3)
31 Horse (5)
32 Acclimatised (7)
34 Requirements (5)
35 Child's bed (3)
36 Taunt (5)
37 Surrendered (5)
38 Glowing coal (5)

DOWN

1 Mosquito-like insect (5)
2 Two-wheeled vehicle (7)
4 Uncommon (4)
5 Reduction in expenditure (6)
6 Exhausted (5)
7 Storey (5)
9 Manage (3)
12 Combined (7)
14 Type of snake (3)
16 Hereditary factors (5)
17 Old Russian rulers (5)
19 Puts in (7)
20 Complete disorder (5)
21 Religious minister's house (5)
23 Made smaller (7)
24 Save (6)
25 Speck (3)
27 Speak (5)
28 Taut (5)
30 Measuring device (5)
32 Tool (4)
33 Show assent (3)

210

ACROSS

1 Be buoyant (5)
6 Wear away (5)
9 Sickness (7)
10 Muscle contraction (5)
11 Sculpt wood etc. (5)
12 Record (5)
13 100 years (7)
15 Equip (3)
17 Minerals (4)
18 Generosity (6)
19 Melodies (5)
20 Bear (6)
22 Dread (4)
24 Period of time (3)
25 Head-cold (7)
26 Warning device (5)
27 Huge (5)
28 Anaesthetic (5)
29 Greenery (7)
30 Possessor (5)
31 Speak at length (5)

DOWN

2 Food store (6)
3 Owns (6)
4 Gratuity (3)
5 Abdomen (5)
6 Portuguese coins (7)
7 Measure of paper (4)
8 Amuse (6)
12 Row (5)
13 Managed (5)
14 Poor (5)
15 Wrath (5)
16 Aromatic substance (5)
18 Started (5)
19 Person guilty of treason (7)
21 Small in breadth (6)
22 Quicker (6)
23 Eager (6)
25 Girl's name (5)
26 Secure (4)
28 Self-image (3)

ACROSS

1 Haphazard (6)
7 Small exterior building (8)
8 Mines (4)
10 Moving crowds (6)
11 Traps (6)
14 Small ocean (3)
16 Name (5)
17 Stagger (4)
19 Teacher (5)
21 Fact (5)
22 Type of fabric (5)
23 Small missile (4)
26 Wise men (5)
28 Adherent (3)
29 Content (6)
30 Fugitive (6)
31 Impulse (4)
32 Fanciful and sentimental (8)
33 Custodian (6)

DOWN

1 Attacker (6)
2 Nonsense (6)
3 Plant that grows on trees, rocks, etc. (4)
4 Spectre (7)
5 Liquid measure (5)
6 Property contract (5)
8 Stance (4)
9 Beverage (3)
12 Simple melody (3)
13 Senior (5)
15 Made silent (5)
18 Equivalent (5)
19 Thrash (3)
20 Barrel (3)
21 Difference of opinion (7)
22 Meadow (3)
23 Hang suspended (6)
24 The Princess Royal (4)
25 Great fear (6)
26 Steeple (5)
27 Bacteria (5)
28 Animal coat (3)
30 Crease (4)

212

ACROSS

4 Yield (6)
7 Reminiscent (8)
8 From side to side (6)
10 Platform (5)
13 Middle East republic (4)
14 Inform (4)
15 Insects (4)
16 Not many (3)
17 Paddles (4)
19 Second-hand (4)
21 Rebuke (9)
23 Many (4)
24 Rod (4)
26 Piece (3)
27 Dry (4)
29 Prepare for publication (4)
32 German song (4)
33 Animal's trail (5)
34 Makes petty objections (6)
35 Made up (8)
36 Be next to (6)

DOWN

1 Baked shell of a pie (5)
2 Perfect (5)
3 Hint (4)
4 Begin (5)
5 Farm building (4)
6 Flowed out (6)
9 Informal (6)
11 Young sheep (3)
12 Dwell on exultantly (5)
13 Unpalatable (7)
15 Skill (3)
16 Professional payment (3)
18 Attack (6)
20 Precipitous (5)
21 Baby's bed (3)
22 Deity (3)
23 Reptile (6)
25 Brazilian port (3)
28 Plant extract used in varnishes, etc. (5)
30 Slightly mad (5)
31 Business (5)
32 Open-air pool (4)
33 Appear (4)

213

ACROSS

3 Imperfections (5)
8 Egyptian embalmed body (5)
10 Bury (5)
11 Flower-garland (3)
12 Telegram (5)
13 State briefly (7)
15 Rips (5)
18 Equip (3)
19 Study (6)
21 Paced (7)
22 Thick cord (4)
23 Ladder step (4)
24 Stupid mistake (7)
26 Loafers (6)
29 Sicken (3)
31 Liquid measure (5)
32 Notches (7)
34 Respond (5)
35 Melody (3)
36 Chaos (5)
37 Poplar (5)
38 Massive horned animal, in short (5)

DOWN

1 Regulations (5)
2 Ape (7)
4 Incline (4)
5 Drooped (6)
6 Show contempt (5)
7 Dreads (5)
9 Males (3)
12 Forces (7)
14 Anger (3)
16 Be an omen (5)
17 Grasslike plant (5)
19 Flag (7)
20 Delicate (5)
21 Upset (5)
23 Set free (7)
24 Part of a gun (6)
25 Performed (3)
27 Backless sofa (5)
28 Mistake (5)
30 Scatter (5)
32 Religious image (4)
33 Pinch (3)

214

ACROSS

1 Shut (5)
6 Emaciated (5)
9 Mild (7)
10 Smooth and shiny (5)
11 Main blood vessel (5)
12 Tempest (5)
13 Takes offence (7)
15 Perform (3)
17 Poems (4)
18 Trader (6)
19 Positioned (5)
20 Astounded (6)
22 Desire (4)
24 Moral wrong (3)
25 Dwarfed (7)
26 Plunder (5)
27 Breed of terrier (5)
28 Elf (5)
29 Stuck (7)
30 Informal trousers (5)
31 Romany (5)

DOWN

2 Lounged (6)
3 Play divisions (6)
4 Large deer (3)
5 Gives out (5)
6 Twisted (7)
7 Small amount (4)
8 Sign (6)
12 Sedate (5)
13 Rosters (5)
14 Portable chair (5)
15 Vigilant (5)
16 Attempted (5)
18 God (5)
19 Moments (7)
21 Illusion (6)
22 Messy (6)
23 Highly-gifted individual (6)
25 Alloy (5)
26 Husks of cereal grain (4)
28 Pin or dowel (3)

215

ACROSS

1 Frightened (6)
7 Adversary (8)
8 Regular (4)
10 Royal seat (6)
11 Priest (6)
14 Aged (3)
16 Name (5)
17 Compass point (4)
19 Cooked in fat (5)
21 Noblemen (5)
22 Snap (5)
23 Stink (4)
26 Concur (5)
28 Pitch (3)
29 Insect (6)
30 Dried grape (6)
31 Church recess (4)
32 Casting off (8)
33 Bear (6)

DOWN

1 Not obvious (6)
2 Rebel (6)
3 Performed (4)
4 Turns (7)
5 Raising agent (5)
6 Small rock (5)
8 Cupid (4)
9 Finish (3)
12 Free (3)
13 Oily fruit (5)
15 Abnormal person, object, etc. (5)
18 Saying (5)
19 Professional payment (3)
20 Vex (3)
21 Musical introduction (7)
22 Wager (3)
23 Elevated (6)
24 Gaelic (4)
25 Set alight (6)
26 Maltreat (5)
27 Allude (5)
28 Pat (3)
30 Fury (4)

216

ACROSS

4	Socialise (6)
7	Great musical artist (8)
8	Singe (6)
10	Furious (5)
13	Costly (4)
14	Nobleman (4)
15	Seeds eaten as a vegetable (4)
16	Cover (3)
17	Wander (4)
19	Second-hand (4)
21	Involve (9)
23	Mislaid (4)
24	Strong wind (4)
26	Unit of weight (3)
27	Metal (4)
29	Curves (4)
32	Burden (4)
33	Slumber (5)
34	Attractively unusual (6)
35	Habitually silent (8)
36	Tempestuous (6)

DOWN

1	Shun (5)
2	Cry of a frog (5)
3	Remedy (4)
4	Hebrew prophet (5)
5	Insensitive person (4)
6	Exotic flower (6)
9	Informal (6)
11	Floor covering (3)
12	Conditions (5)
13	Part mortal, part deity (7)
15	Friend (3)
16	Shelter (3)
18	Choice (6)
20	Take unlawfully (5)
21	Charged particle (3)
22	Tin (3)
23	Voracious insect (6)
25	Expert (3)
28	Bad-tempered (5)
30	Happen again (5)
31	Exhausted (5)
32	Teller of untruths (4)
33	Rotate (4)

217

ACROSS

3 Push (5)
8 Banal (5)
10 Watchful (5)
11 Expert (3)
12 On one's own (5)
13 Function (7)
15 Religious images (5)
18 Suitable (3)
19 Off-course (6)
21 Cunning (7)
22 Fencing foil (4)
23 Protagonist (4)
24 Adept (7)
26 Scuffles (6)
29 Tree (3)
31 Pilot (5)
32 Thwarted (7)
34 Eagle's nest (5)
35 Writing fluid (3)
36 Look amused (5)
37 Vex (5)
38 Precipitous (5)

DOWN

1 Chart (5)
2 Repeat (7)
4 Cavity (4)
5 Disappear (6)
6 Choose (5)
7 Sportsground (5)
9 Frozen water (3)
12 Raids (7)
14 Mimic (3)
16 Bay window (5)
17 Ecclesiastical council (5)
19 Sportsman (7)
20 Unfree persons (5)
21 Worsted fabric (5)
23 Buzzing (7)
24 Public road (6)
25 Go by air (3)
27 Objects (5)
28 Restores to health (5)
30 Black tea (5)
32 Piece of land (4)
33 Pub (3)

218

ACROSS

1 Faith (5)
6 Keen (5)
9 Omen (7)
10 Not fresh (5)
11 Outspoken (5)
12 Cotton fabric (5)
13 Pedagogue (7)
15 Church seat (3)
17 Lazy (4)
18 Dome (6)
19 Tolerates (5)
20 Quake (6)
22 Pain (4)
24 Utter (3)
25 Stifle (7)
26 Cluster (5)
27 Deluge (5)
28 Canvas shelters (5)
29 Common viral disease (7)
30 Snake (5)
31 Musical study (5)

DOWN

2 Decayed (6)
3 Join (6)
4 Foot digit (3)
5 Bullock (5)
6 Jealous (7)
7 Minute fragment (4)
8 Protective coating (6)
12 Postpone (5)
13 Shades (5)
14 Lane (5)
15 Sac (5)
16 Be indecisive (5)
18 Muscle contraction (5)
19 Large rock (7)
21 Raved (6)
22 Bear witness (6)
23 Warmed up (6)
25 Break in pieces (5)
26 Arrive (4)
28 Golf peg (3)

ACROSS

1 Club (6)
7 Lover of art (8)
8 Chess piece (4)
10 Declared (6)
11 Charm (6)
14 Allow (3)
16 Army chaplain (5)
17 Act (4)
19 Celestial body (5)
21 Managed (5)
22 Belief (5)
23 Aim (4)
26 Beer mug (5)
28 Beverage (3)
29 Intones (6)
30 Sadness (6)
31 Throws, informally (4)
32 Think too highly of (8)
33 Marine mammal (6)

DOWN

1 Hateful (6)
2 Jarred (6)
3 Country (4)
4 Halted (7)
5 Surrendered (5)
6 Beautiful woman (5)
8 Wan (4)
9 Very moist (3)
12 Tap (3)
13 Smell (5)
15 Was gloomy and deject-
ed (5)
18 Soil (5)
19 Swindle (3)
20 Encountered (3)
21 One hundred years (7)
22 Can (3)
23 Rodent (6)
24 Sculls (4)
25 Brings down (6)
26 Shovel (5)
27 Artist's support (5)
28 Also (3)
30 Slaughtered (4)

220

ACROSS

4 It contains the twelve star signs (6)
7 Introductory piece of music (8)
8 Combines (6)
10 Glower (5)
13 Tot (4)
14 Tender (4)
15 Tackle (4)
16 Sprint (3)
17 Baptismal bowl (4)
19 Costly (4)
21 Happening repeatedly (9)
23 Only (4)
24 Distinctive air (4)
26 Offer (3)
27 Delicate woven fabric (4)
29 Trim (4)
32 Defensive enclosure (4)
33 Condition (5)
34 Owns (6)
35 Out of use (8)
36 Religious speech (6)

DOWN

1 Percussion instruments (5)
2 Exclude (5)
3 Eye inflammation (4)
4 Striped animal (5)
5 Consider (4)
6 Passion (6)
9 Food store (6)
11 Vulgar (3)
12 Allude (5)
13 Diminish (7)
15 Wildebeest (3)
16 Rodent (3)
18 Feline mammal (6)
20 Play out (5)
21 Colour (3)
22 Regret (3)
23 Centre (6)
25 Piece (3)
28 Fire-raising (5)
30 Subsequently (5)
31 Boy's name (5)
32 Company (4)
33 Anon (4)

221

ACROSS

3 Sections (5)
8 Indian tent (5)
10 Thespian (5)
11 Type of lettuce (3)
12 Stout rope (5)
13 Accountant (7)
15 Relish (5)
18 River barrier (3)
19 Whole (6)
21 Turmoil (7)
22 Prejudice (4)
23 Breed (4)
24 Pried (7)
26 Choose (6)
29 Tear (3)
31 Go in (5)
32 Flightless bird (7)
34 Crest (5)
35 Stray (3)
36 Spring bulb (5)
37 Awry (5)
38 Anaesthetic (5)

DOWN

1 Happen again (5)
2 Moreover (7)
4 Slightly open (4)
5 Gift (6)
6 Perfume (5)
7 Engine (5)
9 Seedcase (3)
12 Remark (7)
14 Sailor, commonly (3)
16 Made jeering remarks (5)
17 Long (5)
19 Sanction (7)
20 Maltreat (5)
21 Flaw (5)
23 Keep under control (7)
24 Writing (6)
25 Mine (3)
27 Boredom (5)
28 Weird (5)
30 Threaded fastener (5)
32 Look amorously at (4)
33 Vex (3)

222

ACROSS

1 Tender (5)
6 Fencing foils (5)
9 Mechanical device (7)
10 Underground vault (5)
11 Snares (5)
12 Female garment (5)
13 Singing voice (7)
15 Attempt (3)
17 Very sentimental (4)
18 Quit premises (6)
19 Piece of turf (5)
20 Dog shelter (6)
22 Spirit (4)
24 Cathedral city (3)
25 People owing money (7)
26 Shoe part (5)
27 Musical work (5)
28 Targeted (5)
29 Clever device (7)
30 Snake (5)
31 Canvas shelters (5)

DOWN

2 Trench (6)
3 Supreme power (6)
4 Rodent (3)
5 Military headdress (5)
6 Implore (7)
7 Saucy (4)
8 Skilful (6)
12 Mollusc (5)
13 Metal or wooden post (5)
14 Small coin (5)
15 Socially disapproved of (5)
16 Shouts (5)
18 Elector (5)
19 Lose hope (7)
21 Ran away to wed (6)
22 Hit (6)
23 Pressing (6)
25 Considers (5)
26 Impulse (4)
28 Deed (3)

223

ACROSS

1 Rarely (6)
7 Incursion (8)
8 Soon (4)
10 Submissive (6)
11 Overnight case (6)
14 Colour (3)
16 Apple drink (5)
17 Prophet (4)
19 Struggle (5)
21 Indistinct (5)
22 Stupid person (5)
23 Cast off (4)
26 Evaluate (5)
28 Shelter (3)
29 Of the teeth (6)
30 Wine bottle (6)
31 Prepare for publication (4)
32 Appreciative (8)
33 Sheen (6)

DOWN

1 Hues (6)
2 Unit of silk weight (6)
3 Pit (4)
4 Style (7)
5 Intense (5)
6 Bury (5)
8 Measure of land (4)
9 Aged (3)
12 Illuminated (3)
13 Fabric (5)
15 Intolerant person (5)
18 Rub out (5)
19 Distant (3)
20 Firearm (3)
21 Traveller (7)
22 Rug (3)
23 Succession of related things (6)
24 Warmth (4)
25 Sprinkle food with flour, etc. (6)
26 Saying (5)
27 Move furtively (5)
28 Boy (3)
30 Prison room (4)

224

ACROSS

4 Refreshments counter (6)
7 Speck (8)
8 Scratch (6)
10 Temporary drop in standard (5)
13 Complain (4)
14 Speech defect (4)
15 Solid mass (4)
16 Beer (3)
17 Freezes (4)
19 Soviet news agency (4)
21 Fierce (9)
23 Strong wind (4)
24 Master (4)
26 Not good (3)
27 So be it (4)
29 Notion (4)
32 Goddess (4)
33 Step (5)
34 Selected (6)
35 Mad, commonly (8)
36 Gentle wind (6)

DOWN

1 Upset (5)
2 Clutches (5)
3 Pleasant (4)
4 Broom (5)
5 Plant which has fronds (4)
6 Ejects (6)
9 One who takes prisoners (6)
11 Goal (3)
12 Patter (5)
13 Biceps, for instance (7)
15 Zodiac sign (3)
16 Fool (3)
18 Fold (6)
20 Inspection of business accounts (5)
21 Temporary craze (3)
22 Charged particle (3)
23 Collect (6)
25 Flower-garland (3)
28 Chop up or grind (5)
30 Old-fashioned (5)
31 Come up (5)
32 Eyot (4)
33 Unwell (4)

ACROSS

3 Wander aimlessly (5)
8 Fury (5)
10 Mistake (5)
11 Perish (3)
12 Not fresh (5)
13 Saves (7)
15 Stratum (5)
18 In favour of (3)
19 Staid (6)
21 Commotion (7)
22 Succulent plant (4)
23 Item of footwear (4)
24 Insolently bold (7)
26 Placard (6)
29 Individual (3)
31 Perspire (5)
32 Melodic (7)
34 Approaches (5)
35 Take illegally (3)
36 Summits (5)
37 Conical tent (5)
38 Simple seat (5)

DOWN

1 Command (5)
2 Spire (7)
4 Rodents (4)
5 One who cuts down trees (6)
6 Walk on (5)
7 Composition for nine musicians (5)
9 Help (3)
12 Suffocate (7)
14 Age (3)
16 Racing vessel (5)
17 Revolt (5)
19 Grave (7)
20 Temporary settlements (5)
21 Thicket (5)
23 Showed contempt (7)
24 Hate (6)
25 Girl's name (3)
27 Possessed (5)
28 Liquid containers (5)
30 Fleshy stem or root (5)
32 Threesome (4)
33 Dandy (3)

226

ACROSS

1 Fold (5)
6 Confidential remark (5)
9 Link (7)
10 Having a pleasant flavour (5)
11 Ringlets (5)
12 Removed (5)
13 Indistinct (7)
15 Consumed (3)
17 Allows (4)
18 Put by for future use (6)
19 Fools (5)
20 Opposed (6)
22 Constructed (4)
24 Sailor, commonly (3)
25 Counselled (7)
26 Smelling old and stale (5)
27 Seraglio (5)
28 Of the ear (5)
29 Fail to give due care (7)
30 Bosses (5)
31 Irritable (5)

DOWN

2 Responsible (6)
3 Thespians (6)
4 Plaything (3)
5 Work dough, etc. (5)
6 Stresses (7)
7 Daze (4)
8 Water down (6)
12 Taut (5)
13 Puff up (5)
14 Speak (5)
15 Regions (5)
16 Gradually moved sideways (5)
18 Shabby (5)
19 Supposes (7)
21 Empty (6)
22 Tiny (6)
23 Leave (6)
25 Coral reef (5)
26 Repair (4)
28 Perform (3)

ACROSS

1 Free (6)
7 Charming (8)
8 Widespread (4)
10 Fumbles (6)
11 Ceremonious (6)
14 Base (3)
16 Cotton yarn (5)
17 Fastened (4)
19 Crawl (5)
21 Staple food (5)
22 Stratum (5)
23 Wail (4)
26 Eastern garments (5)
28 Varnish (3)
29 Invest (6)
30 Tumulus (6)
31 Lazy (4)
32 Brawny (8)
33 Rehearsal (3,3)

DOWN

1 Small mechanical device (6)
2 Three-legged stand (6)
3 Observes (4)
4 Coaxed (7)
5 Movies (5)
6 Nimble (5)
8 Part (4)
9 Not many (3)
12 Tear (3)
13 Let (5)
15 Environment-friendly (5)
18 Perfect (5)
19 Weep (3)
20 Organ of hearing (3)
21 Shy (7)
22 Illuminated (3)
23 Type of grain (6)
24 Measure of land (4)
25 Sheriff or policeman (6)
26 Rogue (5)
27 Awaken (5)
28 Boy (3)
30 Feathered creature (4)

228

ACROSS

4 Mended by sewing (6)
7 Inside (8)
8 Proclamations (6)
10 Small hard fruits (5)
13 Prison (4)
14 Kind (4)
15 Lather (4)
16 Skill (3)
17 Blessing (4)
19 Small rodents (4)
21 Enchant (9)
23 Open pie (4)
24 Stack (4)
26 Sphere (3)
27 Notion (4)
29 Construct (4)
32 Needy (4)
33 Moving (5)
34 Baby (6)
35 Ten hundred (8)
36 Fortified wine (6)

DOWN

1 Prime (5)
2 Soak (5)
3 Weapons (4)
4 Fear (5)
5 Complain bitterly (4)
6 Whole (6)
9 Dreary (6)
11 Organ of sight (3)
12 Exclude (5)
13 Coniferous tree (7)
15 Drunkard (3)
16 Expert (3)
18 Choice (6)
20 Objects (5)
21 Taxi (3)
22 By way of (3)
23 Deep ditch (6)
25 Move on snow (3)
28 Mildly eccentric (5)
30 Book of maps (5)
31 Wear away (5)
32 Couple (4)
33 Fever (4)

229

ACROSS

3 Burst forth (5)
8 Wash (5)
10 Large gathering (5)
11 Snake (3)
12 Dissuade (5)
13 Principal (7)
15 Incursion (5)
18 Male cat (3)
19 Withdraw (6)
21 Speaker at a discussion (7)
22 Agitate (4)
23 In addition (4)
24 Undertaking (7)
26 Exhilarated (6)
29 Wrath (3)
31 Fine fabric (5)
32 Constituent (7)
34 Impudence (5)
35 Unwell (3)
36 Spirit (5)
37 Allude (5)
38 Lifting device (5)

DOWN

1 Tag (5)
2 Idle talk (7)
4 Stagger (4)
5 Like better (6)
6 Fortune-telling cards (5)
7 Transparent (5)
9 Unit of weight (3)
12 Harmed (7)
14 Steal from (3)
16 Firearm (5)
17 Raising agent (5)
19 Cold-blooded creature (7)
20 Tree (5)
21 Backless sofa (5)
23 First in importance (7)
24 Superficial appearance (6)
25 English river (3)
27 Compare (5)
28 Invigorating preparation (5)
30 Small bay (5)
32 Regular (4)
33 Dwarf (3)

230

ACROSS

1 Marks on the skin (5)
6 Walk at a leisurely pace (5)
9 Evasive (7)
10 Daft (5)
11 Edition (5)
12 Operatic songs (5)
13 Spade-like tools (7)
15 Era (3)
17 In this place (4)
18 Hat (6)
19 Postpone (5)
20 Bits (6)
22 Naked (4)
24 Stray (3)
25 Employed delaying tactics (7)
26 Cubicle (5)
27 Express contempt (5)
28 Mollusc (5)
29 Made gassy (7)
30 Said more (5)
31 Pale (5)

DOWN

2 Hackneyed remark (6)
3 Experience once more (6)
4 Crafty (3)
5 Old Russian rulers (5)
6 Pilot (7)
7 Untidy state (4)
8 Living room (6)
12 Succulent plants (5)
13 Form (5)
14 Command (5)
15 Dismay (5)
16 Strayed (5)
18 Cogs (5)
19 Devout (7)
21 Pressed (6)
22 Combines (6)
23 Mock (6)
25 Strip of leather, etc. (5)
26 Scottish hillside (4)
28 Small ocean (3)

ACROSS

1 Fight (6)
7 Show (8)
8 Quote (4)
10 Food cupboard (6)
11 Figure (6)
14 Beer (3)
16 Representative (5)
17 Gown (4)
19 Dance (5)
21 Contradict (5)
22 Challenged (5)
23 Certain (4)
26 Musical instrument (5)
28 Wet ground (3)
29 Spoken (6)
30 Sentimental song (6)
31 Whirlpool (4)
32 Glow (8)
33 Search for food (6)

DOWN

1 Underground room (6)
2 Horse's headgear (6)
3 Row (4)
4 Error (7)
5 Squander (5)
6 Brimless cap (5)
8 Marine crustacean (4)
9 Golf peg (3)
12 Military commander (3)
13 Below (5)
15 Parts (5)
18 Immoderate (5)
19 Each (3)
20 Cover (3)
21 Fruit (7)
22 Pat lightly (3)
23 Fuse metal together (6)
24 Unattractive (4)
25 Bear (6)
26 Open (5)
27 Position on a scale (5)
28 Not good (3)
30 Red meat (4)

232

ACROSS

4 Small box for jewels, etc. (6)
7 Spring bulb (8)
8 Pictures (6)
10 Aromatic substance (5)
13 Open tart (4)
14 Unaccompanied (4)
15 Cunning (4)
16 Era (3)
17 Horse of a mixed colour (4)
19 Secrete (4)
21 Catch (9)
23 Ascend (4)
24 A few (4)
26 Odd (3)
27 Coarse file (4)
29 Scheme (4)
32 Constructed (4)
33 Gaze fixedly (5)
34 Foolish (6)
35 Speck (8)
36 Coming (6)

DOWN

1 Board game (5)
2 Herb (5)
3 Pleasant (4)
4 Cool (5)
5 Aquatic bird (4)
6 Come out (6)
9 Confusion (6)
11 Cooking vessel (3)
12 Tactical army unit (5)
13 Elegant skill (7)
15 Open conflict (3)
16 Say more (3)
18 Musical works (6)
20 Clumsy (5)
21 Goal (3)
22 Leap on one leg (3)
23 Destroyed (6)
25 Counter (3)
28 Skilful (5)
30 Tree (5)
31 At no time (5)
32 Pit (4)
33 Piece of building land (4)

233

ACROSS

3 Small food-fish (5)
8 Rot (5)
10 Blood vessels (5)
11 Auction item (3)
12 Twelve (5)
13 Ripened (7)
15 Picture-puzzle (5)
18 Unconscious (3)
19 Towards the rear (6)
21 Sunup (7)
22 Untruths (4)
23 Long journey (4)
24 Charged (7)
26 Feel aggrieved (6)
29 Staff (3)
31 Happening (5)
32 Deer meat (7)
34 Fragment (5)
35 Paddle (3)
36 Row (5)
37 Jog (5)
38 Hollow (5)

DOWN

1 Take it easy (5)
2 Foolish (7)
4 Poke (4)
5 Opposed (6)
6 Belief (5)
7 Be liable for (5)
9 Baby's bed (3)
12 Take away from (7)
14 Manage (3)
16 Facial hair (5)
17 Reptile (5)
19 Guaranteed (7)
20 Signalling light (5)
21 Become aware of (5)
23 Monotonous (7)
24 Song (6)
25 Male issue (3)
27 Each (5)
28 Follow (5)
30 Smithy (5)
32 Undergarment (4)
33 Unhappy (3)

234

ACROSS

1 Book of maps (5)
6 Donated (5)
9 Figures (7)
10 Pier (5)
11 Halts (5)
12 US state (5)
13 Contented (7)
15 Skill (3)
17 Depend (4)
18 Evening meal (6)
19 Compare (5)
20 Nursed (6)
22 Aquatic bird (4)
24 Finish (3)
25 Yearned (7)
26 Make reparation (5)
27 Sorceress (5)
28 Coral reef (5)
29 Hermit (7)
30 Show respect (5)
31 Excessively prim person (5)

DOWN

2 Triple (6)
3 Out of the right path (6)
4 Pig-pen (3)
5 Horse (5)
6 Edible jelly (7)
7 Egyptian goddess (4)
8 Run out (6)
12 Lukewarm (5)
13 Chatter (5)
14 Antelope (5)
15 Wrath (5)
16 Direction (5)
18 Thick (5)
19 Tanned hide (7)
21 Whole (6)
22 Snigger (6)
23 Staggered (6)
25 Fish (5)
26 Land measure (4)
28 Snake (3)

ACROSS

1 Gentle heat (6)
7 Quick appraisal (4-4)
8 In addition (4)
10 Was unsuccessful (6)
11 Decayed (6)
14 Allow (3)
16 Swarms (5)
17 Final (4)
19 Chinese tea (5)
21 Managed (5)
22 Mountain ash (5)
23 Says more (4)
26 Previous (5)
28 Before (3)
29 Contrasting stripe (6)
30 Stroke (6)
31 Mimicked (4)
32 Floor covering (8)
33 Light tapping sound (6)

DOWN

1 Headstrong (6)
2 Large-headed hammer (6)
3 Cowl (4)
4 Indicated (7)
5 Egg-shaped (5)
6 Networks (5)
8 Afflicts (4)
9 Collection (3)
12 Beverage (3)
13 Make corrections (5)
15 Gemstone (5)
18 Vigilant (5)
19 Show respect (3)
20 Female bird (3)
21 Small boat (7)
22 Fish eggs (3)
23 Apprehend (6)
24 Act (4)
25 Female relative (6)
26 Hymn (5)
27 Girl's name (5)
28 Undemanding reading matter (3)
30 Temporary settlement (4)

236

ACROSS

4 Pantihose (6)
7 Variety of cabbage (8)
8 Overseas (6)
10 Fold (5)
13 Spoken (4)
14 Unfree person (4)
15 Precious stone (4)
16 Perform (3)
17 Ripped (4)
19 Queue (4)
21 Sorry (9)
23 Tender (4)
24 Assistant (4)
26 Aged (3)
27 Cloud precipitation (4)
29 Tatters (4)
32 Den (4)
33 Dry grass (5)
34 Coercion (6)
35 Formal midday meal (8)
36 Pure (6)

DOWN

1 Omits (5)
2 Cry of approval (5)
3 Worry unduly (4)
4 Jewelled headdress (5)
5 Young female (4)
6 Hypnotic state (6)
9 Narrative song (6)
11 Meadow (3)
12 Later (5)
13 Outdoor (4-3)
15 Mineral (3)
16 Insect (3)
18 Musical works (6)
20 Still (5)
21 Staff (3)
22 Can (3)
23 Detective (6)
25 Military commander (3)
28 Gangway (5)
30 Equipped (5)
31 Pig (5)
32 Not so much (4)
33 Ill (4)

237

ACROSS

3 Awry (5)
8 Bundles (5)
10 Fetes (5)
11 Obtained (3)
12 Core (5)
13 Put down (7)
15 Weird (5)
18 Tease (3)
19 Emphasise (6)
21 Hates (7)
22 Press (4)
23 Notion (4)
24 Arrest (7)
26 Moves to music (6)
29 Fasten (3)
31 Sweetener (5)
32 Overdue (7)
34 Pit-worker (5)
35 Allow (3)
36 Beasts of burden (5)
37 Appeal (5)
38 Gain knowledge (5)

DOWN

1 Light-bodied beer (5)
2 Indicate (7)
4 Waxy fat (4)
5 Wading birds (6)
6 Liquid essential to life (5)
7 Cabs (5)
9 Cut (3)
12 Ugly (7)
14 Take a seat (3)
16 Prepared (5)
17 Attempt (5)
19 Speech defect (7)
20 Takes care of (5)
21 Performing (5)
23 Perfectly (7)
24 Dark red (6)
25 Lubricant (3)
27 Presage (5)
28 Ship of the desert (5)
30 Flower-part (5)
32 Ale (4)
33 Peg (3)

238

ACROSS

1 Brittle (5)
6 Pungent (5)
9 Discolour (7)
10 Begin (5)
11 Brindled cat (5)
12 Exclusive story (5)
13 Foretell (7)
15 Recede (3)
17 Bet (4)
18 Whine (6)
19 Trade name (5)
20 Unexpected (6)
22 Performs (4)
24 Before (3)
25 Ghost (7)
26 Sieves (5)
27 Caucasian (5)
28 Correct (5)
29 Mean (7)
30 Trap (5)
31 Finished (5)

DOWN

2 Come back (6)
3 Take long steps (6)
4 Tap (3)
5 Perform (5)
6 Astonish (7)
7 Fellow (4)
8 Drink (6)
12 Mock (5)
13 Out-of-date (5)
14 Musical study (5)
15 Forcibly remove (5)
16 Lacking enthusiasm (5)
18 Breaks noisily (5)
19 Credit (7)
21 Roguish child (6)
22 Discernment (6)
23 Hypnotic state (6)
25 Harsh (5)
26 Celebrity (6)
28 Era (3)

ACROSS

1 Body-guard (6)
7 Physical training (8)
8 Highest point (4)
10 Expose (6)
11 Facet (6)
14 Finish (3)
16 Carries (5)
17 Missile (4)
19 Metal fastener (5)
21 Peeled (5)
22 Belief (5)
23 Dress (4)
26 Storey (5)
28 Taxi (3)
29 Outbuilding (4-2)
30 Empty (6)
31 Lazy (4)
32 Moving (8)
33 Chopped (6)

DOWN

1 Spoiled (6)
2 Proper (6)
3 Stagger (4)
4 Relied upon (7)
5 Catlike mammal (5)
6 Encounters (5)
8 Assert (4)
9 Insane (3)
12 Cooking vessel (3)
13 Coniferous tree (5)
15 Sacked (5)
18 Nimble (5)
19 Managed (3)
20 Examine (3)
21 Trouble (7)
22 Unit of weight (3)
23 French (6)
24 Competent (4)
25 Proverbial example (6)
26 Bottle (5)
27 Fertile spot (5)
28 Food fish (3)
30 Lofty (4)

240

ACROSS

4 Sweet (6)
7 Nonsense (8)
8 Monster (6)
10 Helicopter blade (5)
13 Fossil fuel (4)
14 Paradise (4)
15 Shape (4)
16 Zodiac sign (3)
17 Bridge (4)
19 Reared (4)
21 Horrified (9)
23 Routine (4)
24 Destiny (4)
26 Golf peg (3)
27 Ran away (4)
29 Type of cabbage (4)
32 Dread (4)
33 Poplar (5)
34 Leave (6)
35 Legacy (8)
36 Harsh (6)

DOWN

1 Twenty (5)
2 Hurry (5)
3 Move (4)
4 Track (5)
5 Young woman (4)
6 Relaxed (6)
9 Opening move (6)
11 Poem (3)
12 Beginning (5)
13 Evergreen tree (7)
15 Distant (3)
16 Guided (3)
18 Favour (6)
20 Stinks (5)
21 Digit (3)
22 Craze (3)
23 Respect (6)
25 Beer (3)
28 Boring machine (5)
30 Shock (5)
31 Go in (5)
32 Renown (4)
33 Sour (4)

ACROSS

3 Cut (5)
8 Rear of a vessel (5)
10 Open (5)
11 Mineral (3)
12 Din (5)
13 Distant (7)
15 Faith (5)
18 Took a seat (3)
19 Hot spring (6)
21 Even (7)
22 Chief (4)
23 Long dispute between families, etc. (4)
24 Leopard (7)
26 Rogue (6)
29 Era (3)
31 Rows (5)
32 Exact (7)
34 Book of maps (5)
35 Type (3)
36 Taut (5)
37 Still bay (5)
38 Move furtively (5)

DOWN

1 Weasel-like mammal (5)
2 Wrinkled (7)
4 Be excessively sweet (4)
5 Rota (6)
6 Each (5)
7 Come up (5)
9 Stray (3)
12 Not synthetic (7)
14 Wit (3)
16 Wedding attendant (5)
17 Skilled job (5)
19 Stocking supports (7)
20 Brief (5)
21 Elevate (5)
23 Fighting with foils (7)
24 Crayon (6)
25 Garden tool (3)
27 Ventilated (5)
28 Stupid (5)
30 Enquired (5)
32 Chesspiece (4)
33 Unwell (3)

242

ACROSS

1 Severe (5)
6 Easily angered (5)
9 Small established position (7)
10 Frighten (5)
11 Lament for the dead (5)
12 Brawl (5)
13 Fan (7)
15 Vapour (3)
17 Miserly (4)
18 Variety of polecat (6)
19 Strayed (5)
20 Room for manoeuvre (6)
22 Italian wine (4)
24 Consume (3)
25 Let fall (7)
26 Messenger (5)
27 Shop (5)
28 Once more (5)
29 Foolish (7)
30 Icy deposit (5)
31 Conditions (5)

DOWN

2 Covered shopping area (6)
3 Strive (6)
4 Garden tool (3)
5 Very steep (5)
6 Defrauded (7)
7 Lazy (4)
8 West Indian music (6)
12 Happy (5)
13 Stroll (5)
14 French painter (5)
15 Grip (5)
16 Sedate (5)
18 Type of ship (5)
19 Serious (7)
21 Christian festival (6)
22 The highest point (6)
23 Monotony (6)
25 Rolling uplands (5)
26 Ages (4)
28 Insect (3)

243

ACROSS

1 Wince (6)
7 Unstable (8)
8 Halt (4)
10 Religious service (6)
11 Act upon (6)
14 Expert (3)
16 Looks at suggestively (5)
17 Uncommon (4)
19 Pulp (5)
21 Gem unit of weight (5)
22 Idiot (5)
23 Constructed (4)
26 Title of respect (5)
28 Rocky hill (3)
29 Seizes a throne (6)
30 Reason (6)
31 Amongst (4)
32 Convey (8)
33 Set alight (6)

DOWN

1 Previous (6)
2 Sign (6)
3 Fruits of the rose (4)
4 Pamphlet (7)
5 Indian currency unit (5)
6 Examines (5)
8 Celebrity (4)
9 An individual (3)
12 Professional payment (3)
13 Throng(5)
15 'Great ' N. American lake (5)
18 Operatic songs (5)
19 Average (3)
20 Managed (3)
21 Write music (7)
22 Spoil (3)
23 Movement (6)
24 Dry (4)
25 Come out (6)
26 Old-smelling (5)
27 Old gold coin (5)
28 Male cat (3)
30 Scratch (4)

244

ACROSS

4 Pulses (6)
7 Inside (8)
8 Approximately (6)
10 Turning device (5)
13 Chilled (4)
14 Region (4)
15 Insects (4)
16 Cake (3)
17 Firewood? (4)
19 Object (4)
21 Confined (9)
23 Break suddenly (4)
24 Regrets (4)
26 Deer (3)
27 Baking chamber (4)
29 Labels(4)
32 Employs (4)
33 Man-made material (5)
34 Categories (6)
35 Boring (8)
36 Against (6)

DOWN

1 Country house (5)
2 Condition (5)
3 Liberate (4)
4 Area (of land) (5)
5 Cross (4)
6 Nonsense (6)
9 Live (6)
11 Skill (3)
12 Board game (5)
13 Protects against risk, etc. (7)
15 In the past (3)
16 Four-poster, for example (3)
18 Counter (6)
20 Irritable (5)
21 Writing fluid (3)
22 Sister (3)
23 Part of a garment (6)
25 Self-image (3)
28 Underwear items (5)
30 Let (5)
31 Show contempt (5)
32 Vaselike receptacles (4)
33 Require (4)

ACROSS

3 Cooks (5)
8 Swift (5)
10 Lane (5)
11 Outfit (3)
12 Male relative (5)
13 Witty replies (7)
15 Stop (5)
18 Youngster (3)
19 Made a light explosive sound (6)
21 Old soldier (7)
22 Put down (4)
23 Stir (4)
24 Sure (7)
26 Smiled broadly (6)
29 Zero (3)
31 Enlist (5)
32 Giving goods for money (7)
34 Operating handle (5)
35 Public-house (3)
36 Might (5)
37 Card game (5)
38 Slender girl (5)

DOWN

1 Challenged (5)
2 Narrow minded (7)
4 Female bird (4)
5 Bird of prey (6)
6 Rest (5)
7 Taut (5)
9 Mine (3)
12 Spoke (7)
14 Decay (3)
16 Protective covering (5)
17 Borders (5)
19 Companion (7)
20 Sphere (5)
21 Clergyman (5)
23 Large figure (7)
24 Salad vegetable (6)
25 Sicken (3)
27 Take pleasure in (5)
28 Burrowing mammals (5)
30 Add territory by conquest (5)
32 Ooze (4)
33 Writing fluid (3)

246

ACROSS

1 At no time (5)
6 Stage of development, etc. (5)
9 Type of pasta (7)
10 Small food fish (5)
11 Chosen few (5)
12 Flower part (5)
13 Facets (7)
15 Network (3)
17 Pip, for example (4)
18 Long for (6)
19 Wide (5)
20 Turn upside-down (6)
22 Celebrity (4)
24 Actor's signal (3)
25 Held up (7)
26 Exposed (5)
27 Finished (5)
28 Sweetener (5)
29 Artist's studio (7)
30 Large open area (5)
31 Go in (5)

DOWN

2 Reveal (6)
3 Rubbed out (6)
4 Rodent (3)
5 Plunges into water (5)
6 Arranged in folds (7)
7 Mound (4)
8 Breed of dog (6)
12 Begin (5)
13 Savoury jelly (5)
14 Vex (5)
15 Cleverly amusing (5)
16 Facial hair (5)
18 Old-fashioned (5)
19 Width (7)
21 Subtle difference in meaning, etc. (6)
22 Planet (6)
23 Make gassy (6)
25 Trade agreements (5)
26 Thrash (4)
28 Observe (3)

ACROSS

1 Goes (6)
7 Fully stated (8)
8 Musical instrument (4)
10 Exchanged (6)
11 Trapped (6)
14 Show assent (3)
16 Lees (5)
17 Board game (4)
19 Seraglio (5)
21 Outstanding (5)
22 Use a broom (5)
23 Fictitious person or thing (4)
26 Film (5)
28 Shelter (3)
29 Hooded jacket (6)
30 Legislative body (6)
31 Animal's den (4)
32 Fuse (8)
33 Digs deeply (6)

DOWN

1 Beam over a door (6)
2 Type of witchcraft (6)
3 Transmit (4)
4 Stupid mistake (7)
5 Frighten (5)
6 Metal fasteners (5)
8 Part of the body (4)
9 Colour (3)
12 Equip (3)
13 Wading bird (5)
15 Escapade (5)
18 Alliance (5)
19 Shade (3)
20 Agent (3)
21 Jumper (7)
22 Title of respect (3)
23 Servile (6)
24 Period of time (4)
25 'Laughing' mammals (6)
26 Month (5)
27 Of the voice (5)
28 Meadow (3)
30 Snow vehicle (4)

248

ACROSS

4 Wooded area (6)
7 Enlarge (8)
8 Noise of leaves (6)
10 Useful (5)
13 Hypocrisy (4)
14 Row (4)
15 Gangster's girlfriend (4)
16 Vegetable (3)
17 M East country (4)
19 Frozen (4)
21 Passed (9)
23 Kiln (4)
24 M East port (4)
26 Epoch (3)
27 Threesome (4)
29 Story (4)
32 Principal (4)
33 Pale (5)
34 Dangers (6)
35 Stretch (8)
36 Catch-phrase (6)

DOWN

1 Vision (5)
2 Doughy cake (5)
3 Extremely (4)
4 Wild (5)
5 Corrosion (4)
6 Seasoned (6)
9 Dissimilar to (6)
11 Target (3)
12 Force (5)
13 Include (7)
15 Spoil (3)
16 Enclosure (3)
18 Hire charge (6)
20 US coins (5)
21 Eggs (3)
22 Fuss (3)
23 Trial (6)
25 Beer (3)
28 Got up (5)
30 Leading (5)
31 Concluded (5)
32 Chinese dynasty (4)
33 Relative (4)

249

ACROSS

3 Vote into office (5)
8 Prestige (5)
10 Rub out (5)
11 Male issue (3)
12 Unaccompanied (5)
13 Hidden trap (7)
15 Stories (5)
18 Frozen water (3)
19 Passionate (6)
21 Trespass (7)
22 Queue (4)
23 Smugly self-righteous person (4)
24 Lumberjacks (7)
26 Put away for future use (6)
29 Era (3)
31 Type of accommodation (5)
32 Halted (7)
34 Roofing material (5)
35 Tune (3)
36 Christmas show, in short (5)
37 Rear (5)
38 Aquatic birds (5)

DOWN

1 Harmonious sound (5)
2 Limit (7)
4 Calm interval (4)
5 Middle (6)
6 Walk (5)
7 Pale (5)
9 Speck (3)
12 Warned to prepare for action (7)
14 Perform (3)
16 Eyes lasciviously (5)
17 Phase (5)
19 Worship (7)
20 Confrontation (5)
21 Block of cast metal (5)
23 Get ready (7)
24 Chap (6)
25 Self-image (3)
27 Semi-precious stone (5)
28 Pauses (5)
30 Brimless cap (5)
32 Daze (4)
33 Baked dish (3)

250

ACROSS

1 Contagious fear (5)
6 Royal (5)
9 Marked with spots (7)
10 Avarice (5)
11 Sieves (5)
12 Apples, pears, etc. (5)
13 Bloated (7)
15 Untruth (3)
17 Thames at Oxford (4)
18 Moment (6)
19 Slides (5)
20 Invited people (6)
22 Surrender (4)
24 Finish (3)
25 Stages of a meal (7)
26 Rare gas (5)
27 Dot (5)
28 Book of maps (5)
29 White ant (7)
30 Enquired (5)
31 Rub out (5)

DOWN

2 Missiles (6)
3 Goals (6)
4 Bounder (3)
5 Reject (5)
6 Lives (7)
7 Prepare for publication (4)
8 Reach (6)
12 Senses (5)
13 Offensive operation (5)
14 Lubricated (5)
15 Feels great affection for (5)
16 Borders (5)
18 Eating implement (5)
19 Began (7)
21 Releases (6)
22 Large depression (6)
23 Rots (6)
25 Swollen underground stems (5)
26 Betting stake (4)
28 Consumed (3)

251

ACROSS

1 Touched down (6)
7 Unsteady (8)
8 Genuine (4)
10 Large wood (6)
11 Old name for Iran (6)
14 Expert (3)
16 Out of practice, commonly (5)
17 Engrossed (4)
19 Item of bed-linen (5)
21 Challenged (5)
22 Honey badger (5)
23 Specific job (4)
26 French capital (5)
28 Goal (3)
29 On fire (6)
30 Warning devices (6)
31 Scheme (4)
32 Become dull from inaction (8)
33 Considered (6)

DOWN

1 Idler (6)
2 Straightforward (6)
3 Composition for two (4)
4 Spoke (7)
5 Chasm (5)
6 Hold-up (5)
8 Snare (4)
9 Employ (3)
12 Groove or furrow (3)
13 Objects (5)
15 Chop finely (5)
18 Dismay (5)
19 Took a seat (3)
20 Food fish (3)
21 Spirited and stylish (7)
22 Manipulate fraudulently (3)
23 Vitriolic speech (6)
24 So be it (4)
25 Touched with the lips (6)
26 Old-fashioned (5)
27 Contender (5)
28 Sicken (3)
30 Raced (4)

252

ACROSS

4	Spoiled (6)
7	Italian coffee (8)
8	Tubular bells (6)
10	Declare (5)
13	Cast off (4)
14	Ballet skirt (4)
15	Box in training (4)
16	Still (3)
17	Rip (4)
19	Overt (4)
21	Prerequisite (9)
23	Challenge (4)
24	Upper part of a bottle (4)
26	Piece (3)
27	Fury (4)
29	Organs of hearing (4)
32	Unattractive (4)
33	Moan (5)
34	Stage of animal development (6)
35	Related (8)
36	Declare upon oath (6)

DOWN

1	Raising agent (5)
2	Food fish (5)
3	Gala (4)
4	Dark brown coffee (5)
5	Attack (4)
6	Team in football, etc. (6)
9	Brave (6)
11	Pull sharply (3)
12	Teacher (5)
13	Bouncy (7)
15	Unhappy (3)
16	Japanese monetary unit (3)
18	Vim (6)
20	Card game (5)
21	Household pet (3)
22	Golf peg (3)
23	Dreary (6)
25	Age (3)
28	Unaccompanied (5)
30	Main blood vessel (5)
31	Maliciously derogatory (5)
32	Press (4)
33	Young female (4)

253

ACROSS

3 Shut (5)
8 Gush or declaim (5)
10 Presses (5)
11 Sicken (3)
12 Go in (5)
13 Drooping (7)
15 Firm (5)
18 Skill (3)
19 Layers (6)
21 Inactivity (7)
22 Peruvian Indian (4)
23 Baby's bed (4)
24 Loud and harsh (7)
26 Common finch (6)
29 Organ of hearing (3)
31 Divine messenger (5)
32 Irregular and unpredictable (7)
34 Eagle's nest (5)
35 Light brown (3)
36 Gain knowledge (5)
37 Drilled (5)
38 Scatter (5)

DOWN

1 EC country (5)
2 Dried grape (7)
4 Yearn (4)
5 Afternoon nap (6)
6 Mistake (5)
7 Out of condition (5)
9 Lubricate (3)
12 Implore (7)
14 Anger (3)
16 Animal's dens (5)
17 Smears (5)
19 Genuine (7)
20 Country house (5)
21 Sweet topping (5)
23 Head of a museum (7)
24 Become more amenable (6)
25 Paddle (3)
27 Bury (5)
28 Approaches (5)
30 Queues (5)
32 Republic of Ireland (4)
33 Sailor, commonly (3)

254

ACROSS

1 Detest (5)
6 Outdoor garments (5)
9 Floating bridge (7)
10 Vault (5)
11 Extreme (5)
12 Each (5)
13 Sadly thoughtful (7)
15 Observe (3)
17 Succulent plant (4)
18 Representatives (6)
19 Worship (5)
20 Snow vehicle (6)
22 Travel permit (4)
24 Fish (3)
25 Kings, queens, etc. (7)
26 Slaughtered (5)
27 Semi-precious stone (5)
28 Directed (5)
29 Road-surfacing material (7)
30 Periods of time (5)
31 Telling untruths (5)

DOWN

2 Keg (6)
3 Resist (6)
4 Decay (3)
5 Cooker (5)
6 Bravery (7)
7 Just (4)
8 Small tower (6)
12 Elude (5)
13 Old-fashioned (5)
14 New (5)
15 Mollusc (5)
16 Attempt (5)
18 Rare gas (5)
19 Eternal (7)
21 Alliance (6)
22 Excessive pride (6)
23 Scattered (6)
25 Correct (5)
26 Celebrity (4)
28 Everyone (3)

ACROSS

1 Prohibit (6)
7 Increase in extent, etc. (8)
8 Golfer's warning (4)
10 Puma (6)
11 Occupation (6)
14 Holy Sister (3)
16 Groups (5)
17 Deposit of ore (4)
19 Having an edge or point (5)
21 Form (5)
22 Piece of poetry (5)
23 Satisfy (4)
26 Row (5)
28 Dog (3)
29 Hard and unfeeling (6)
30 Narrow sword (6)
31 Region (4)
32 Abstruse (8)
33 Glowing coals (6)

DOWN

1 Relating to financial matters (6)
2 Gentle accent (6)
3 Elk, etc. (4)
4 Gruesome (7)
5 Harbour (5)
6 Dreads (5)
8 Reserve of money (4)
9 Managed (3)
12 Knock (3)
13 Decree (5)
15 Disgrace (5)
18 Open (5)
19 Reserved (3)
20 Mimic (3)
21 Put aside or postponed (7)
22 Regret (3)
23 Terrific (6)
24 Operatic song (4)
25 Mistakes (6)
26 Pale (5)
27 Italian city (5)
28 Vehicle (3)
30 Contest of speed (4)

256

ACROSS

4 Rider's seat (6)
7 Might (8)
8 Movement (6)
10 Sure-footed mammals (5)
13 Shallow receptacle (4)
14 Woman's name (4)
15 Cast off (4)
16 Humorist (3)
17 Couple (4)
19 Regular (4)
21 Deformed (9)
23 Planet (4)
24 Bird's home (4)
26 Young male (3)
27 Second-hand (4)
29 Talk idly (4)
32 Flower (4)
33 Tint (5)
34 Selected (6)
35 Hoodlum (8)
36 Turn to ice (6)

DOWN

1 Custom (5)
2 Of the town or city (5)
3 Burden (4)
4 Portion (5)
5 Government tax (4)
6 Pay a short visit (4,2)
9 Trainee officers (6)
11 Strange (3)
12 Animal with long snout (5)
13 Royal seats (7)
15 Take a seat (3)
16 Marry (3)
18 Convince (6)
20 Climbing plant (5)
21 Period of time (3)
22 Colour (3)
23 Parent (6)
25 Unhappy (3)
28 Scorch (5)
30 Rash (5)
31 Rips (5)
32 Small island (4)
33 Notice (4)

257

ACROSS

3 Slender young woman (5)
8 Indifferent to pleasure or pain (5)
10 Tears (5)
11 Concealed (3)
12 Sacrificial table (5)
13 Strong bag (7)
15 New (5)
18 Illuminated (3)
19 Disregard (6)
21 Lowers in dignity, etc. (7)
22 Vehicles (4)
23 Enthusiastic (4)
24 Strikes Out (7)
26 Depended (6)
29 Born (3)
31 Fake (5)
32 Modified (7)
34 Goads (5)
35 Charged particle (3)
36 Follow (5)
37 Show contempt (5)
38 Rub out (5)

DOWN

1 Distinctive spirit (5)
2 Puzzles (7)
4 Shout (4)
5 Accidents (6)
6 Wading bird (5)
7 Snake (5)
9 Lubricate (3)
12 Changed (7)
14 Goal (3)
16 Chooses a candidate (5)
17 Inclines (5)
19 Means (7)
20 Muffler (5)
21 Teach by rigorous exercises (5)
23 Retaining (7)
24 More profound (6)
25 Beverage (3)
27 Makes money from work (5)
28 Edition (5)
30 Belief (5)
32 Equips (4)
33 Foot digit (3)

258

ACROSS

1 Assumed name (5)
6 Operating handle (5)
9 Window cover (7)
10 Common flower (5)
11 Leg joint (5)
12 Trap (5)
13 Eying lasciviously (7)
15 Fool (3)
17 Press (4)
18 Fireside (6)
19 Managed (5)
20 Talk flirtatiously to (4,2)
22 Idiot (4)
24 Poor actor (3)
25 Anti (7)
26 Flat-bottomed vessel (5)
27 Gem unit of weight (5)
28 Youngster (5)
29 Income from taxation (7)
30 Borders (5)
31 Offensively loud (5)

DOWN

2 Head (6)
3 Guarantee (6)
4 Timid (3)
5 Smart (5)
6 Wise (7)
7 River in N. Ireland (4)
8 Join up (6)
12 Pry (5)
13 Midday meal (5)
14 Town in Surrey (5)
15 Fireraising (5)
16 Item of bedlinen (5)
18 Row of bushes acting as a boundary (5)
19 Clergymen (7)
21 Risk (6)
22 Be indecisive (6)
23 Holy songs (6)
25 Concur (5)
26 Naked (4)
28 Young of certain animals (3)

ACROSS

1 Somewhat (6)
7 Turned upside down (8)
8 Break noisily (4)
10 Cows, bulls, oxen, etc. (6)
11 Elder (6)
14 "Slippery" fish (3)
16 Scope (5)
17 Obscene (4)
19 Clutch (5)
21 Light brown (5)
22 Name (5)
23 Pole for sails, flags, etc. (4)
26 Conductor's stick (5)
28 Taxi (3)
29 Antelopes (6)
30 Money-pouch (6)
31 Lazy (4)
32 Meant (8)
33 Goes in (6)

DOWN

1 Scoundrel (6)
2 Intimated (6)
3 Mature (4)
4 Drive backwards (7)
5 Blemish (5)
6 Worship (5)
8 Dish of meat, vegetables, etc. (4)
9 Everyone (3)
12 Snooze (3)
13 Monsters (5)
15 Bore (5)
18 Identical in size, quantity, etc. (5)
19 Obtain (3)
20 Time (3)
21 Book covering (7)
22 Unit of weight (3)
23 Wooden hammer (6)
24 Competent (4)
25 Teachers (6)
26 Contradict (5)
27 Sample (5)
28 Bounder (3)
30 Extensive (4)

260

ACROSS

4 Subjects for discussion (6)
7 Pieces of paper thrown at weddings etc. (8)
8 Missing (6)
10 Rubbish (5)
13 Flower (4)
14 Every one (4)
15 Difficulty (4)
16 Young male (3)
17 Aid criminally (4)
19 Overt (4)
21 Objected (9)
23 Bearing (4)
24 Bird's home (4)
26 Youngster (3)
27 Facial feature (4)
29 Young sheep (4)
32 Lake (4)
33 Man-made material (5)
34 Corsair (6)
35 Forebear (8)
36 Actually (6)

DOWN

1 Sharp (5)
2 Australian or New Zealand WW1 soldier (5)
3 Net (4)
4 Headdress (5)
5 Go by (4)
6 Heavy piece of artillery (6)
9 Narrow-minded people (6)
11 Rodent (3)
12 Portion (5)
13 Keen (7)
15 Collection (3)
16 Item of furniture (3)
18 Hat (6)
20 Trifling (5)
21 Mine (3)
22 Observe (3)
23 Movement (6)
25 In the past (3)
28 Mountain nymph (5)
30 Exhilarate (5)
31 Show contempt (5)
32 Construct (4)
33 Require (4)

ACROSS

3 An assumed name (5)
8 Power or influence (5)
10 Member of the nobility (5)
11 Nocturnal bird (3)
12 Piece of turf (5)
13 Artist's studio (7)
15 Cut into small cubes (5)
18 Skill (3)
19 Indicate (6)
21 Wrinkles (7)
22 Substance formed from milk (4)
23 Inform (4)
24 Cut (7)
26 Jogs (6)
29 Assist (3)
31 Shop (5)
32 Of least quantity, etc. (7)
34 Traffic light colour (5)
35 Paddle (3)
36 Dish up (5)
37 Silenced (5)
38 Borders (5)

DOWN

1 Material (5)
2 Stupid person (7)
4 Animal's den (4)
5 Dwellings (6)
6 Shiny material (5)
7 Celestial body (5)
9 Be indebted (3)
12 Holds back (7)
14 Anger (3)
16 Managed (5)
17 Transactions (5)
19 Lose hope (7)
20 Scrutinises (5)
21 Belief (5)
23 Monotonous (7)
24 Appeared (6)
25 Metal fastener (3)
27 Complete (5)
28 Solemn (5)
30 Showed concern (5)
32 Mountain lake (4)
33 Floor covering (3)

262

ACROSS

1 Stupid (5)
6 Pale (5)
9 Net hung for use as a bed (7)
10 Wander (5)
11 Apple drink (5)
12 Brimless cap (5)
13 Avaricious person (7)
15 Beverage (3)
17 Tax (4)
18 Be present (6)
19 Indications (5)
20 Place of worship (6)
22 Ooze (4)
24 Collection (3)
25 Drop (7)
26 Move down (5)
27 Wilt (5)
28 Exists (5)
29 Worships (7)
30 Thick woollen cloth (5)
31 Gather (5)

DOWN

2 Go to bed (6)
3 Drab (6)
4 Express in words (3)
5 Burning coal (5)
6 Takes what's offered (7)
7 Theatrical sketch (4)
8 Football of cricket team (6)
12 Contradict (5)
13 Tumbler (5)
14 Avoid (5)
15 Conical tent (5)
16 Skilful (5)
18 Wrath (5)
19 Pried (7)
21 Official language of Israel (6)
22 Split (6)
23 Goes in (6)
25 Postpone (5)
26 Body of knowledge on a subject (4)
28 Meadow (3)

263

ACROSS

1 Inclinations (6)
7 Post (8)
8 Fairy (4)
10 Taken unlawfully (6)
11 Find (6)
14 Guided (3)
16 Painful afflictions (5)
17 Elderly (4)
19 Disturbances (5)
21 Story (5)
22 Quick (5)
23 Female deer (4)
26 Javelin (5)
28 Free (3)
29 Talkative (6)
30 Affectionate (6)
31 Paradise (4)
32 Impedes (8)
33 Poser (6)

DOWN

1 Afternoon nap (6)
2 Skinned (6)
3 Rotate (4)
4 Reply (7)
5 Monetary unit (5)
6 Mountain range (5)
8 Eastern European (4)
9 Colour (3)
12 Lettuce (3)
13 Anxious (5)
15 Shinbone (5)
18 Grid (5)
19 Knock (3)
20 Elderly (3)
21 More distant (7)
22 Traitor (3)
23 Deflect (6)
24 Norse god (4)
25 Italian "Mr" (6)
26 Range (5)
27 Keen (5)
28 Staff (3)
30 Not as much (4)

264

ACROSS

4 Band (6)
7 Flower (8)
8 Counterbalance (6)
10 Bloodsucking creature (5)
13 Boxing match (4)
14 Sport (4)
15 Pieces (4)
16 Strike (3)
17 Bard (4)
19 Wading bird (4)
21 Hanging (9)
23 Supreme (4)
24 Quite a few (4)
26 Obtained (3)
27 Frozen (4)
29 Dash (4)
32 So be it (4)
33 Small fruit (5)
34 Assassins (6)
35 Thrashed (8)
36 Hire contracts (6)

DOWN

1 Young animal (5)
2 Collar part (5)
3 Desire (4)
4 Bud (5)
5 Fissure (4)
6 Summary (6)
9 Joining (6)
11 Age (3)
12 Manages (5)
13 Road surface (7)
15 Cot (3)
16 Belonging to him (3)
18 Punctual (2,4)
20 Purchaser (5)
21 Favourite (3)
22 Boy (3)
23 Cattle-like (6)
25 Faucet (3)
28 US coins (5)
30 Tree (5)
31 Poor (5)
32 Units of current (4)
33 Food, commonly (4)

ACROSS

3 Unruly children (5)
8 Brimless cap (5)
10 Fruit (5)
11 Type of lettuce (3)
12 Steel rope (5)
13 Accountant (7)
15 Diplomat (5)
18 River barrier (3)
19 Whole (6)
21 Section (7)
22 Tears (4)
23 Excavates (4)
24 Pried (7)
26 Choose (6)
29 Knock (3)
31 Go in (5)
32 Flightless bird (7)
34 Crest (5)
35 Stray (3)
36 Spring bulb (5)
37 Awry (5)
38 Anaesthetic (5)

DOWN

1 Happen again (5)
2 Moreover (7)
4 Breed (4)
5 Gift (6)
6 Exhausted (5)
7 Storey (5)
9 Stick (3)
12 Remark (7)
14 Label (3)
16 Intense (5)
17 Raising agent (5)
19 Sanction (7)
20 Come up (5)
21 Upset (5)
23 Push down (7)
24 Writing (6)
25 Tap (3)
27 Boredom (5)
28 Weird (5)
30 Threaded fastener (5)
32 Monster (4)
33 Vex (3)

266

ACROSS

1 Grain used to make flour (5)
6 Finished (5)
9 Lay on the back (7)
10 Packing box (5)
11 Brownish-grey (5)
12 Begin (5)
13 Singing voice (7)
15 Attempt (3)
17 Three in cards (4)
18 Roof of the mouth (6)
19 Piece of turf (5)
20 Herb (6)
22 Spirit (4)
24 Cook in fat (3)
25 Those owing money (7)
26 Shoe-part (5)
27 Jewelled headdress (5)
28 Pointed at a target (5)
29 Clever device (7)
30 Operating handle (5)
31 Cogs (5)

DOWN

2 Dread (6)
3 Blood vessel (6)
4 Golf peg (3)
5 Planet (5)
6 Beg (7)
7 Tidy (4)
8 Ace (6)
12 Mollusc (5)
13 Workforce (5)
14 Small coin (5)
15 Socially frowned upon (5)
16 Shouts (5)
18 Might (5)
19 Lose hope (7)
21 Stoat's fur (6)
22 Hit (6)
23 Pressing (6)
25 Considers (5)
26 Impulse (4)
28 Perform (3)

ACROSS

1 Fluid part of blood (6)
7 Inert (8)
8 Cast off (4)
10 Pointless (6)
11 Purify (6)
14 Enquire (3)
16 Tree of the birch family (5)
17 Expression (4)
19 Spacious (5)
21 Visits (5)
22 Subdued (5)
23 Section (4)
26 Take unlawfully (5)
28 Hit (3)
29 Almost (6)
30 Picture-house (6)
31 Overt (4)
32 Magician (8)
33 Make certain (6)

DOWN

1 Gain (6)
2 Division (6)
3 Assistant (4)
4 Piercing cries (7)
5 Furious (5)
6 Allude (5)
8 Celebrity (4)
9 Large deer (3)
12 Go by air (3)
13 At no time (5)
15 Actor's parts (5)
18 Exclusive (5)
19 Male sheep (3)
20 Aged (3)
21 Uncaring (7)
22 By-product of coal (3)
23 Flat sections in a door, etc. (6)
24 So be it (4)
25 Hypnotic state (6)
26 Light meal (5)
27 Gains by labour (5)
28 Rim (3)
30 Heart (4)

268

ACROSS

4 Uncommon (6)
7 Reprove (8)
8 Agreement (6)
10 Bearskin (5)
13 Fencing foil (4)
14 Gaelic (4)
15 Slaughtered (4)
16 Arid (3)
17 Mature (4)
19 Fever (4)
21 Jewish place of worship (9)
23 Friends (4)
24 Region (4)
26 Rule (3)
27 Sea-eagle (4)
29 Flower-holder (4)
32 Let it stand (4)
33 Manservant (5)
34 Husband or wife (6)
35 Shabby or worn (3-5)
36 Fresh and windy (6)

DOWN

1 Perhaps (5)
2 Gather (5)
3 Black (4)
4 Form (5)
5 Church recess (4)
6 Middle (6)
9 Waste matter (6)
11 Vaselike receptacle (3)
12 Semi-precious stone (5)
13 Dignified (7)
15 Health resort (3)
16 Owing (3)
18 Diagrams placed within others (6)
20 Tropical fruit (5)
21 Hand tool (3)
22 Mineral (3)
23 Coddle (6)
25 Employ (3)
28 Shrill (5)
30 Warning device (5)
31 Musical study (5)
32 Certain (4)
33 Scene (4)

269

ACROSS

3 Smell (5)
8 Female (5)
10 Ball game (5)
11 Opening (3)
12 Cheroot, for instance (5)
13 Livid (7)
15 Ingenuous (5)
18 Dark viscid substance (3)
19 Sweet (6)
21 Diverse (7)
22 Precious stone (4)
23 Former (4)
24 Polishing (7)
26 Star sign (6)
29 Before (3)
31 Beer mug (5)
32 Gift (7)
34 Plunges into water (5)
35 Light brown (3)
36 Tropical fruit (5)
37 Wading bird (5)
38 Access (5)

DOWN

1 Sham (5)
2 Country's seat of government (7)
4 Raised platform (4)
5 Planet (6)
6 Rustic (5)
7 Over (5)
9 Spoil (3)
12 Inquisitive (7)
14 Paddle (3)
16 Sweet topping (5)
17 Woman's name (5)
19 Useless persons (7)
20 Makes a sound like an owl (5)
21 Unclear (5)
23 Dance (3-4)
24 Swelling on the toe (6)
25 Anger (3)
27 Book of maps (5)
28 Raised edge (5)
30 Vex (5)
32 Soft fruit (4)
33 Spike of corn, etc. (3)

270

ACROSS

1. Sharp (5)
6. Test (5)
9. Person held as security (7)
10. Long (5)
11. Teller of fables (5)
12. Once more (5)
13. Favourable outcome (7)
15. Small drops of moisture (3)
17. Wind instrument (4)
18. Cunning (6)
19. Traded (5)
20. Slight injury (6)
22. Corrosive substance (4)
24. Age (3)
25. Unfortunate (7)
26. Lance (5)
27. Enlist (5)
28. Object (5)
29. Build-up of work (7)
30. Untidy (5)
31. Poor (5)

DOWN

2. Angel (6)
3. Three times (6)
4. Period of time (3)
5. Adult male deer (5)
6. Anti (7)
7. Observed (4)
8. Shore bird (6)
12. Kind of poplar (5)
13. Pickling liquid (5)
14. Snake (5)
15. Slow learner (5)
16. Unwanted plants (5)
18. Sacrificial table (5)
19. Show (7)
21. Royal son (6)
22. Assert (6)
23. Supplied (6)
25. Poor journalists (5)
26. Weeps convulsively (4)
28. Put on (3)

ACROSS

1 Trouble (6)
7 Lover (8)
8 Blaze (4)
10 Prepared (6)
11 Greek capital (6)
14 Stage of a race (3)
16 Queues (5)
17 Lofty (4)
19 Stared open-mouthed (5)
21 Satisfied (5)
22 Let (5)
23 Injure (4)
26 State of harmony (5)
28 Network (3)
29 Coming (6)
30 Closed securely (6)
31 In this place (4)
32 Generosity (8)
33 Rehearsal (3,3)

DOWN

1 Casserole (6)
2 Beast (6)
3 Raced (4)
4 Fought (7)
5 Twelve (5)
6 Frock (5)
8 Make full (4)
9 Corded fabric (3)
12 Concealed (3)
13 At no time (5)
15 Conductor's stick (5)
18 Equipped (5)
19 Girl (3)
20 Church seat (3)
21 Slim (7)
22 Expert (3)
23 Sincere and
   unrestrained (6)
24 Competent (4)
25 Up-to-date (6)
26 Buckets (5)
27 Avoid (5)
28 Small (3)
30 Outhouse (4)

272

ACROSS

4 Morally wrong (6)
7 Pull back (8)
8 Towards the rear (6)
10 Financial reserves (5)
13 Little devils (4)
14 Large woody plant (4)
15 Eastern ruler (4)
16 Welsh river (3)
17 Rounded leafbase of daffodils, etc. (4)
19 Kiln for hops (4)
21 Deface (9)
23 Flying insect (4)
24 Sink the teeth into (4)
26 Baby's bed (3)
27 Regular (4)
29 Recent information (4)
32 Reared (4)
33 Manservant (5)
34 Wood (6)
35 Woodwind instrument (8)
36 Fireside (6)

DOWN

1 Rapid (5)
2 Rock (5)
3 Poems (4)
4 Hindu religious instructor (5)
5 Mad, informally (4)
6 Disturbance (6)
9 Shoot (6)
11 Vase (3)
12 Sum owing in an account (5)
13 Drank (7)
15 Small legendary being (3)
16 Employ (3)
18 Wedding attendants (6)
20 Sportsground (5)
21 Speck (3)
22 Trap (3)
23 Gloomy (6)
25 Be indebted (3)
28 Forage plant (5)
30 Antelope (5)
31 Condition (5)
32 Ale (4)
33 Extremely (4)

273

ACROSS

3 Aquatic birds (5)
8 Fortress (5)
10 Anaesthetic (5)
11 Hit lightly (3)
12 Sacrificial table (5)
13 Competition (7)
15 Stories (5)
18 Vex (3)
19 Account (6)
21 Char (7)
22 Pain (4)
23 Old (4)
24 Get (7)
26 Lower in rank (6)
29 Sound made by a cow (3)
31 Rep (5)
32 Flimsy (7)
34 Positioned (5)
35 Took a seat (3)
36 Operating handle (5)
37 Allude (5)
38 Conditions of agreement (5)

DOWN

1 Engine (5)
2 Cold-blooded vertebrate (7)
4 Droop (4)
5 Tidier (6)
6 Strip of leather, etc. (5)
7 More up-to-date (5)
9 Pale (3)
12 Obliquely (7)
14 Before (3)
16 Home of the beaver, etc. (5)
17 Investigation (5)
19 Took up again (7)
20 Bearlike mammal (5)
21 Ring (5)
23 Awoken (7)
24 Dress (6)
25 Charged particle (3)
27 Wading bird (5)
28 Start (5)
30 Silenced (5)
32 Side (4)
33 Lout (3)

274

ACROSS

1 Untrue (5)
6 Small plot of land (5)
9 Leopard (7)
10 Its winter coat is ermine (5)
11 Harvests (5)
12 Smell (5)
13 Russian warrior (7)
15 Beer (3)
17 Formerly (4)
18 Flow (6)
19 Counterfeit (5)
20 Seem (6)
22 Only (4)
24 Shelter (3)
25 Bung (7)
26 Steep slope (5)
27 Parody (5)
28 Notions (5)
29 Large bird of prey (7)
30 Fisherman's basket (5)
31 Mistake (5)

DOWN

2 Movement (6)
3 Scanty (6)
4 Consume (3)
5 Wading bird (5)
6 Allows (7)
7 Region (4)
8 Dome (6)
12 Thespian (5)
13 Reef-forming substance (5)
14 Range (5)
15 Writer of fables (5)
16 Piece of burning coal (5)
18 Set (5)
19 Shy (7)
21 Condiment (6)
22 Arachnid (6)
23 Smoothly, in music (6)
25 Condition (5)
26 Inlet (4)
28 Anger (3)

275

ACROSS

1 Slight convexity on a road, etc. (6)
7 Small shed (8)
8 Volcano (4)
10 Slice of bacon (6)
11 Bear (6)
14 Favourite (3)
16 Fooled (5)
17 Playthings (4)
19 Inexperienced (5)
21 Face-protector (5)
22 Churchman (5)
23 Flightless bird (4)
26 Male singer (5)
28 Observe (3)
29 Derivation (6)
30 Inscription (6)
31 Unit of length (4)
32 Magician (8)
33 Secure by intimidation (6)

DOWN

1 Root vegetable (6)
2 Washes (6)
3 Bellow (4)
4 Loud booming sound (7)
5 Amass (3,2)
6 Surrendered (5)
8 Catch sight of (4)
9 After deduction (3)
12 Press for payment (3)
13 Entertainment (5)
15 Fire-raising (5)
18 External (5)
19 Spirit (3)
20 Age (3)
21 Miscellaneous (7)
22 Tooth (3)
23 Rue (6)
24 Pay attention (4)
25 Passionate (6)
26 Feel (5)
27 Fool (5)
28 Ocean (3)
30 Old instrument (4)

276

ACROSS

4 Filament (6)
7 Elation (8)
8 Mixes (6)
10 Furious (5)
13 Fossil fuel (4)
14 Information (4)
15 Needy (4)
16 Perform (3)
17 Ogle (4)
19 Small missile (4)
21 Part (9)
23 Solitary (4)
24 Informer (4)
26 Rodent (3)
27 Harvest (4)
29 Weaving device (4)
32 Eons (4)
33 Border (5)
34 Dealer in fabrics (6)
35 Lower in quality (8)
36 Snow vehicle (6)

DOWN

1 Lukewarm (5)
2 Brisling (5)
3 Wander (5)
4 Socially frowned upon (5)
5 Stagger (4)
6 Kidnap (6)
9 Food store (6)
11 Uncooked (3)
12 Claw (5)
13 Small crowns (7)
15 Energy (3)
16 Skill (3)
18 Come out (6)
20 Leg joint (5)
21 Baby's bed (3)
22 Short sleep (3)
23 Bay tree (6)
25 Wet spongy ground (3)
28 Weird (5)
30 Path of a satellite (5)
31 Happy (5)
32 Mimicked (4)
33 Swerve to avoid (4)

ACROSS

3 Apartments (5)
8 Summarise, in short (5)
10 Mr Presley (5)
11 Decay (3)
12 Sports ground (5)
13 Disgusting (7)
15 Period of darkness (5)
18 Item of headgear (3)
19 End (6)
21 Grave (7)
22 Chilly (4)
23 Scheme (4)
24 Inquisitive (7)
26 Yearn (6)
29 Belonging to us (3)
31 In that place (5)
32 Dead skin round the nails (7)
34 Fertile spot (5)
35 Youngster (3)
36 Overcooked (5)
37 Lucifer (5)
38 Supposedly lucky number (5)

DOWN

1 Aromatic plants (5)
2 Corresponded to (7)
4 Entice (4)
5 Racket game (6)
6 Slaughtered (5)
7 Expresses relief, etc. (5)
9 Lettuce (3)
12 Valuable old object (7)
14 Organ of hearing (3)
16 Young females (5)
17 Ponder (5)
19 Livid (7)
20 Showy display (5)
21 Incline (5)
23 Strict moralist (7)
24 Make (6)
25 Not in (3)
27 Yell (5)
28 Presses (5)
30 Sacrificial table (5)
32 Quote (4)
33 Baby's bed (3)

278

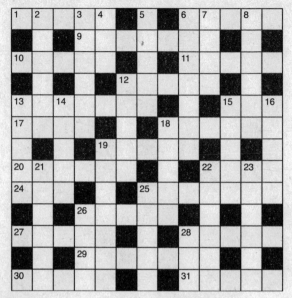

ACROSS

1 Tender (5)
6 Range (5)
9 Stroll (7)
10 Oneness (5)
11 Steel rope (5)
12 Healthily plump (5)
13 Melodic (7)
15 Ocean (3)
17 Quantity of paper (4)
18 Grown-ups (6)
19 Tires (5)
20 Cooked in hot water (6)
22 Give up (4)
24 Stray (3)
25 Pried (7)
26 Impatient, colloquially (5)
27 Dog's lead (5)
28 Worm that feeds on blood (5)
29 Beginner (7)
30 Speak (5)
31 Make reparation (5)

DOWN

2 Swiss cheese dish (6)
3 Respect (6)
4 Beam (3)
5 Cancel (5)
6 Moments (7)
7 Stuff (4)
8 Young hen (6)
12 Construct (5)
13 Clan (5)
14 Lowest point (5)
15 Slumber (5)
16 Enquired (5)
18 Torment (5)
19 Plume (7)
21 The East (6)
22 Concealed (6)
23 Ordained minister in the RC church (6)
25 Portion (5)
26 Small island (4)
28 Meadow (3)

ACROSS

1 Stiffener (6)
7 Welcoming (8)
8 Rotate (4)
10 Send goods out of the country (6)
11 Freebooter (6)
14 Employ (3)
16 Regions (5)
17 Tender (4)
19 Ranked (5)
21 Conductor's stick (5)
22 Spear (5)
23 Give food to (4)
26 Comfort (5)
28 Flightless bird (3)
29 Dress (6)
30 Put in order (6)
31 Garments, colloquially (4)
32 Drug or remedy (8)
33 Pool (6)

DOWN

1 Guides (6)
2 Rest (6)
3 Clue (4)
4 Community member (7)
5 Giant (5)
6 Eyes lasciviously (5)
8 Goad (4)
9 Anger (3)
12 Staff (3)
13 Taut (5)
15 Observe (5)
18 Should (5)
19 Managed (3)
20 Foot digit (3)
21 Jeer (7)
22 Flower garland (3)
23 Made in a smithy (6)
24 Consumes (4)
25 Infer (6)
26 Makes tranquil (5)
27 Musical study (5)
28 Sound made by a cow (3)
30 Pace (4)

280

ACROSS

4 Put money, etc., into (6)
7 Clattering (8)
8 Group of animal off spring (6)
10 Sphere (5)
13 Charged particles (4)
14 Team (4)
15 Soon (4)
16 Reserved (3)
17 Type (4)
19 Succulent plant (4)
21 Tortured (9)
23 Capital of Italy (4)
24 Require (4)
26 Dandy (3)
27 Blast of wind (4)
29 Stare open-mouthed (4)
32 Brief letter (4)
33 Gem (5)
34 Mother or father (6)
35 Cut (8)
36 Dread (6)

DOWN

1 Residue in liquids (5)
2 Got up (5)
3 Paste (4)
4 Eskimo dwelling (5)
5 Large containers for liquid (4)
6 Boil with rage (6)
9 Inborn (6)
11 Rim (3)
12 Broom (5)
13 Keen (7)
15 Equip (3)
16 Turf (3)
18 American state (6)
20 Shelf (5)
21 Highest part (3)
22 Catch (3)
23 Turn (6)
25 Mimic (3)
28 Complete (5)
30 Expect (5)
31 Antelope (5)
32 Close (4)
33 Prison (4)

281

ACROSS

3 Gather (5)
8 Wed (5)
10 Jetties (5)
11 Youngster (3)
12 Loaded (5)
13 Piece of furniture (7)
15 Rep (5)
18 Collection (3)
19 Give a sermon (6)
21 Rags (7)
22 Type of horse (4)
23 One who inherits (4)
24 Confided in (7)
26 Runs away to wed (6)
29 Fish (3)
31 Reveal (3,2)
32 Broke suddenly (7)
34 Fool (5)
35 Charged particle (3)
36 Untrue (5)
37 Excessive (5)
38 Strayed (5)

DOWN

1 Deadly (5)
2 Craftsman (7)
4 Flesh (4)
5 Lances (6)
6 Scorch (5)
7 French currency unit (5)
9 Steal from (3)
12 Written communications (7)
14 After deductions (3)
16 Soothed (5)
17 Unit of heat (5)
19 Gift (7)
20 Fisherman's basket (5)
21 Fortune-telling cards (5)
23 Portion of food (7)
24 Offer (6)
25 Hot drink (3)
27 Licit (5)
28 Composure (5)
30 Meeting place (5)
32 Only (4)
33 Seed case (3)

282

ACROSS

1 Belief (5)
6 Indian instrument (5)
9 Enlightenment (7)
10 Person held as property (5)
11 Eagle's nest (5)
12 Kingdom (5)
13 Avoided (7)
15 Lettuce (3)
17 Saucy (4)
18 Wood (6)
19 Be maliciously exultant (5)
20 Lariats (6)
22 Delicate decorative fabric (4)
24 Before (3)
25 Cut off (7)
26 Panics, informally (5)
27 Fashion (5)
28 Blacksmith's block (5)
29 Weird (7)
30 Angry (5)
31 Bordered (5)

DOWN

2 Experience once again (6)
3 Amuse (6)
4 An individual (3)
5 Sacked (5)
6 Edible bulb (7)
7 Object (4)
8 Spanish for friends (6)
12 Staggers (5)
13 Fruit (5)
14 Rub out (5)
15 Type of wood (5)
16 Horse (5)
18 Sums charged for bus, train travel, etc. (5)
19 Drinking vessels (7)
21 Protective covering (6)
22 Inclined (6)
23 Dark red (6)
25 Utter (5)
26 Ado (4)
28 Grow old (3)

283

ACROSS

1 Recompense (6)
7 Fine cotton fabric (8)
8 Arrived (4)
10 Car's stopping device (6)
11 Visitor (6)
14 Stitch (3)
16 Demon (5)
17 Paradise (4)
19 Weary (5)
21 Vessels for cut flowers (5)
22 Ran a cloth over (5)
23 Blaze (4)
26 Glossy fabric (5)
28 Male issue (3)
29 Attractive (6)
30 Big top (6)
31 Be impatient, commonly (4)
32 Haughty (8)
33 Tolerate (6)

DOWN

1 Pieces of broken stones (6)
2 Rouse (6)
3 Female deer, rabbits, etc. (4)
4 Wine bottles (7)
5 Confuse (5)
6 Facial hair (5)
8 Matter (4)
9 Sound made by a cat (3)
12 Cover (3)
13 Go in (5)
15 Skinflint (5)
18 Monetary unit of several countries (5)
19 Hit lightly (3)
20 Colour (3)
21 Wine from a harvest, in an exceptional year (7)
22 Humorist (3)
23 Coerced (6)
24 Unit of length (4)
25 Guarantee (6)
26 Aerosol (5)
27 Type of fabric (5)
28 Take a seat (3)
30 Quote (4)

284

ACROSS

4 Die (6)
7 In the open air (8)
8 Verse form (6)
10 Perfect (5)
13 Saucy (4)
14 Coil of hair (4)
15 Farm building (4)
16 Askew (3)
17 Prescribed range of food (4)
19 Not present (4)
21 Created (9)
23 Master (4)
24 Chilled (4)
26 Club (3)
27 Small island (4)
29 Express awe (4)
32 Encounter (4)
33 Measuring device (5)
34 Fleet of ships (6)
35 Famous (8)
36 Typewriter roller (6)

DOWN

1 Fundamental (5)
2 Tender (5)
3 Dropped (4)
4 Baffling question (5)
5 Rave (4)
6 Fortified wine (6)
9 Fancy (6)
11 Owing (3)
12 Tree (5)
13 Lover of one's country (7)
15 Buzzing insect (3)
16 Small ball or bundle (3)
18 In fact (6)
20 V-shaped slice (5)
21 Obtained (3)
22 Perform (3)
23 Bay (6)
25 Employ (3)
28 Long (5)
30 Make reparation (5)
31 Conceit (5)
32 Vertical spar on a vessel (4)
33 State of mind (4)

ACROSS

3 Animal's trail (5)
8 Food fish (5)
10 Contests of speed (5)
11 Stray (3)
12 Attempt (5)
13 Custodians (7)
15 Invigorating drink (5)
18 Paddle (3)
19 Cheerful (6)
21 Pieces of landed property (7)
22 Part (4)
23 Confidence trick (4)
24 Error (7)
26 Bookmaker's sign language (3-3)
29 Cathedral city (3)
31 Go in (5)
32 Roars (7)
34 Regal (5)
35 Beer (3)
36 Trunk of the body (5)
37 Command (5)
38 Finished (5)

DOWN

1 Immature (5)
2 Aim (7)
4 Go by (4)
5 Speaks (6)
6 Man-made material (5)
7 Reddish-brown (5)
9 Mineral (3)
12 Inconsistent (7)
14 Consume (3)
16 Female relation (5)
17 Cluster (5)
19 Well-bred (7)
20 Beast (5)
21 Choose (5)
23 Songbird (7)
24 Firework (6)
25 Everyone (3)
27 Piece of cast metal (5)
28 Abrupt (5)
30 Dessert (5)
32 Naked (4)
33 Aged (3)

286

ACROSS

1 Pale (5)
6 Tarnish (5)
9 Disappointment (3-4)
10 Eastern dish (5)
11 Smell (5)
12 Forbidden (5)
13 Overall (7)
15 Beverage (3)
17 Heavy metal (4)
18 Proclaim (6)
19 Helped (5)
20 Strip (6)
22 Only (4)
24 Before (3)
25 Coach (7)
26 Guide (5)
27 Below (5)
28 Drilling-tool (5)
29 Sickness (7)
30 Decorate (5)
31 Irritable (5)

DOWN

2 Evening music party (6)
3 Overjoyed (6)
4 Novel (3)
5 Perfect (5)
6 Descended suddenly (7)
7 Release (4)
8 Bay (6)
12 Unspoken (5)
13 Move smoothly (5)
14 Artless (5)
15 Removed (5)
16 Snake (5)
18 Core (5)
19 Painkiller (7)
21 Pressed (6)
22 Tiny (6)
23 Up-to-date (6)
25 Private in the British Army (5)
26 Fruit (4)
28 Insect (3)

ACROSS

1 Covered in spots (6)
7 Demote (8)
8 In addition (4)
10 Part of the foot (6)
11 Hit (6)
14 Golf-peg (3)
16 Wading-bird (5)
17 Network (4)
19 Liberated (5)
21 Tree (5)
22 Cringe (5)
23 Hit with the open hand (4)
26 Carrying-chair (5)
28 Meadow (3)
29 Attractive (6)
30 Cause (6)
31 Lubricates (4)
32 Worshipped (8)
33 Final part (6)

DOWN

1 Bold (6)
2 Inclined (6)
3 Fall (4)
4 Animal skin (7)
5 Lowest point (5)
6 Lucky number (5)
8 Italian wine (4)
9 Observe (3)
12 Colour (3)
13 Australian marsupial (5)
15 Command (5)
18 Large stream (5)
19 Not many (3)
20 Organ of hearing (3)
21 Comprise (7)
22 Feline (3)
23 Tightly closed (6)
24 Girl (4)
25 Longing (6)
26 Spray (5)
27 Devil (5)
28 Flower-garland (3)
30 Went by bicycle, etc. (4)

288

ACROSS

4 Dreary (6)
7 One who gives work (8)
8 Did as told (6)
10 Mad, informally (5)
13 Scheme (4)
14 Above (4)
15 Seasoning (4)
16 Enquire (3)
17 Object of worship (4)
19 Carry (4)
21 Continue regardless (9)
23 Musical tailpiece (4)
24 Nurse (4)
26 Show assent (3)
27 Unit of power (4)
29 Fencing foil (4)
32 Surrender (4)
33 Cook by direct heat (5)
34 Look at (6)
35 Surround (8)
36 Declared (6)

DOWN

1 Time, in music (5)
2 Malice (5)
3 Small horse (4)
4 Amusing (5)
5 Observed (4)
6 Loath (6)
9 Strip of wood (6)
11 Eggs (3)
12 Attempted (5)
13 Artist's mixing-board (7)
15 Distress signal (3)
16 Consumed (3)
18 Sliding boxlike container (6)
20 Arrangement (5)
21 Seed-case (3)
22 Examine (3)
23 Secret (6)
25 Take shape (3)
28 Said more (5)
30 Nip (5)
31 Senior (5)
32 Throw (4)
33 Grasp firmly (4)

289

ACROSS

3 Water vapour (5)
8 Irritable (5)
10 Clergyman (5)
11 Flower garland (3)
12 Citrus fruit (5)
13 Gossip (7)
15 Surrendered (5)
18 Decay (3)
19 Calm (6)
21 Sake (7)
22 Study (4)
23 Gloomy (4)
24 Gate fastenings (7)
26 Plant used in salads, etc. (6)
29 Age (3)
31 Prongs of a fork (5)
32 Light winds (7)
34 Edition (5)
35 Raised edge (3)
36 French river (5)
37 Pleased (5)
38 Deliberate insults (5)

DOWN

1 Brawl (5)
2 Agitated (7)
4 Three in cards (4)
5 Shore bird (6)
6 Pit worker (5)
7 Harbour (5)
9 Area of water (3)
12 Relating to the side (7)
14 Male offspring (3)
16 Trades (5)
17 Considers (5)
19 Heartfelt (7)
20 Icy deposit (5)
21 In Scottish dialect, a child (5)
23 Overall (7)
24 Belittle (6)
25 Garden tool (3)
27 Lubricated (5)
28 They control horses (5)
30 Musical speed (5)
32 Hyacinth or daffodil for instance (4)
33 Fastening device (3)

290

ACROSS

1 Adhere (5)
6 Religion of Muslims (5)
9 Increase (7)
10 Started (5)
11 Causes pain (5)
12 Pale (5)
13 Below (7)
15 Skill (3)
17 Notion (4)
18 Steal (6)
19 Defect (5)
20 Stringed instruments (6)
22 Sports umpires (4)
24 Fodder (3)
25 Young hare (7)
26 Lukewarm (5)
27 Eye inflammations (5)
28 Food dressing (5)
29 Proof of purchase (7)
30 Salt water (5)
31 Raising agent (5)

DOWN

2 Looked at suggestively (6)
3 Revulsion (6)
4 Firearm (3)
5 Break (5)
6 Succeed as heir (7)
7 Daze (4)
8 Wear (6)
12 Book of maps (5)
13 Tree (5)
14 Recently (5)
15 Subsequently (5)
16 Confidence (5)
18 Sold (5)
19 Predict (7)
21 Christian festival (6)
22 Narrate (6)
23 Barriers (6)
25 Organ of the body (5)
26 Aquatic bird (4)
28 Snoop (3)

ACROSS

1 Crucial turning point (6)
7 Dolt (8)
8 Split (4)
10 Paltry (6)
11 Author (6)
14 Reserved (3)
16 Watchful (5)
17 Spellbound (4)
19 Spot (5)
21 Female garment (5)
22 Aviator (5)
23 Fruit of a palm (4)
26 Light boat (5)
28 Agent (3)
29 Harvester (6)
30 Small mammal (6)
31 Lazy (4)
32 Bloomed (8)
33 Coarse (6)

DOWN

1 More placid (6)
2 Snub (6)
3 Piece of land (4)
4 Take back (7)
5 Ski-slope (5)
6 Core (5)
8 File (4)
9 Cook in fat (3)
12 Type (3)
13 Put up (5)
15 Salesman's patter (5)
18 Seaweed (5)
19 Move on snow (3)
20 Stray (3)
21 Simple earring (7)
22 Dandy (3)
23 Trader (6)
24 Church recess (4)
25 Speech in praise of a person, etc. (6)
26 Small farm (5)
27 Rich man (5)
28 Colour (3)
30 Extensive (4)

292

ACROSS

4 Declared (6)
7 Intrude upon (8)
8 Made accessible (6)
10 Sharp (5)
13 Back (4)
14 Old instrument (4)
15 Joke (4)
16 Appropriate (3)
17 Verse composition (4)
19 Leave out (4)
21 Graphic (9)
23 Constructed (4)
24 Reddish coating on iron (4)
26 Church seat (3)
27 Mislaid (4)
29 Hint (4)
32 Small bay (4)
33 Brief (5)
34 Canine mammal (6)
35 Rose up (8)
36 Young swan (6)

DOWN

1 Wild (5)
2 Reconnoitre (5)
3 Tender (4)
4 Items of footwear (5)
5 Declare (4)
6 Excuse (6)
9 Regional dialect (6)
11 Dog (3)
12 Lukewarm (5)
13 Deep regret (7)
15 Nozzle (3)
16 Trouble (3)
18 Feline mammal (6)
20 Exact copy (5)
21 Animal's foot (3)
22 Furrow in a road (3)
23 Tune (6)
25 Animal coat (3)
28 Open (5)
30 Simple (5)
31 Musical study (5)
32 Metal money (4)
33 Ooze (4)

ACROSS

3 Underground chamber (5)
8 Swift (5)
10 Scottish landlord (5)
11 Vapour (3)
12 Wrath (5)
13 Prayer books (7)
15 Main blood vessel (5)
18 Lubricate (3)
19 Regard highly (6)
21 Huge (7)
22 Conceal (4)
23 Peel (4)
24 Women (7)
26 Positioned (6)
29 Cooking vessel (3)
31 Firm (5)
32 Mends (7)
34 Had a nap (5)
35 Foot digit (3)
36 Measuring device (5)
37 Notes, coins, etc. (5)
38 Large gathering (5)

DOWN

1 Sorcery (5)
2 Lithe (7)
4 Manages (4)
5 Content (6)
6 Fortune-telling cards (5)
7 Banal (5)
9 Ballet step (3)
12 Stated without proof (7)
14 Goal (3)
16 Stinks (5)
17 Alter (5)
19 Fled (7)
20 Pommes frites (5)
21 Perfect (5)
23 US politician (7)
24 Soft felt hat (6)
25 Circuit of a race track (3)
27 Felt great affection for (5)
28 Alcoholic apple drink (5)
30 Raise (5)
32 Stagger (4)
33 Charged particle (3)

294

ACROSS

1 Wishes (5)
6 Wash out (5)
9 Tells (7)
10 Fold (5)
11 Liquid measures (5)
12 Dunces (5)
13 Small grain (7)
15 Vegetable (3)
17 Not as much (4)
18 Frightened (6)
19 Italian city (5)
20 Steps (6)
22 Border (4)
24 Boy's name (3)
25 Colonist (7)
26 Cold dish (5)
27 Start (5)
28 Regimens (5)
29 Final game (7)
30 Enquired (5)
31 At no time (5)

DOWN

2 Fascination (6)
3 Coaches (6)
4 Ready (3)
5 Paddle-boat (5)
6 Copy (7)
7 Egyptian goddess (4)
8 Sofa (6)
12 Insects (5)
13 Drinking vessel (5)
14 Indian state (5)
15 Conceit (5)
16 Viper (5)
18 Sturdy (5)
19 Sounded frustrated (7)
21 Narrows (6)
22 Whole (6)
23 Moderate (6)
25 Sudden fear (5)
26 Team (4)
28 Lair (3)

ACROSS

1 Crops up (6)
7 Definite (5-3)
8 Celebration (4)
10 Tidier (6)
11 Angry speech (6)
14 Body of water (3)
16 Drive back (5)
17 Serpents (4)
19 Ranted (5)
21 Taunts (5)
22 Insurgent (5)
23 Region (4)
26 Counterfeit (5)
28 Greeting (3)
29 Representatives (6)
30 Talks (6)
31 Nurse (4)
32 Address angrily (8)
33 Molluscs (6)

DOWN

1 Schedule (6)
2 Roofing tiles (6)
3 Mark (4)
4 Lampoons (7)
5 Discard (5)
6 Alloy (5)
8 Sudden intake of breath (4)
9 Meadow (3)
12 Colour (3)
13 Dig (5)
15 Log (5)
18 Baby, commonly (5)
19 Chest bone (3)
20 Solidify (3)
21 Fooling (7)
22 Manage (3)
23 Tree-lined street (6)
24 Peruse (4)
25 Things of value (6)
26 Wash (5)
27 Type (5)
28 Mimic (3)
30 Casserole (4)

296

ACROSS

4 Nearly (6)
7 Court of justice (8)
8 Collect (6)
10 Sphere (5)
13 Show concern (4)
14 Unaided (4)
15 Sonnet, for instance (4)
16 Aged (3)
17 Precipitation (4)
19 Says more (4)
21 Not sure (9)
23 Raised (4)
24 Muslim religious leader (4)
26 Bar (3)
27 Speech defect (4)
29 Employed (4)
32 Lake (4)
33 Sportsground (5)
34 Chirping insect (6)
35 Elegant (8)
36 Dairy product (6)

DOWN

1 Adult male deer (5)
2 Area of Austria (5)
3 Unsullied (4)
4 Seaweed (5)
5 Dumb (4)
6 Gets bigger (6)
9 Fleet of ships (6)
11 Record (3)
12 Carried (5)
13 Brief (7)
15 Baked dish (3)
16 Strange (3)
18 Confused (6)
20 Object (5)
21 Vessel (3)
22 Little devil (3)
23 Drive away (6)
25 Information (3)
28 Furious (5)
30 Unfree persons (5)
31 Dawdle (5)
32 Construct (4)
33 Stake (4)

297

ACROSS

3 Dairy product (5)
8 Missile (5)
10 Stringed instrument (5)
11 Consume (3)
12 Wrong (5)
13 Characters (7)
15 Weird (5)
18 Skill (3)
19 Apprehend (6)
21 Anti (7)
22 English resort (4)
23 Despatch (4)
24 Detestable (7)
26 Deteriorate (6)
29 Summit (3)
31 Subsequently (5)
32 Smoked fish (7)
34 Contagious fear (5)
35 Be indebted (3)
36 Demon (5)
37 Iron (5)
38 Snake (5)

DOWN

1 Unripe (5)
2 Country house (7)
4 Batters (4)
5 Declare (6)
6 Skinflint (5)
7 Eastern garments (5)
9 Rodent (3)
12 Craftsman (7)
14 Age (3)
16 Rise up (5)
17 Musical study (5)
19 Abstemious person (7)
20 Wrap (5)
21 Avoid (5)
23 Prop (7)
24 Harbinger (6)
25 Dandy (3)
27 Fertile spots (5)
28 Reddish-brown pigment (5)
30 Frock (5)
32 Bird of prey (4)
33 Female sheep (3)

298

ACROSS

1 Group of workers (5)
6 Hymn (5)
9 Soused herring (7)
10 Spirit (5)
11 Sword (5)
12 Below (5)
13 Flag (7)
15 Insect (3)
17 Rush (4)
18 Fruit (6)
19 Sieves (5)
20 Take away (6)
22 Sound made by a cat (4)
24 Cathedral city (3)
25 Gossip (7)
26 Lid (5)
27 Perfect (5)
28 Ape (5)
29 Weds (7)
30 Loafer (5)
31 At no time (5)

DOWN

2 Wigwam (6)
3 Ally (6)
4 Enemy (3)
5 Gleam (5)
6 Affected types (7)
7 Box (4)
8 Enticing (6)
12 Out of condition (5)
13 Haughtiness (5)
14 Poor (5)
15 Former Scottish county (5)
16 Type of fabric (5)
18 Aquatic animal (5)
19 Student (7)
21 Avoided (6)
22 Laud (6)
23 Gorge (6)
25 Core (5)
26 Arrived (4)
28 Males (3)

ACROSS

1 Stopped temporarily (6)
7 Thin slice of meat (8)
8 Narrow way (4)
10 Frightened (6)
11 Inclines (6)
14 Stitch (3)
16 Surrey town (5)
17 Collections (4)
19 Map (5)
21 Areas of waste ground (5)
22 Breast (5)
23 Dirt (4)
26 Happen (5)
28 Ban (3)
29 Small rocks (6)
30 Marked by heat (6)
31 Enquires (4)
32 Frees from blame (8)
33 Loathing (6)

DOWN

1 Goes by (6)
2 Shows mercy (6)
3 Act (4)
4 Visitors (7)
5 Highland valleys (5)
6 Muscular contraction (5)
8 Final (4)
9 Novel (3)
12 Fitting (3)
13 Subject (5)
15 Fire (5)
18 Oust (5)
19 Kind of lettuce (3)
20 Equip (3)
21 Type of cherry (7)
22 Small cake (3)
23 Demand for goods (6)
24 Vases (4)
25 Teased (6)
26 Academy Award (5)
27 Thicket (5)
28 Public vehicle (3)
30 Hit (4)

300

ACROSS

4 Young child (6)
7 Shy (8)
8 Solicitor (6)
10 Position (5)
13 Nee (4)
14 Meat substitute (4)
15 Black deposit (4)
16 Deciduous tree (3)
17 Needy(4)
19 Liberate (4)
21 Endless (9)
23 String (4)
24 Puppet (4)
26 Club (3)
27 Famous school (4)
29 Rules (4)
32 Pack tightly (4)
33 Man-made textile (5)
34 Fondle (6)
35 Short rest at work (3-5)
36 Cloak (6)

DOWN

1 Snares (5)
2 Wander (5)
3 Genuine (4)
4 Eskimo house (5)
5 Young deer (4)
6 Sewing implement (6)
9 Cunning (6)
11 Sever (3)
12 Cavort (5)
13 Ennui (7)
15 Concession (3)
16 Fish (3)
18 Commands (6)
20 Large gathering (5)
21 Cooking vessel (3)
22 Unit of weight (3)
23 N. American country (6)
25 A pair (3)
28 Discretion (5)
30 Strange (5)
31 Reptile (5)
32 Foreign coin (4)
33 Arrests, informally (4)

ACROSS

3 Ways (5)
8 Musical composition (5)
10 Make amends (5)
11 Managed (3)
12 Type of wood (5)
13 Electric cell (7)
15 Begin (5)
18 Fish-eggs (3)
19 Detective (6)
21 Swagger (7)
22 Metal fastener (4)
23 Destroy (4)
24 Tremble violently (7)
26 Threat (6)
29 Not in (3)
31 Age (5)
32 Knitted garment (7)
34 Examines (5)
35 Charged particle (3)
36 Broom (5)
37 Show contempt (5)
38 Breeds (5)

DOWN

1 Ethical (5)
2 Positioned in the middle (7)
4 Not present (4)
5 Great deal of trouble (6)
6 Condition (5)
7 Inactive (5)
9 Make lace (3)
12 Take in air (7)
14 Age (3)
16 Presage (5)
17 Ponder on (5)
19 Follows stealthily (7)
20 Garden ornament (5)
21 Musical instrument (5)
23 Keeps (7)
24 Plan (6)
25 Owing (3)
27 Fencing foils (5)
28 Thespian (5)
30 Belief (5)
32 Agitate (4)
33 Foot digit (3)

302

ACROSS

1 Range (5)
6 Cringe (5)
9 Beginner (7)
10 Take unlawfully (5)
11 Rule (5)
12 Hits sharply (5)
13 Dejected (7)
15 Period of time (3)
17 Primates (4)
18 Precious metal (6)
19 Claw (5)
20 Fisherman (6)
22 Prong of a fork (4)
24 Shelter (3)
25 Split (7)
26 Rate (5)
27 Declare (5)
28 Soil (5)
29 Amaze (7)
30 Core (5)
31 Put off (5)

DOWN

2 Doze (6)
3 Shallow dishes (6)
4 Fish (3)
5 Creep (5)
6 Sure (7)
7 Minerals (4)
8 Hire (6)
12 Sweetener (5)
13 Trite (5)
14 Shelf (5)
15 Avert (5)
16 Strayed (5)
18 Firm (5)
19 Storm (7)
21 Lie snug (6)
22 Angry speech (6)
23 Stinging plant (6)
25 Warehouse (5)
26 Celebrity (4)
28 Finish (3)

ACROSS

1 Get smaller (6)
7 Scrutinises (8)
8 Gemstone (4)
10 New (6)
11 Pillaged (6)
14 Large deer (3)
16 Sift (5)
17 Headland (4)
19 Temporary accommodation (5)
21 Lukewarm (5)
22 Thick (5)
23 Use the teeth (4)
26 Pale (5)
28 Unopened flower (3)
29 Monkey nut (6)
30 Moves slowly sideways (6)
31 Rim (4)
32 Sufficient (8)
33 Went by (6)

DOWN

1 Food fish (6)
2 Forces (6)
3 Potter's oven (4)
4 Countered (7)
5 Sharp (5)
6 Confidential remark (5)
8 Poems (4)
9 Noah's vessel (3)
12 Lubricate (3)
13 Happening (5)
15 Thicket (5)
18 Rub out (5)
19 Female bird (3)
20 Fasten (3)
21 Flimsy (7)
22 Study (3)
23 Moves slightly (6)
24 Lazy (4)
25 Followed (6)
26 Dismay (5)
27 Loathed (5)
28 Offer (3)
30 Ooze (4)

304

ACROSS

4 Heavy cloth (6)
7 Devilish (8)
8 Landed property (6)
10 Use a broom (5)
13 Entrance (4)
14 Mountain lake (4)
15 Distinctive air (4)
16 Favourite (3)
17 Pause (4)
19 Travel around (4)
21 Cramp (9)
23 Religious group (4)
24 Every one (4)
26 Very warm (3)
27 Merit (4)
29 Prank (4)
32 Equips (4)
33 Thighbone (5)
34 Sea trip (6)
35 Drivel (8)
36 Taunted (6)

DOWN

1 Prime (5)
2 Subsequently (5)
3 Journey (4)
4 Transparent (5)
5 Short communication (4)
6 Flower-part (6)
9 Still (6)
11 Humorist (3)
12 Register (5)
13 Rainwater channels (7)
15 Fool (3)
16 Place (3)
18 Goes in (6)
20 Natural pigment (5)
21 Snip (3)
22 Raced (3)
23 Force (6)
25 Flightless bird (3)
28 Alter (5)
30 Signs (5)
31 Dress the feathers (5)
32 Goals (4)
33 Ado (4)

305

ACROSS

3 Last (5)
8 Pig (5)
10 Tote (5)
11 Deed (3)
12 Jokes (5)
13 Liberty (7)
15 Academy Award (5)
18 No (3)
19 Awaken (6)
21 Speech (7)
22 Consumes (4)
23 Incline (4)
24 Counsels (7)
26 Hang freely (6)
29 Quantity (3)
31 Take unlawfully (5)
32 Paced (7)
34 Melodies (5)
35 Illuminated (3)
36 Tree (5)
37 Measuring device (5)
38 Shabby (5)

DOWN

1 Move in large numbers (5)
2 Means (7)
4 Object (4)
5 Performers (6)
6 Lariat (5)
7 Regions (5)
9 Frozen water (3)
12 Pleasure-drive in a stolen car (3-4)
14 Father (3)
16 Remedies (5)
17 Tears (5)
19 Helps (7)
20 Twists (5)
21 Make reparation (5)
23 Places of worship (7)
24 Charm (6)
25 Start legal proceedings against (3)
27 Coral reef (5)
28 Entrances (5)
30 Put off (5)
32 Remit (4)
33 Mine (3)

306

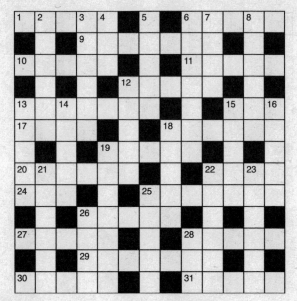

ACROSS

1 Perspire (5)
6 Perceive (5)
9 Order (7)
10 Choose (5)
11 Eskimo house (5)
12 Canal boat (5)
13 Wander aimlessly (7)
15 Allow (3)
17 Prepare for publication (4)
18 Lower (6)
19 Guide (5)
20 Hotel patrons (6)
22 Periods of time (4)
24 Finish (3)
25 Sportsman (7)
26 Mounds (5)
27 Female fox (5)
28 Unclear (5)
29 Withdrew (7)
30 Surrendered (5)
31 Short (5)

DOWN

2 Drooped (6)
3 Stress (6)
4 Youngster (3)
5 Smudge (5)
6 Laugh derisively (7)
7 Border (4)
8 Cuts (6)
12 Hits (5)
13 Blend (5)
14 Helped (5)
15 Big (5)
16 Taut (5)
18 Small hollows (5)
19 Blemished (7)
21 Foolish (6)
22 Refer (6)
23 Musical studies (6)
25 Change (5)
26 In this place (4)
28 Encountered (3)

307

ACROSS

1 Protect from harm (6)
7 Swap (8)
8 Scrutinise (4)
10 Awning (6)
11 Conduct (6)
14 Skill (3)
16 Urns (5)
17 Drug (4)
19 Crave (5)
21 Shows concern (5)
22 Trainee officer (5)
23 Flower (4)
26 Antitoxin (5)
28 Gender (3)
29 Correct (6)
30 Skips playfully (6)
31 Overt (4)
32 Hypocritical (3-5)
33 Goes in (6)

DOWN

1 Moved to music (6)
2 Cry meaning 'more' (6)
3 Reject as false (4)
4 Prospers (7)
5 Leg-joints (5)
6 Great deeds (5)
8 Break suddenly (4)
9 Suitable (3)
12 Rodent (3)
13 Prison rooms (5)
15 Drilled (5)
18 Freshwater mammal (5)
19 Bounder (3)
20 Examine (3)
21 Photographic devices (7)
22 Drinking vessel (3)
23 Feel remorse (6)
24 Bovine mammals (4)
25 Follows (6)
26 Malice (5)
27 Automaton (5)
28 Drain of energy (3)
30 Cipher (4)

308

ACROSS

4 High-pitched (6)
7 Contender coming second (6-2)
8 Protective covering (6)
10 Confidence (5)
13 Prejudice (4)
14 Stop (4)
15 Canvas shelter (4)
16 Wager (3)
17 Press (4)
19 Drag (4)
21 Innocent (9)
23 Matted fabric (4)
24 Eating implement (4)
26 Wrath (3)
27 Journey (4)
29 Otherwise (4)
32 Strip of wood (4)
33 Take as one's own (5)
34 Herb (6)
35 Askew (8)
36 Room to move (6)

DOWN

1 Thin soup (5)
2 Cancel (5)
3 Saucy (4)
4 European country (5)
5 Thrusts violently (4)
6 Bay tree (6)
9 Somewhat (6)
11 Uncooked (3)
12 Unmoving (5)
13 Advantage (7)
15 Male cat (3)
16 Public vehicle (3)
18 Child's toy (6)
20 Enquired (5)
21 Buzzing insect (3)
22 Cut off (3)
23 Decorative border (6)
25 Snake (3)
28 Mass gathering (5)
30 Burdens (5)
31 Musical study (5)
32 Ice crystals in flakes (4)
33 Church recess (4)

309

ACROSS

3 Hit (5)
8 Alloy (5)
10 Soothed (5)
11 Agent (3)
12 Animal (5)
13 Professions (7)
15 Egg's outer layer (5)
18 Yes (3)
19 Oil-yielding seeds (6)
21 Contents (7)
22 Misfortunes (4)
23 Ban (4)
24 Break in pieces (7)
26 Embraces (6)
29 Charged particle (3)
31 Edge along (5)
32 This evening (7)
34 Consumed (5)
35 Observe (3)
36 Pilot (5)
37 Was very fond of (5)
38 Hymn (5)

DOWN

1 Wander (5)
2 Revokes (7)
4 Shades of colour (4)
5 Makes untidy (6)
6 Narrow ways (5)
7 Kingdom (5)
9 Always (3)
12 Puffs of air (7)
14 Organ of vision (3)
16 Keen (5)
17 Citrus fruit (5)
19 Division (7)
20 Records (5)
21 Appeal (5)
23 Deer meat (7)
24 Lances (6)
25 Unit of weight (3)
27 Catalogues (5)
28 Slumber (5)
30 Woolly animals (5)
32 Inform (4)
33 Obtain (3)

310

ACROSS

1 Blunder (5)
6 Filament (5)
9 Disproved (7)
10 Blacksmith's block (5)
11 Chosen few (5)
12 Fine net fabric (5)
13 Trap (7)
15 Meadow (3)
17 Old (4)
18 Goes in (6)
19 Smart (5)
20 Hypnotic state (6)
22 Bet (4)
24 Female bird (3)
25 Made up (7)
26 Ranked (5)
27 Fragment (5)
28 Walks unevenly (5)
29 Sure (7)
30 Surrenders (5)
31 Wading bird (5)

DOWN

2 Canopy (6)
3 Ally (6)
4 Fish (3)
5 Organ composition (5)
6 Sensation (7)
7 Lazy (4)
8 Cad (6)
12 Banal (5)
13 Soil (5)
14 Portable chair (5)
15 Inclines (5)
16 Enquired (5)
18 Finished (5)
19 Removes by rubbing (7)
21 Save (6)
22 Sickening (6)
23 Place of worship (6)
25 Greek letter (5)
26 Contest of speed (4)
28 Untruth (3)

311

ACROSS

1 Agree (6)
7 Draw near (8)
8 Animal skin (4)
10 Positions (6)
11 Remember (6)
14 Definite article (3)
16 Famous (5)
17 Fencing foil (4)
19 Satisfied (5)
21 Shock (5)
22 Unadorned (5)
23 Of sound mind (4)
26 Wall-painting (5)
28 Evergreen tree (3)
29 Worshipped (6)
30 Duty (6)
31 Region (4)
32 Obscure (8)
33 Wrestle (6)

DOWN

1 Pair (6)
2 Day nursery (6)
3 Rodents (4)
4 Ammunition store (7)
5 Gem weight (5)
6 Tot (5)
8 Meat paste (4)
9 Shelter (3)
12 Food fish (3)
13 Reveal (3,2)
15 Swift (5)
18 Haughty (5)
19 Resort (3)
20 Yellowish-brown (3)
21 Accused (7)
22 Standard (3)
23 Warning devices (6)
24 Operatic song (4)
25 Obliterate (6)
26 Female horses (5)
27 Automaton (5)
28 Distant (3)
30 Diplomacy (4)

312

ACROSS

4 Bird (6)
7 Spring bulb (8)
8 Evades (6)
10 Compass point (5)
13 Smear (4)
14 Large plant (4)
15 Eats (4)
16 Court (3)
17 Breed of dog, informally (4)
19 Sour (4)
21 Likewise (9)
23 Go by car, etc. (4)
24 Fibbed (4)
26 Gratuity (3)
27 Rush (4)
29 Send out (4)
32 Got older (4)
33 Wear away (5)
34 Evening meal (6)
35 Notorious (8)
36 Set on fire (6)

DOWN

1 Simple song (5)
2 Cavalry sword (5)
3 Lofty (4)
4 Inexpensive (5)
5 Bat (4)
6 Valued fur (6)
9 Sheen (6)
11 Mineral (3)
12 Lukewarm (5)
13 Fought to the death (7)
15 Move on snow (3)
16 Sardonic (3)
18 Come out (6)
20 Shrub or tree (5)
21 Drink daintily (3)
22 Help (3)
23 Ascending (6)
25 Free (3)
28 Weird (5)
30 Engine (5)
31 Abrupt (5)
32 Against (4)
33 Dutch cheese (4)

313

ACROSS

3 Rows (5)
8 Goods (5)
10 Before time (5)
11 Apt (3)
12 On high (5)
13 Accounts (7)
15 Eagle's nest (5)
18 Outfit (3)
19 Wandering (6)
21 Wins back (7)
22 Arabian sultanate (4)
23 Female deer (4)
24 Expressed disgust (7)
26 Shuts (6)
29 Fish (3)
31 Loaned (5)
32 Young frog (7)
34 Manservant (5)
35 Obese (3)
36 Metal fastener (5)
37 Wall-painting (5)
38 Breeds (5)

DOWN

1 Very light biscuit (5)
2 Indicate (7)
4 Misfortunes (4)
5 Alludes (6)
6 Woodland deity (5)
7 Slaughtered (5)
9 Tear (3)
12 Reaches (7)
14 Manipulate fraudulently (3)
16 Swift (5)
17 Musical study (5)
19 Beg (7)
20 Flashlight (5)
21 Shaving implement (5)
23 Cooperative (7)
24 Staid (6)
25 Make hay (3)
27 Furious (5)
28 Cut off (5)
30 Sacrificial table (5)
32 Rend (4)
33 Paddle (3)

314

ACROSS

1 Herb (5)
6 Weird (5)
9 Very old (7)
10 Booth (5)
11 Empties (5)
12 Start (5)
13 Antennae (7)
15 Expert (3)
17 Lazy (4)
18 Piece let into a garment (6)
19 Naps (5)
20 Avoided (6)
22 Only (4)
24 Start legal proceedings against (3)
25 Warship (7)
26 Cut (5)
27 Not fresh (5)
28 Own (5)
29 Wind flower (7)
30 Skilful (5)
31 Cord (5)

DOWN

2 Loathing (6)
3 Mutilate (6)
4 Finish (3)
5 Artful ploys (5)
6 Jealous (7)
7 Boy's public school (4)
8 Persuade (6)
12 Ponder morbidly (5)
13 Discovers (5)
14 Evade (5)
15 Fools (5)
16 Anaesthetic (5)
18 Category (5)
19 Downward slope (7)
21 Expelled (6)
22 Plant disease (6)
23 Step down (6)
25 Offence (5)
26 Hit with the open hand (4)
28 Insect (3)

315

ACROSS

1 Plumlike fruit (6)
7 Upholstered seat (8)
8 Ray (4)
10 Disinclined (6)
11 Time of year (6)
14 Noah's vessel (3)
16 Watchful (5)
17 Reject as false (4)
19 Censure (5)
21 Oozes (5)
22 Sturdy box (5)
23 Ripped (4)
26 Row (5)
28 Each (3)
29 Flow (6)
30 Scold (6)
31 Nobleman (4)
32 Proof (8)
33 In a robust manner (6)

DOWN

1 Insist on (6)
2 Fortified wine (6)
3 Title (4)
4 Yells (7)
5 Old-fashioned (5)
6 Bestow (5)
8 Edible seed (4)
9 Enquire (3)
12 Beer (3)
13 Command (5)
15 Meat (5)
18 Turn inside out (5)
19 Buzzing insect (3)
20 Fitting (3)
21 Bundles (7)
22 Actor's signal (3)
23 Great fear (6)
24 Spoken (4)
25 Vim (6)
26 Awry (5)
27 Small seedlike fruit (5)
28 Vegetable (3)
30 Red meat (4)

316

ACROSS

4 Forward flow (6)
7 Wayward behaviour (8)
8 Tip over (6)
10 Showy and vulgar (5)
13 Sum owed (4)
14 Fencing foil (4)
15 Canvas shelter (4)
16 Lubricant (3)
17 Wail (4)
19 Distinctive air (4)
21 Pet (9)
23 Female horse (4)
24 Small hollow (4)
26 Counter (3)
27 Require (4)
29 Soothe (4)
32 Reserve of money (4)
33 Heartless (5)
34 Opening (6)
35 Imagine (8)
36 Bloom (6)

DOWN

1 Picture (5)
2 Edition (5)
3 Watery part of milk (4)
4 Frequently (5)
5 Engrossed (4)
6 Garden flower (6)
9 Get (6)
11 Mimic (3)
12 Exclude (5)
13 Deceived (7)
15 A pair (3)
16 Mineral (3)
18 Broad street (6)
20 Speak (5)
21 Distant (3)
22 Colour (3)
23 Handbook (6)
25 Employ (3)
28 Go in (5)
30 Of the ear (5)
31 Senior (5)
32 Blemish (4)
33 Baby's bed (4)

317

ACROSS

3 Bush (5)
8 Bad-tempered (5)
10 At no time (5)
11 And not (3)
12 Shoot (5)
13 Treats meanly (7)
15 Peaceful (5)
18 Friend (3)
19 Sprinter (6)
21 Entourage (7)
22 Eons (4)
23 Peruse (4)
24 Stammer (7)
26 Frightens (6)
29 Circuit (3)
31 Italian city (5)
32 African country (7)
34 Adder (5)
35 Also (3)
36 Basket (5)
37 Den (5)
38 Anxious (5)

DOWN

1 Jousting weapon (5)
2 Bands (7)
4 Beer ingredient (4)
5 One of a kind (6)
6 Started (5)
7 Commotion (5)
9 Hill (3)
12 Broken bone supports (7)
14 Floor covering (3)
16 Bury (5)
17 Deal (5)
19 Cattle thief (7)
20 Creature (5)
21 Navigation aid (5)
23 Iterates (7)
24 Of old age (6)
25 Brown (3)
27 Indian dish (5)
28 Metal fastener (5)
30 Golfer's assistant (5)
32 Groups (4)
33 Wildebeest (3)

318

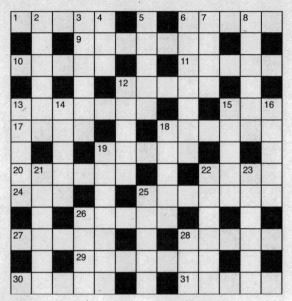

ACROSS

1 Destroy (5)
6 Malice (5)
9 Nursing home (7)
10 Magnificent (5)
11 Pale (5)
12 Item of clothing (5)
13 Dream (7)
15 Sun (3)
17 Alack (4)
18 Want (6)
19 Custom (5)
20 Stringed instrument (6)
22 Miserly (4)
24 Conclude (3)
25 Versus (7)
26 Gambling game (5)
27 Comedian (5)
28 Ancient symbols (5)
29 Pigeon house (7)
30 Principle (5)
31 Party (5)

DOWN

2 Wonder (6)
3 Forms (6)
4 Very warm (3)
5 Talked (5)
6 Red (7)
7 Nuisance (4)
8 Quake (6)
12 Indian instrument (5)
13 Extent (5)
14 Acceptable (5)
15 Alarm (5)
16 Inclined (5)
18 Wild dog (5)
19 Bean (7)
21 Opened (6)
22 Tiny (6)
23 At the back (6)
25 Concur (5)
26 Stay (4)
28 Thieve (3)

319

ACROSS

1 Second drink (6)
7 Breed of dog (8)
8 Indian dress (4)
10 Catch-phrase (6)
11 Find (6)
14 Lair (3)
16 Satisfies (5)
17 Celebrity (4)
19 Narrow (5)
21 Rants (5)
22 Deserve (5)
23 Reared (4)
26 Teams (5)
28 Meadow (3)
29 Box (6)
30 Complained (6)
31 Aid in crime (4)
32 Relative (8)
33 Names (6)

DOWN

1 Turning point (6)
2 Veteran (6)
3 Precipitation (4)
4 Reclines (7)
5 Unit of gem's weight (5)
6 Yields (5)
8 Sparkling water (4)
9 Managed (3)
12 Vehicle (3)
13 Curt (5)
15 Sorcery (5)
18 Shinbone (5)
19 Sailor (3)
20 Favourite (3)
21 Holiday locations (7)
22 Encountered (3)
23 Deprived (6)
24 Attentive (4)
25 Evades (6)
26 Neckwear item (5)
27 Amusing (5)
28 Scientist's room (3)
30 Hypocrisy (4)

SECTION 2

The Solutions

SOLUTIONS

No 1 - ACROSS: 3 Heart 8 Mines 10 Error 11 Tot 12 Rouse 13 Stripes 15 Tames 18 Ref 19 Return 21 Reputed 22 Raid 23 Halo 24 Capital 26 Vassal 29 Sob 31 Elect 32 Denizen 34 Redid 35 Tip 36 Molar 37 Taper 38 Psalm
DOWN: 1 Ditty 2 Retired 4 Eros 5 Rested 6 Treat 7 Mower 9 Nor 12 Refusal 14 Pep 16 Mural 17 Snoop 19 Revised 20 Crave 21 Rinse 23 Habitat 24 Caters 25 Ton 27 Allot 28 Scrap 30 Repel 32 Dial 33 Zip

No 2 - ACROSS: 1 Haste 6 Lends 9 Untried 10 Child 11 Virgo 12 Sweet 13 Tropics 15 Ten 17 Reps 18 Retire 19 Duvet 20 Mentor 22 Bend 24 See 25 Derides 26 Habit 27 Bigot 28 Health 29 Polemic 30 Ryder 31 Steel
DOWN: 2 Ashore 3 Tulips 4 Ends 5 Grows 6 Leveret 7 Edit 8 Dagger 12 Scour 13 Trims 14 Opine 15 Tired 16 Needs 18 Reset 19 Donator 21 Eerily 22 Bisect 23 Nestle 25 Diver 26 Hope 28 His

No 3 - ACROSS: 1 Grieve 7 Cashmere 8 Bath 10 Voodoo 11 Encode 14 Rep 16 Nomad 17 Lees 19 Jewel 21 Caber 22 Habit 23 Pads 26 Ashen 28 Pen 29 Sturdy 30 Barter 31 Onus 32 Entreaty 33 Sleeps
DOWN: 1 Gravel 2 Evades 3 Echo 4 Thinner 5 Besom 6 Ceded 8 Bore 9 Top 12 Col 13 Dated 15 Debit 18 Exist 19 Jab 20 Wet 21 Candles 22 Her 23 Peruse 24 Ants 25 Strips 26 Aspen 27 Hurts 28 Pan 30 Boys

No 4 - ACROSS: 4 Subtle 7 Trappist 8 Alfred 10 Erect 13 Clef 14 Rota 15 Area 16 Paw 17 Biro 19 Dray 21 Cartwheel 23 Solo 24 Bone 26 Bet 27 Neat 29 Lord 32 Dear 33 Osier 34 Beards 35 Eighteen 36 Merges
DOWN: 1 Steer 2 Cadet 3 Spot 4 Stale 5 Buff 6 Leeway 9 Leaden 11 Row 12 Cabal 13 Crowbar 15 Art 16 Pal 18 Ironed 20 Reels 21 Cot 22 Hot 23 Severe 25 Ore 28 Eases 30 Oiled 31 Drink 32 Drag 33 Oche

No 5 - ACROSS: 3 Grips 8 Crave 10 Leers 11 Ice 12 Straw 13 Inertia 15 Never 18 Ram 19 Serene 21 Variant 22 Then 23 Sure 24 Carpets 26 Gather 29 Par 31 Sisal 32 Ceramic 34 Blood 35 Nor 36 Media 37 Adder 38 Tread
DOWN: 1 Bring 2 Overran 4 Rota 5 Planet 6 Sewer 7 Green 9 Ace 12 Similar 14 Tar 16 Venus 17 Refer 19 Snapped 20 Stags 21 Vents 23 Strands 24 Cellar 25 Ear 27 Aided 28 Habit 30 Siren 32 Coda 33 Mod

No 6 - ACROSS: 1 Offal 6 Merge 9 Sedated 10 Flute 11 Rinse 12 Tacit 13 Sneaked 15 Hen 17 Tell 18 Melody 19 Snood 20 Ladies 22 Oslo 24 Ere 25 Canteen 26 Minor 27 Heron 28 Serum 29 Painter 30 Utter 31 Aspen
DOWN: 2 Feline 3 Astral 4 Lee 5 Salad 6 Merited 7 Edit 8 Gushed 12 Terns 13 Stale 14 Elude 15 House 16 Nylon 18 Molar 19 Seminar 21 Arrest 22 Otters 23 Legume 25 Corny 26 Mope 28 Sea

No 7 - ACROSS: 1 Spades 7 American 8 Omen 10 Rebuke 11 Sparse 14 Ire 16 Plead 17 Date 19 Label 21 Fever 22 Ceded 23 Feed 26 Tutor 28 Rod 29 Starve 30 Cement 31 Open · 32 Relented 33 Extent

DOWN: 1 Shared 2 Demure 3 Sane 4 Trapper 5 Score 6 Ended 8 Obit 9 Eke 12 All 13 Sabre 15 Raven 18 About 19 Led 20 Bed 21 Fervent 22 Cor 23 Foment 24 Eden 25 Detect 26 Tsars 27 Table 28 Rep 30 Code

No 8 - ACROSS: 4 Brazil 7 Reappear 8 Ethics 10 Trade 13 Fare 14 Hero 15 Dime 16 Wet 17 Near 19 Apes 21 Commented 23 Carp 24 Must 26 Top 27 Iran 29 Ales 32 Grin 33 Sleep 34 Spared 35 Grandson 36 Writhe

DOWN: 1 Wrath 2 Radar 3 Apse 4 Bream 5 Ache 6 Inches 9 Treats 11 Red 12 Donor 13 Fireman 15 Dam 16 Wed 18 Empire 20 Petal 21 Cap 22 Nun 23 Copper 25 Bee 28 Ridge 30 Least 31 Spine 32 Grit 33 Sent

No 9 - ACROSS: 3 Avers 8 Widen 10 Eider 11 Nil 12 Niece 13 Ignited 15 Overt 18 Get 19 Dreamy 21 Chatted 22 Heat 23 Once 24 Veneers 26 Grapes 29 And 31 Satan 32 In-depth 34 Studs 35 Rot 36 Piste 37 Alter 38 Addle

DOWN: 1 Bingo 2 Delight 4 Void 5 Record 6 Sieve 7 Rearm 9 Din 12 Nettles 14 Tea 16 Earns 17 Types 19 Demeans 20 Thugs 21 Carat 23 Orderly 24 Vented 25 End 27 Radio 28 Pasta 30 Utter 32 Idol 33 Pot

No 10 - ACROSS: 1 Smith 6 Rouse 9 Reciter 10 In-law 11 Vault 12 Label 13 Lampoon 15 Sea 17 Ices 18 Almond 19 Rills 20 Heroic 22 Site 24 Try 25 Chancer 26 Sepia 27 Stoat 28 Study 29 Genetic 30 Acted 31 Third

DOWN: 2 Maniac 3 Tramps 4 Hew 5 Divan 6 Reveals 7 Oral 8 Sullen 12 Logic 13 Light 14 Merry 15 Sonic 16 Adder 18 Alpha 19 Riveted 21 Erotic 22 Snatch 23 Tender 25 Cider 26 Sage 28 Sit

No 11 - ACROSS: 1 Chores 7 Evermore 8 Acre 10 Repaid 11 Appear 14 End 16 Penny 17 East 19 Beret 21 Sated 22 Strap 23 Tier 26 Altar 28 Lit 29 Vermin 30 Sirens 31 Edam 32 Increase 33 Pledge

DOWN: 1 Charge 2 Recant 3 Seed 4 Trapped 5 Coven 6 Berry 8 Apes 9 Rid 12 Pet 13 Angle 15 Petal 18 Agile 19 Bar 20 Rep 21 Striker 22 Sam 23 Tirade 24 Item 25 Rescue 26 Avoid 27 Trace 28 Lid 30 Seep

No 12 - ACROSS: 4 Pastor 7 Reprisal 8 Earned 10 Spire 13 lamb 14 Tine 15 Also 16 Cow 17 Pail 19 Rout 21 Replicate 23 Help 24 Colt 26 Hod 27 Lair 29 Eden 32 Pest 33 Prone 34 Recess 35 Educated 36 Strict

DOWN: 1 Trust 2 Spain 3 File 4 Pleas 5 Serb 6 Ocelot 9 Amoral 11 Pit 12 Repel 13 Illicit 15 Ail 16 Cue 18 Apples 20 Otter 21 Red 22 Cor 23 Honest 25 Pen 28 Asset 30 Dotty 31 Needs 32 Peri 33 Pick

No 13 - ACROSS: 3 Tract 8 Birch 10 Rests 11 Mar 12 Steep 13 Riposte 15 Dials 18 Boa 19 Tidily 21 Cabinet 22 Halt 23 Clap 24 Fertile 26 Absurd 29 Ere 31 Posse 32 Tremble 34 Hears 35 Eat 36 Jerez 37 Under 38 Reaps

    DOWN: 1 Timid 2 Acrobat 4 Rote 5 Credit 6 Tepid 7 Stall 9 Rap 12 Stained 14 Sob 16 Aisle 17 Sylph 19 Testers 20 Cheap 21 Class 23 Clement 24 Freeze 25 Ire 27 Boxes 28 Usher 30 Alter 32 Trip 33 Bad

No 14 - ACROSS: 1 Tribe 6 Pinch 9 Rampart 10 Utter 11 Actor 12 Broth 13 Glisten 15 Wet 17 Rent 18 Please 19 Scare 20 Breath 22 Lees 24 Sex 25 Remorse 26 Spoon 27 Canoe 28 Antic 29 Snoring 30 Snood 31 Depot

    DOWN: 2 Rattle 3 Breast 4 Ear 5 Spurn 6 Prattle 7 Itch 8 Chores 12 Bench 13 Grabs 14 Index 15 Water 16 Tense 18 Preen 19 Stipend 21 Regain 22 Lounge 23 Eskimo 25 Roars 26 So-so 28 And

No 15 - ACROSS: 1 Stress 7 Commerce 8 Asia 10 Tavern 11 Copper 14 Elk 16 Ratty 17 Errs 19 Feral 21 Coral 22 First 23 Pure 26 Saris 28 Ton 29 Thirty 30 Police 31 Omit 32 Clear-cut 33 Sheets

    DOWN: 1 Settle 2 Easels 3 Scan 4 Immoral 5 Crept 6 Ferry 8 Aver 9 Irk 12 Pal 13 Ether 15 Verse 18 Rajah 19 For 20 Rat 21 Cistern 22 Fir 23 Polite 24 Unit 25 Events 26 Stick 27 Risen 28 Tom 30 Pots

No 16 - ACROSS: 4 Affray 7 Trespass 8 Stench 10 Fishy 13 Pert 14 Flea 15 Erse 16 Spy 17 Rave 19 Meet 21 Telescope 23 Limb 24 Sure 26 Din 27 Ever 29 Edit 32 Arid 33 Osier 34 Agents 35 Impacted 36 Truant

    DOWN: 1 Staff 2 Lease 3 Spry 4 Asses 5 Feet 6 Accept 9 Tremor 11 Ill 12 Harem 13 Pressed 15 Eve 16 See 18 Albert 20 Epees 21 Tin 22 Cur 23 Linger 25 Tie 28 Visit 30 Ditty 31 Trade 32 Anna 33 Opal

No 17 - ACROSS: 3 Pairs 8 Capri 10 Acute 11 Lea 12 Diana 13 Forward 15 Crate 18 Lie 19 Mister 21 Meddled 22 Thor 23 Sago 24 Beetles 26 Rushed 29 Oar 31 Stead 32 Ordinal 34 Slams 35 Oil 36 Delta 37 Duped 38 Emend

    DOWN: 1 Talon 2 Trawler 4 Arid 5 Rancid 6 Scars 7 State 9 Per 12 Dredged 14 Aid 16 Atlas 17 Error 19 Mentors 20 Stars 21 Morse 23 Serious 24 Bedlam 25 Lad 27 Utter 28 Haste 30 Dales 32 Omen 33 Nip

No 18 - ACROSS: 1 Epoch 6 Elder 9 Outline 10 Grime 11 Dated 12 Begun 13 Fencers 15 Bet 17 Iris 18 Serene 19 Scold 20 Struck 22 Bent 24 Tee 25 Sprites 26 Paste 27 Macaw 28 Agate 29 Intrude 30 Stony 31 Order

    DOWN: 2 Porter 3 Comics 4 Hue 5 Flies 6 Endured 7 Lean 8 Eleven 12 Brick 13 First 14 Nitre 15 Beret 16 Tents 18 Slope 19 Scrawny 21 Tenant 22 Bigger 23 Nestle 25 Stork 26 Pain 28 Ado

No 19 - ACROSS: 1 Bamboo 7 Recharge 8 Plug 10 Sultry 11 Braise 14 Eon 16 Actor 17 Scan 19 Trade 21 Those 22 Deeds 23 Says 26 Sapid 28 Gem 29 Torpid 30 Rowers 31 Eden 32 Pictures 33 Tester

DOWN: 1 Bursts 2 Bolton 3 Orgy 4 Charade 5 Trait 6 Fewer 8 Plea 9 Urn 12 Ace 13 Sorry 15 Erode 18 Cacao 19 The 20 Ass 21 Tedious 22 Dip 23 Sewers 24 Amen 25 Sister 26 Stops 27 Price 28 God 30 Rest

No 20 - ACROSS: 4 School 7 Withdraw 8 Evades 10 Grave 13 Beet 14 Sake 15 Vats 16 Cod 17 Rain 19 Soon 21 Endangers 23 Fled 24 Eels 26 Yak 27 Earl 29 Over 32 Orbs 33 Snore 34 Radish 35 Overrule 36 Lesser

DOWN: 1 Twigs 2 Steak 3 Adze 4 Sweet 5 Heat 6 Oregon 9 Vessel 11 Raw 12 Verne 13 Banners 15 Via 16 Cos 18 Adders 20 Orson 21 Elk 22 Gel 23 Facade 25 Her 28 Abhor 30 Vogue 31 Rebel 32 Oils 33 Sure

No 21 - ACROSS: 3 Scalp 8 Metal 10 Irate 11 Cog 12 Iraqi 13 Currant 15 Uncle 18 Arc 19 Mitres 21 Enticed 22 Hurt 23 Beta 24 Doleful 26 Sadder 29 Nor 31 Steel 32 Utensil 34 Beano 35 Ion 36 Carat 37 Onset 38 Rents

DOWN: 1 Recur 2 Vagrant 4 Curt 5 Liquid 6 Print 7 Stole 9 Tor 12 Incisor 14 Art 16 Cruel 17 Essay 19 Memento 20 Chess 21 Erode 23 Burning 24 Delete 25 Foe 27 Atlas 28 Debar 30 Tines 32 Unit 33 SOS

No 22 - ACROSS: 1 Llama 6 Lords 9 October 10 Smile 11 Cello 12 Ports 13 Tension 15 Ate 17 Edit 18 Brazen 19 Snore 20 Accent 22 Erse 24 See 25 Pioneer 26 Freed 27 Bleak 28 Dupes 29 Learner 30 Drill 31 Never

DOWN: 2 Limped 3 Molest 4 Ace 5 Colon 6 Lecture 7 Ores 8 Dilute 12 Point 13 Texas 14 Niece 15 Azure 16 Enter 18 Braid 19 Snorkel 21 Cellar 22 Ensure 23 Severe 25 Pears 26 Fall 28 Den

No 23 - ACROSS: 1 Sandal 7 Alderman 8 Aces 10 Recent 11 Visage 14 Hid 16 Girls 17 Stet 19 Lemon 21 Coped 22 Begin 23 Deer 26 Bosun 28 Led 29 Roasts 30 Parent 31 Odin 32 Adequate 33 Teeter

DOWN: 1 Shares 2 Deceit 3 Last 4 Demigod 5 Smear 6 Andes 8 Ache 9 End 12 Sin 13 Glade 15 Tepid 18 Taboo 19 Log 20 Men 21 Centaur 22 Bus 23 Deride 24 Eden 25 Rotter 26 Broad 27 Saves 28 Lad 30 Poet

No 24 - ACROSS: 4 Suffer 7 Elephant 8 Adored 10 Slide 13 Bled 14 Tone 15 Feel 16 Apt 17 Nail 19 Unit 21 Estranged 23 Fret 24 Toes 26 Cur 27 Iced 29 Trip 32 Grid 33 Aside 34 Turret 35 Eviction 36 Seemed

DOWN: 1 Least 2 Begin 3 Shoe 4 Stale 5 Food 6 Exempt 9 Deluge 11 Lot 12 Dense 13 Belated 15 Fir 16 Aid 18 Attire 20 Nests 21 Err 22 Nod 23 Future 25 Bid 28 Cited 30 Rigid 31 Penny 32 Gram 33 Arch

No 25 - ACROSS: 3 Grips 8 Cater 10 Logic 11 Rip 12 Pagan 13 Recited 15 Yacht 18 Car 19 Berate 21 Striker 22 Alps 23 Asks 24 Educate 26 Churns 29 Hit 31 Hated 32 Herring 34 Fumes 35 Are 36 Steer 37 Ocean 38 Ready

DOWN: 1 Harem 2 Depicts 4 Road 5 Player 6 Sonar 7 Sight 9 Tic 12 Periods 14 Tar 16 Cause 17 Tense 19 Benches 20 Catch 21 Spout 23 Attract 24 Endure 25 Air 27 Haste 28 Refer 30 Sneak 32 Heed 33 Ire

No 26 - ACROSS: 1 Usage 6 Coven 9 Oration 10 Globe 11 Rural 12 Seats 13 Accepts 15 Tee 17 Meat 18 Aghast 19 Agate 20 Stance 22 Food 24 Sat 25 Balance 26 Feels 27 Stain 28 Wails 29 Stamped 30 Edits 31 Tests

DOWN: 2 Solace 3 Goblet 4 Ere 5 Sties 6 Cortege 7 Onus 8 Erases 12 Stage 13 Amass 14 Carat 15 Talon 16 Etude 18 Atlas 19 Accents 21 Tasted 22 Facade 23 Ocelot 25 Blame 26 Fist 28 Wet

No 27 - ACROSS: 1 Gaucho 7 Pastoral 8 Hare 10 Eleven 11 Finite 14 Led 16 Rotor 17 Asps 19 Sewer 21 Fired 22 Rapid 23 Sort 26 Pesos 28 Bap 29 Sweets 30 Palace 31 Oral 32 Luminous 33 Thieve

DOWN: 1 Geneva 2 Craves 3 Open 4 Attired 5 Trait 6 Alter 8 Help 9 Red 12 Nor 13 Tower 15 Merit 18 Strew 19 Sip 20 Wed 21 Fastens 22 Roe 23 Salami 24 Opal 25 Thence 26 Psalm 27 Seams 28 Bar 30 Post

No 28 - ACROSS: 4 Glance 7 Repairer 8 Avoids 10 Bathe 13 Scan 14 Erse 15 Aces 16 Old 17 Much 19 Sure 21 Captivate 23 Lane 24 Silt 26 Don 27 Name 29 Eden 32 Adds 33 Prone 34 Valise 35 Password 36 Defect

DOWN: 1 Tribe 2 Spots 3 Fine 4 Grace 5 Anon 6 Cuddle 9 Vassal 11 Arm 12 He-man 13 Schisms 15 Act 16 Ore 18 Upends 20 Utter 21 Can 22 Vie 23 Locate 25 Pen 28 Adept 30 Donor 31 Needy 32 Aide 33 Pest

No 29 - ACROSS: 3 Style 8 Depot 10 Onion 11 Bun 12 Limit 13 Dutiful 15 Tenet 18 Tic 19 Peruse 21 Conifer 22 Rear 23 Asks 24 Respite 26 Better 29 Lot 31 Sleet 32 Reneged 34 Piled 35 Nod 36 Stair 37 Adder 38 Dense

DOWN: 1 Rebut 2 Monitor 4 Toil 5 Loiter 6 Enter 7 Notes 9 Put 12 Lucifer 14 Fin 16 Nurse 17 Terse 19 Peopled 20 Grabs 21 Caste 23 Attends 24 Retire 25 Ion 27 Elite 28 Tepid 30 Ceded 32 Reps 33 God

No 30 - ACROSS: 1 Abuse 6 Plead 9 Capable 10 Order 11 Ended 12 Broad 13 Restore 15 Sue 17 Ants 18 Rested 19 Diced 20 Abated 22 Zinc 24 Rip 25 Cabinet 26 Silly 27 Venus 28 Shuts 29 Residue 30 Steed 31 Pried

DOWN: 2 Burden 3 Scents 4 Ear 5 Sabre 6 Pleased 7 Lend 8 Avenue 12 Braid 13 Radar 14 Strap 15 Stain 16 Edict 18 Repay 19 Devised 21 Bisect 22 Zither 23 Nestle 25 Claim 26 Sure 28 Sup

No 31 - ACROSS: 1 Acacia 7 Potholer 8 Pale 10 Sieves 11 Ethics 14 Rat 16 Tires 17 Emit 19 Hopes 21 Later 22 Roman 23 Rest 26 Satan 28 Bad 29 Cringe 30 Ripens 31 Odin 32 Relented 33 Strand

DOWN: 1 Aussie 2 Cravat 3 Apes 4 Chatter 5 Flair 6 Dross 8 Peri 9 Let 12 His 13 Cents 15 Total 18 Molar 19 Ham 20 Pen 21 Longing 22 Ran 23 Rapier 24 Eden 25 Tested 26 Score 27 Tills 28 Bid 30 Rods

No 32 - ACROSS: 4 Citrus 7 Admonish 8 Acidic 10 Needs 13 Biro 14 Sole 15 Very 16 Red 17 Mien 19 Prod 21 Contented 23 Font 24 Fuss 26 Bit 27 Edit 29 Trip 32 Knit 33 Osier 34 Chants 35 Chuckled 36 Aspens

DOWN: 1 Pains 2 Impel 3 Onus 4 Chair 5 Trio 6 United 9 Crypts 11 Eon 12 Demon 13 Benefit 15 Vet 16 Rod 18 Intent 20 Rests 21 Cot 22 Nut 23 Fights 25 Die 28 Discs 30 Rifle 31 Pride 32 Knee 33 Once

No 33 - ACROSS: 3 Flare 8 Signs 10 Enter 11 Bet 12 Numbs 13 Deleted 15 Augur 18 Gap 19 Stereo 21 Reptile 22 Hair 23 Gear 24 Enliven 26 Saline 29 Gin 31 Spent 32 Cheetah 34 Girls 35 Rot 36 Manor 37 Canal 38 Tenet

DOWN: 1 Tiber 2 Integer 4 Loud 5 Rebate 6 Ensue 7 Venue 9 Gel 12 Neptune 14 Tap 16 Green 17 Roars 19 Sleighs 20 Chess 21 Rifle 23 General 24 Entire 25 Vie 27 Appal 28 Ingot 30 Fatal 32 Clue 33 Ton

No 34 - ACROSS: 1 Reach 6 Count 9 Ruction 10 Rivet 11 Musty 12 Stops 13 Dispute 15 Ace 17 Arts 18 Scares 19 Light 20 Craven 22 Beta 24 Eel 25 Someday 26 Treat 27 Robin 28 Skids 29 Reverie 30 Steed 31 Crime

DOWN: 2 Elixir 3 Creeps 4 Hut 5 State 6 Compact 7 Onus 8 Notice 12 Stain 13 Dance 14 Steal 15 Armed 16 Essay 18 Shoot 19 Learned 21 Resort 22 Beaker 23 Tandem 25 Saved 26 Tire 28 Sic

No 35 - ACROSS: 1 Alaska 7 Pamphlet 8 Vile 10 Drives 11 Tavern 14 Sea 16 Rates 17 Scar 19 Haven 21 Rebel 22 Nonet 23 Rote 26 Bogus 28 Rep 29 Lean-to 30 Potent 31 Lean 32 Denounce 33 Annual

DOWN: 1 Abodes 2 Shiver 3 Apes 4 Apparel 5 Sleet 6 Stuns 8 Visa 9 Lea 12 Van 13 React 15 Label 18 Canoe 19 Hen 20 Vet 21 Rostrum 22 Nun 23 Retain 24 Open 25 Entail 26 Blade 27 Gains 28 Roe 30 Plea

No 36 - ACROSS: 4 Kidnap 7 Kangaroo 8 Almost 10 Prude 13 Elan 14 Seer 15 Span 16 Win 17 Isis 19 Duel 21 Reprimand 23 Code 24 Laud 26 Shy 27 Atop 29 Etui 32 Grin 33 Trend 34 Robust 35 Lenience 36 Lessee

DOWN: 1 Skips 2 Undue 3 Lame 4 Koala 5 Damn 6 Abseil 9 Landau 11 Red 12 Dried 13 Epsilon 15 Sir 16 Wed 18 Spears 20 Under 21 Roy 22 Map 23 Choose 25 Sun 28 Title 30 Terns 31 Idles 32 Guns 33 Thin

No 37 - ACROSS: 3 Falls 8 Refer 10 Opted 11 Rip 12 Since 13 Narrows 15 Anger 18 Are 19 Attire 21 Overage 22 Pace 23 Snap 24 Deficit 26 Curbed 29 Not 31 Sleep 32 Assuage 34 Limit 35 Age 36 Relic 37 Stone 38 Ether

DOWN: 1 Feral 2 Deprave 4 Axis 5 Locate 6 Spent 7 Sewer 9 Fir 12 Swerved 14 Ore 16 Giant 17 Reaps 19 Against 20 Epics 21 Ochre 23 Situate 24 Depict 25 Cos 27 Ulcer 28 Belie 30 Agent 32 Aide 33 Ago

No 38 - ACROSS: 1 Farce 6 Reedy 9 Averted 10 Haste 11 Leers 12 Token 13 Shelter 15 Ass 17 Here 18 Assist 19 Prose 20 Orders 22 Plan 24 Tee 25 Collect 26 Idiot 27 Maori 28 Manor 29 Accedes 30 Front 31 Tense

DOWN: 2 Apache 3 Cattle 4 Eve 5 Prior 6 Release 7 Eden 8 Duress 12 Tears 13 Shoot 14 Erode 15 Aisle 16 Stunt 18 Ascot 19 Predict 21 Repair 22 Please 23 Actors 25 Coded 26 Iran 28 Met

No 39 - ACROSS: 1 Grappa 7 Crescent 8 Pair 10 Stance 11 Unsaid 14 See 16 Darns 17 Ants 19 Coped 21 Later 22 Siren 23 Lets 26 Basis 28 Cor 29 Alerts 30 Docile 31 Elan 32 Shrunken 33 Thence

DOWN: 1 Geisha 2 Planes 3 Acre 4 Asunder 5 Debar 6 Studs 8 Past 9 Ice 12 Sad 13 Ingot 15 Hotel 18 Natal 19 Car 20 Pen 21 Listens 22 Sir 23 Locate 24 Erin 25 Sleeve 26 Balsa 27 Seers 28 Col 30 Dent

No 40 - ACROSS: 4 Flouts 7 Reproval 8 Onions 10 Stock 13 Iron 14 Sane 15 Gnat 16 Row 17 Duet 19 Icon 21 Sentenced 23 Pest 24 Reel 26 Lot 27 Rent 29 Laps 32 Buns 33 Asset 34 Rolled 35 Engaging 36 Ascend

DOWN: 1 Crass 2 Spoon 3 Work 4 Flora 5 Odin 6 Tendon 9 Notice 11 Tap 12 Cedes 13 Interns 15 Get 16 Rod 18 Untrue 20 Cells 21 Set 22 Net 23 Porous 25 Ape 28 Ended 30 Astir 31 Stage 32 Blue 33 Away

No 41 - ACROSS: 3 Drive 8 Silly 10 Ended 11 Lea 12 Tenet 13 Glinted 15 Rebut 18 Cad 19 Berate 21 Derived 22 Lard 23 Sham 24 Cubicle 26 Genres 29 Due 31 Steel 32 Repeats 34 Pesos 35 Pit 36 Deter 37 Beret 38 Lyres

DOWN: 1 Pills 2 Glanced 4 Rued 5 Veered 6 Enter 7 Debut 9 Lei 12 Tedious 14 Tar 16 Bathe 17 Teams 19 Besides 20 Flags 21 Drone 23 Sleeper 24 Celery 25 Cup 27 Ether 28 Repel 30 Utter 32 Rose 33 Air

No 42 - ACROSS: 1 Traps 6 Dated 9 Apparel 10 Every 11 Spade 12 Grips 13 Sectors 15 Asp 17 Awry 18 Astute 19 Spine 20 Ravine 22 Burn 24 Ere 25 Viceroy 26 Comic 27 Kayak 28 Atlas 29 Replete 30 Paper 31 Erred

DOWN: 2 Review 3 Parity 4 Spy 5 Pairs 6 Despise 7 Alps 8 Eldest 12 Grape 13 Sabre 14 Crave 15 Augur 16 Penny 18 Antic 19 Snooker 21 Armada 22 Better 23 Rotate 25 Villa 26 Care 28 Ate

No 43 - ACROSS: 1 Dulcet 7 Sideways 8 Saga 10 Tailor 11 Polite 14 Pet 16 Risen 17 Last 19 Roost 21 Cable 22 Rated 23 Step 26 Siren 28 Per 29 Credit 30 Aiding 31 Leap 32 Nauseous 33 Ocelot

DOWN: 1 Dental 2 Chalet 3 Tsar 4 Remorse 5 Saris 6 Ashen 8 Sips 9 Got 12 Lit 13 Tense 15 Robes 18 Astir 19 Rat 20 Old 21 Canines 22 Red 23 Sedate 24 Trip 25 Piglet 26 Scone 27 Recur 28 Pie 30 Also

No 44 - ACROSS: 4 Lifted 7 Hitherto 8 Scents 10 Alibi 13 Mere 14 Peru 15 Hero 16 Ice 17 Gnat 19 Cure 21 Playhouse 23 Feet 24 Apse 26 Din 27 Tint 29 Race 32 Cede 33 Osier 34 Nature 35 Appalled 36 Reveal

DOWN: 1 Cheap 2 Stair 3 Peri 4 Loser 5 Flee 6 Entice 9 Crocus 11 Lee 12 Bugle 13 Methane 15 Hay 16 Ire 18 Natter 20 Users 21 Pen 22 Opt 23 Finale 25 Ace 28 Ideal 30 Aisle 31 Erode 32 Cute 33 Oval

No 45 - ACROSS: 3 Robot 8 Rolls 10 Radio 11 Leo 12 Regal 13 Plaster 15 Tonic 18 Sad 19 Donate 21 Forever 22 Roam 23 Oral 24 Immerse 26 Morass 29 Nut 31 Basis 32 Ocelots 34 Suave 35 Err 36 Lisle 37 Break 38 Erode

DOWN: 1 Holly 2 Blossom 4 Over 5 Orator 6 Talon 7 Limit 9 Lea 12 Redeems 14 Tar 16 Nacre 17 Cells 19 Defence 20 Crumb 21 Fairs 23 Ostlers 24 Issuer 25 Rue 27 Oasis 28 Aisle 30 Strap 32 Ovid 33 Ore

No 46 - ACROSS: 1 Troop 6 Tense 9 Greater 10 Scary 11 Noble 12 Folds 13 Missile 15 One 17 Ills 18 Pilots 19 Revel 20 Hamper 22 Beta 24 Tip 25 Holiday 26 Heron 27 Pined 28 Story 29 Reverie 30 Egged 31 Trust

DOWN: 2 Recoil 3 Ogress 4 Pry 5 Canoe 6 Tendril 7 Eros 8 Silent 12 Flier 13 Might 14 Slump 15 Oozed 16 Essay 18 Peron 19 Receded 21 Aiding 22 Bitter 23 Taurus 25 Hotel 26 Here 28 Sit

No 47 - ACROSS: 1 Chaste 7 Debonair 8 Pace 10 Oberon 11 Stares 14 Rob 16 Upset 17 Spin 19 Count 21 Norse 22 Lapse 23 Rhea 26 Asses 28 Hoe 29 Depict 30 Cobalt 31 Edit 32 Licensed 33 Ensued

DOWN: 1 Crooks 2 Sharon 3 Eden 4 Fortune 5 Pairs 6 Crest 8 Peri 9 Cob 12 Apt 13 Eerie 15 Morse 18 Prise 19 Cop 20 Use 21 Nascent 22 Lei 23 Robins 24 Heat 25 Attend 26 Addle 27 Speck 28 Hod 30 Cede

No 48 - ACROSS: 4 Noting 7 Hysteria 8 Scents 10 Poise 13 Rare 14 Each 15 Tale 16 Boy 17 Amid 19 Amen 21 Emaciated 23 Over 24 Aver 26 Ire 27 Kite 29 Idol 32 Mere 33 State 34 Reside 35 Nurtured 36 Estate

DOWN: 1 Shape 2 Aspic 3 Sere 4 Nasal 5 Tree 6 Notion 9 Create 11 Oar 12 Shame 13 Radiate 15 Tic 16 Bed 18 Marked 20 Merit 21 Eve 22 Ave 23 Orders 25 Lot 28 Irene 30 Dairy 31 Leads 32 Mica 33 Site

No 49 - ACROSS: 3 Trust 8 Later 10 Proof 11 Cow 12 Aware 13 Shrimps 15 Enter 18 Tap 19 Radish 21 Scraped 22 Loth 23 Stun 24 Refutes 26 Verbal 29 Rum 31 Exert 32 Entitle 34 Atlas 35 Nil 36 Devil 37 Bacon 38 Nests

DOWN: 1 Cache 2 Bewitch 4 Rows 5 Spread 6 Trend 7 Hones 9 Tor 12 Apparel 14 Mar 16 Tints 17 Rhino 19 Returns 20 Slave 21 Store 23 Seminal 24 Rattle 25 Tut 27 Expel 28 Brain 30 Allow 32 East 33 Tic

No 50 - ACROSS: 1 Adage 6 Rival 9 Related 10 Enrol 11 Plead 12 Scale 13 Testate 15 His 17 Espy 18 Stream 19 Bathe 20 Portal 22 Oval 24 Ore 25 Austere 26 Stunt 27 Anvil 28 Lemur 29 Decider 30 Cedes 31 Aside

DOWN: 2 Dunces 3 Grotty 4 Eel 5 Lance 6 Replete 7 Idle 8 Acacia 12 Steal 13 Tempo 14 Spire 15 Heave 16 Smile 18 Shout 19 Battles 21 Orange 22 Others 23 Argued 25 Antic 26 Side 28 Lea

No 51 - ACROSS: 1 Luring 7 Lengthen 8 Apse 10 Dilute 11 Dismal 14 Pry 16 Niece 17 Rise 19 Least 21 Remit 22 Regal 23 Wren 26 Dream 28 Lea 29 Rental 30 Badger 31 Edge 32 Syringes 33 Tassel

DOWN: 1 Ladder 2 Impure 3 Glee 4 Against 5 Chime 6 Angle 8 Alps 9 Sty 12 Sit 13 Acute 15 He-man 18 Inure 19 Leg 20 Ail 21 Remains 22 Rat 23 Wedges 24 Rage 25 Normal 26 Dress 27 Entry 28 Lad 30 Best

No 52 - ACROSS: 4 Canopy 7 Reappear 8 Impels 10 Sheen 13 Emus 14 Sell 15 Ales 16 Tea 17 Face 19 Lead 21 Directing 23 Zinc 24 Tins 26 Den 27 Hoop 29 Urns 32 Near 33 Heath 34 Alters 35 Irritate 36 Stones

DOWN: 1 Cress 2 Gavel 3 Open 4 Crime 5 Nips 6 Pulled 9 Muslin 11 Hew 12 Elfin 13 Elector 15 Ace 16 Tag 18 Archer 20 Ensue 21 Din 22 Tip 23 Zealot 25 Ant 28 Oasis 30 Radar 31 Shred 32 Neon 33 Hail

No 53 - ACROSS: 3 Shoot 8 Stool 10 Camps 11 Ear 12 Sleep 13 Referee 15 Lends 18 Mum 19 Morose 21 Cabinet 22 Oman 23 Uses 24 Machine 26 Logger 29 Ore 31 Sword 32 Ideally 34 Edits 35 Rot 36 Repel 37 Utter 38 Deems

DOWN: 1 Steel 2 Foreman 4 Hole 5 Ocelot 6 Taper 7 Spuds 9 Oaf 12 Seminar 14 Rub 16 Noose 17 Sense 19 Methods 20 Tools 21 Cargo 23 Unearth 24 Meddle 25 Ire 27 Owner 28 Greed 30 Alter 32 Item 33 Lot

No 54 - ACROSS: 1 Sprat 6 Riots 9 Nibbles 10 Mince 11 Piano 12 Fuels 13 Acrobat 15 Led 17 Rear 18 Beware 19 Scold 20 Mutate 22 Ales 24 Any 25 Compete 26 Dream 27 Squat 28 Tepid 29 Regalia 30 Feted 31 Crass

DOWN: 2 Prince 3 Anchor 4 Tie 5 About 6 Replied 7 Isis 8 Tinder 12 Farce 13 Aroma 14 Ratty 15 Ladle 16 Dense 18 Bloom 19 Started 21 Unique 22 Appear 23 Ethics 25 Carat 26 Dare 28 Tic

No 55 - ACROSS: 1 Trusts 7 Permeate 8 Plea 10 Dealer 11 Polite 14 Gel 16 Water 17 Amen 19 Coped 21 Layer 22 Koran 23 Glee 26 Tibia 28 Pea 29 Amends 30 Banger 31 Arts 32 Endanger 33 Events

DOWN: 1 Tundra 2 Sullen 3 Spar 4 Empower 5 Habit 6 Deter 8 Page 9 Eel 12 Lad 13 Tense 15 Royal 18 Minim 19 Car 20 Pen 21 Loading 22 Kin 23 Gentle 24 Lags 25 Enrols 26 Tales 27 Bends 28 Par 30 Bare

No 56 - ACROSS: 4 Repeat 7 Relegate 8 Visits 10 Merge 13 Rune 14 Ever 15 Diet 16 Act 17 Amid 19 Each 21 Abundance 23 Mist 24 Lido 26 Col 27 Tied 29 Rent 32 Lens 33 Enter 34 Cohere 35 Panthers 36 Septet

DOWN: 1 Crime 2 Flare 3 Ogle 4 Revue 5 Pose 6 Attach 9 Intend 11 Eve 12 Grabs 13 Riddles 15 Din 16 Ace 18 Mutter 20 Acorn 21 Ail 22 Aid 23 Morose 25 One 28 Inept 30 Ether 31 Tress 32 Lent 33 Eats

No 57 - ACROSS: 3 Tract 8 Hovel 10 Hotel 11 Wit 12 Spoon 13 Seattle 15 Rises 18 Lei 19 Buckle 21 Lenders 22 Hoes 23 Flat 24 Unravel 26 Musing 29 Tie 31 Blend 32 Shelter 34 Noble 35 Ion 36 Yemen 37 Inert 38 Ready

DOWN: 1 Cower 2 Settles 4 Ripe 5 Chorus 6 Tonic 7 Rebel 9 Via 12 Sliding 14 Ten 16 Skill 17 Seats 19 Breathe 20 Thumb 21 Lease 23 Feeling 24 Undone 25 Vie 27 Ulcer 28 Inner 30 Genre 32 Sled 33 Toe

No 58 - ACROSS: 1 Cache 6 Cable 9 Ashtray 10 Scarp 11 Sense 12 Abets 13 Lessers 15 Led 17 Asps 18 Beside 19 Galas 20 Trills 22 Size 24 Set 25 Shutter 26 Smile 27 Radio 28 Boils 29 Lustful 30 Floor 31 Sloth

DOWN: 2 Arches 3 Harass 4 ESP 5 Stubs 6 Castles 7 Ayes 8 Lashed 12 Areas 13 Lasts 14 Split 15 Limit 16 Deter 18 Bathe 19 Glamour 21 Recall 22 Stroll 23 Zealot 25 Slats 26 Silo 28 Bus

No 59 - ACROSS: 1 Fleece 7 Polyglot 8 Brie 10 Stance 11 Dapper 14 Nee 16 Misty 17 Oder 19 Sweat 21 Sears 22 Scare 23 Rock 26 Tapir 28 Rep 29 Amoral 30 Repaid 31 Idol 32 Overload 33 Seeped

DOWN: 1 Fiasco 2 Earner 3 Epee 4 Pyjamas 5 Slips 6 Story 8 Bane 9 Ice 12 Pit 13 Ethic 15 Aware 18 Dream 19 Sea 20 Ere 21 Scrawls 22 Sir 23 Repose 24 Opal 25 Kidded 26 Talon 27 Power 28 Red 30 Rids

No 60 - ACROSS: 4 Encode 7 Chaplain 8 Scampi 10 Offer 13 Curt 14 Reel 15 Ghee 16 Ash 17 Dane 19 Tune 21 Reluctant 23 Part 24 Kind 26 Pry 27 Even 29 Earn 32 Grid 33 Prune 34 Latest 35 Applause 36 Chisel

DOWN: 1 Actor 2 Gaffe 3 Slur 4 Ensue 5 Chat 6 Depose 9 Cretan 11 Fee 12 Elder 13 Checked 15 Gnu 16 Ant 18 Alters 20 Under 21 Ray 22 Tin 23 Preach 25 Urn 28 Vital 30 Augur 31 Never 32 Gels 33 Pull

No 61 - ACROSS: 3 Trait 8 Bacon 10 Manor 11 Tor 12 Okapi 13 Deserve 15 Onset 18 See 19 Asters 21 Caprice 22 Prow 23 Over 24 Deprive 26 Degree 29 ECU 31 Slain 32 Useless 34 Towns 35 Are 36 Tenet 37 Stern 38 Seats

DOWN: 1 Hated 2 Foresaw 4 Rake 5 Impose 6 Taint 7 Lower 9 Cos 12 Oversee 14 Rep 16 Serve 17 Tsars 19 Actress 20 Spuds 21 Conga 23 Ovulate 24 Denote 25 Ice 27 Elder 28 Rites 30 Users 32 Unit 33 Ere

No 62 - ACROSS: 1 Scrap 6 Pride 9 Censure 10 Costa 11 Enter 12 Beast 13 Chariot 15 Age 17 Lets 18 Untied 19 Erupt 20 Roasts 22 Pelt 24 Ass 25 Reposes 26 Treat 27 Clean 28 Bites 29 Cabinet 30 Drool 31 Tends

DOWN: 2 Clothe 3 Actors 4 Pea 5 Asset 6 Present 7 Rent 8 Dredge 12 Boars 13 Clara 14 Atlas 15 Aides 16 Edits 18 Upset 19 Eternal 21 Ostler 22 Polite 23 Legend 25 Rabid 26 Taco 28 Bet

No 63 - ACROSS: 1 Decamp 7 Overalls 8 Gale 10 Chalet 11 Refine 14 Log 16 Timid 17 Scan 19 Power 21 Famed 22 Motet 23 Teem 26 Swear 28 Tip 29 Hearts 30 Patent 31 Able 32 Cleaning 33 Endear

DOWN: 1 Dunces 2 Avalon 3 Poet 4 Greeted 5 Claim 6 Asked 8 Gala 9 Leg 12 Fir 13 Niece 15 Homer 18 Crewe 19 Pat 20 Wet 21 Fortune 22 Mar 23 Titled 24 Epee 25 Matter 26 Shack 27 Eager 28 Tab 30 Page

No 64 - ACROSS: 4 Desist 7 Pristine 8 Psalms 10 Tribe 13 Woks 14 Soda 15 Site 16 Ham 17 Smut 19 Isis 21 Elephants 23 Ewer 24 Erse 26 Axe 27 Germ 29 Eden 32 Lens 33 Spite 34 Retire 35 Molested 36 Steely

DOWN: 1 Spots 2 Rigid 3 Stye 4 Depot 5 Seas 6 Sambas 9 Skeins 11 Row 12 Basle 13 Withers 15 Sup 16 His 18 Merger 20 Steep 21 Ewe 22 Arm 23 Expect 25 Get 28 Enemy 30 Ditto 31 Needs 32 Lime 33 Seem

No 65 - ACROSS: 3 Hands 8 Madam 10 Rites 11 Jam 12 Beret 13 Rampart 15 Augur 18 Ego 19 Empire 21 Pretext 22 Eros 23 Sloe 24 Hermits 26 Dancer 29 Pro 31 Sitar 32 Clerics 34 Bathe 35 MOT 36 Scull 37 Tenet 38 Edict

DOWN: 1 Rajah 2 Hampers 4 Abet 5 Dreamt 6 Sit up 7 Recur 9 Dam 12 Brother 14 Age 16 Girls 17 Reset 19 Example 20 Lends 21 Point 23 Stormed 24 Herald 25 Ire 27 Aitch 28 Cable 30 Acted 32 Chic 33 Ion

No 66 - ACROSS: 1 Accra 6 Rests 9 Enliven 10 Crept 11 Pinch 12 Triad 13 Regalia 15 Ale 17 Ally 18 Proven 19 Pairs 20 Ordain 22 Fire 24 Nee 25 Smaller 26 Fable 27 Nomad 28 Tunes 29 Contain 30 Never 31 Ether

DOWN: 2 Cartel 3 Replay 4 Ant 5 Tiara 6 Repairs 7 Enid 8 Tackle 12 Titan 13 Rayon 14 Glade 15 Avail 16 Enter 18 Prime 19 Picador 21 Remove 22 Flaunt 23 Recede 25 Slate 26 Face 28 Tie

No 67 - ACROSS: 1 Chilli 7 Debonair 8 Emil 10 Ripple 11 Ethics 14 Eel 16 Earls 17 Sled 19 Pawns 21 Rivet 22 Honed 23 Perm 26 Serum 28 Par 29 Climax 30 Person 31 Rate 32 Negligee 33 Yodels

DOWN: 1 Chores 2 Limped 3 Idle 4 Portent 5 Tapir 6 Dross 8 Epee 9 Ill 12 Has 13 Clear 15 Gavel 18 Label 19 Pin 20 Wed 21 Romania 22 Hum 23 Parted 24 Erse 25 Minims 26 Scent 27 Rings 28 Pea 30 Prey

No 68 - ACROSS: 4 Subtle 7 Romansch 8 Offend 10 Spate 13 Calf 14 Peri 15 Polo 16 Bet 17 Maul 19 Road 21 Complaint 23 Guru 24 Ends 26 Tap 27 Sect 29 Ewes 32 Test 33 Steep 34 Chords 35 Ascended 36 Grumpy

DOWN: 1 Grasp 2 Smear 3 Once 4 Shoal 5 Buff 6 Lanced 9 Florid 11 Pet 12 Timor 13 Collect 15 Pup 16 Bat 18 Amused 20 Onset 21 Cup 22 Ant 23 Gather 25 Lee 28 Essay 30 Weeds 31 Spade 32 Trim 33 Seep

No 69 - ACROSS: 3 Snoop 8 Medal 10 Pinch 11 Ail 12 Begin 13 Greeted 15 Never 18 Rid 19 Reside 21 Emerged 22 Halo 23 Dent 24 Rooster 26 Random 29 Out 31 Endow 32 Intends 34 Dials 35 Cod 36 Reign 37 Utter 38 Egham

DOWN: 1 Heart 2 Palermo 4 Need 5 Opined 6 Pines 7 Ached 9 Die 12 Bedroom 14 Tie 16 Viper 17 Rents 19 Reasons 20 Share 21 Eland 23 Detects 24 Rowing 25 Tut 27 Anger 28 Dodge 30 Added 32 ILEA 33 Not

No 70 - ACROSS: 1 Essay 6 Point 9 Lampoon 10 Scalp 11 Nurse 12 Carts 13 Network 15 Elk 17 Errs 18 Worsen 19 Swoon 20 Redden 22 Rest 24 Sue 25 Relents 26 Bison 27 Rodeo 28 Bully 29 Lustful 30 Eyots 31 Stash

DOWN: 2 Soccer 3 Allows 4 Yap 5 Speak 6 Pontoon 7 Onus 8 Nestle 12 Crown 13 Nears 14 Trade 15 Essen 16 Knots 18 Women 19 Serious 21 Eulogy 22 Result 23 Stylus 25 Routs 26 Belt 28 Bus

No 71 - ACROSS: 1 Chafes 7 Contrive 8 Plea 10 Crater 11 Ribald 14 Gel 16 Panes 17 Seer 19 Caper 21 Fakes 22 Tenet 23 Pure 26 Actor 28 Car 29 Starve 30 Purged 31 Erse 32 Evacuate 33 Punnet

DOWN: 1 Crocus 2 Falter 3 Scar 4 Stripes 5 Titan 6 Lends 8 Page 9 Eel 12 Bar 13 Lever 15 Taken 18 Erect 19 Can 20 Pet 21 Fervour 22 Tor 23 Parson 24 Urge 25 Eldest 26 Aspen 27 Tapas 28 Cur 30 Peep

No 72 - ACROSS: 4 Packet 7 Elegance 8 Scouts 10 Chore 13 Stop 14 Home 15 Atom 16 And 17 Pale 19 Bent 21 Repentant 23 Help 24 Cite 26 Pod 27 Eric 29 Magi 32 Tail 33 Nylon 34 Report 35 Engineer 36 Assets

DOWN: 1 Teach 2 Besom 3 Late 4 Pesto 5 Crop 6 Extent 9 Combat 11 Hod 12 Repel 13 Stencil 15 Ale 16 Ant 18 Appear 20 Enemy 21 Red 22 Tic 23 Hotels 25 Ago 28 Rites 30 Alter 31 Inert 32 Tome 33 Nail

No 73 - ACROSS: 3 Truro 8 Infer 10 Optic 11 Eel 12 Strut 13 Deducts 15 Tepid 18 Doe 19 Reduce 21 Pesetas 22 Read 23 Slur 24 Closets 26 Ashore 29 Are 31 Diana 32 Scatter 34 Stack 35 Sag 36 Melee 37 Logic 38 Tribe

DOWN: 1 Sneer 2 Deluded 4 Rats 5 Routes 6 Opted 7 Mimic 9 Fed 12 Steeple 14 Cos 16 Pulls 17 Decry 19 Ransack 20 Broad 21 Pasha 23 Stetson 24 Crater 25 Era 27 Sited 28 Onset 30 Legit 32 Scab 33 Tag

No 74 - ACROSS: 1 Brats 6 Saint 9 Holdall 10 Ashen 11 Elder 12 Corny 13 Delight 15 Set 17 Odes 18 Deride 19 Order 20 Stripe 22 Ales 24 Eon 25 Austere 26 Flair 27 Canoe 28 Timid 29 Integer 30 Moult 31 Never

DOWN: 2 Rushed 3 Thesis 4 Son 5 Idiot 6 Slender 7 Ally 8 Needed 12 Chore 13 Douse 14 Learn 15 Sidle 16 Tense 18 Demur 19 Opulent 21 Tomato 22 Attire 23 Ermine 25 Aided 26 Foil 28 Ten

No 75 - ACROSS: 1 Pursue 7 Plimsoll 8 Lore 10 Brogue 11 Tragic 14 Vat 16 Tiers 17 Even 19 Taper 21 Baton 22 Nonet 23 Reed 26 Laser 28 Per 29 Alters 30 Bovine 31 Eden 32 Renowned 33 Swerve

DOWN: 1 Pebble 2 Slogan 3 Epee 4 Smarten 5 Forge 6 Blocs 8 Love 9 Rut 12 Air 13 Irate 15 Sated 18 Vital 19 Tan 20 Pot 21 Borrows 22 Nee 23 Revere 24 Erin 25 Dredge 26 Laird 27 Stone 28 Pod 30 Beds

No 76 - ACROSS: 4 Ogress 7 Mushroom 8 Astern 10 Sieve 13 Rhea 14 Hate 15 Gear 16 Own 17 Rand 19 Earn 21 Endurance 23 Aged 24 Ever 26 Ado 27 Lose 29 Esau 32 Reps 33 Tsars 34 Arcade 35 Negation 36 Adonis

DOWN: 1 Smash 2 Asset 3 Free 4 Omaha 5 Rota 6 Strewn 9 Serene 11 Ian 12 Verne 13 Redress 15 Gnu 16 Ore 18 Addled 20 Acres 21 Ego 22 Ave 23 Adored 25 Tar 28 Opens 30 Satin 31 Using 32 Rain 33 Teal

No 77 - ACROSS: 3 Chide 8 Revel 10 Every 11 Ail 12 Drive 13 Plaudit 15 Onset 18 Gel 19 Futile 21 Rebuilt 22 Ties 23 Sloe 24 Textile 26 Inured 29 Try 31 Peril 32 Teenage 34 Floor 35 Err 36 Agile 37 Asked 38 Erode

DOWN: 1 Realm 2 Deluges 4 Hurt 5 Devout 6 Event 7 Creel 9 Via 12 Diluted 14 Deb 16 Sidle 17 Tenet 19 Flutter 20 Strip 21 Recur 23 Slyness 24 Teller 25 Ire 27 Neigh 28 Rifle 30 Agree 32 Told 33 Ark

No 78 - ACROSS: 1 Trace 6 Pairs 9 Almanac 10 Whisk 11 Crepe 12 Choke 13 Panache 15 Use 17 Oral 18 Agents 19 Grace 20 Secure 22 Beta 24 Ely 25 Remarry 26 Epees 27 Scalp 28 Limps 29 Albumen 30 Stone 31 Ogles

DOWN: 2 Rehear 3 Casual 4 Elk 5 Cache 6 Package 7 Acre 8 Repast 12 Chore 13 Poise 14 Nancy 15 Under 16 Essay 18 Aches 19 Grapple 21 Elicit 22 Basing 23 Triple 25 Rebut 26 Elan 28 Leo

No 79 - ACROSS: 1 Thieve 7 Dowagers 8 Late 10 Chosen 11 Minute 14 Sea 16 Notes 17 Sled 19 Taper 21 Makes 22 Lager 23 Pier 26 Stair 28 Tar 29 Torpid 30 Tirade 31 Open 32 Proverbs 33 Sitter

DOWN: 1 Tracks 2 Erased 3 Eden 4 Ravines 5 Debut 6 Asses 8 Lose 9 Tea 12 Nor 13 Tense 15 Rakes 18 Lento 19 Tag 20 Per 21 Marines 22 Lip 23 Parent 24 Iran 25 Reefer 26 Stops 27 Arrow 28 Tip 30 Toss

No 80 - ACROSS: 4 Molest 7 Evaluate 8 Lesson 10 Sweat 13 Dent 14 Temp 15 Peer 16 Bet 17 Rail 19 Omen 21 Disturbed 23 Bolt 24 Does 26 Wet 27 Even 29 Sage 32 Grid 33 Nylon 34 Latest 35 Activate 36 Weasel

DOWN: 1 Least 2 Harem 3 Curt 4 Melee 5 Lest 6 Spoken 9 Enrobe 11 Wed 12 April 13 Deluded 15 Pit 16 Bed 18 Asters 20 Messy 21 Dot 22 Ron 23 Berate 25 Ago 28 Vital 30 Altar 31 Enter 32 Gets 33 Nail

No 81 - ACROSS: 3 Impel 8 Feral 10 Vital 11 Dam 12 Minim 13 Damaged 15 Niche 18 Dud 19 Action 21 Mandate 22 Moan 23 Mere 24 Wellies 26 Razors 29 IRA 31 There 32 Beeswax 34 Baker 35 Lad 36 Tacit 37 Renal 38 Thorn

DOWN: 1 Medal 2 Ramadan 4 Maid 5 Evince 6 Limit 7 Basho 9 Ram 12 Meddles 14 Gun 16 Cites 17 Enter 19 Atelier 20 Smart 21 Maize 23 Measles 24 Wreath 25 Ire 27 Ahead 28 Orbit 30 Radar 32 Beer 33 Wan

No 82 - ACROSS: 1 Aspic 6 Tombs 9 Monitor 10 Grips 11 Rests 12 Loots 13 Cabinet 15 Men 17 Emir 18 Priory 19 Spire 20 Lights 22 Solo 24 One 25 Aspirin 26 Crane 27 Carat 28 Speed 29 Retinue 30 Added 31 Prays

DOWN: 2 Scream 3 Impair 4 Cos 5 Pilot 6 Torture 7 Ores 8 Better 12 Leaps 13 Cello 14 Binge 15 Motor 16 Nylon 18 Prise 19 Started 21 In hand 22 Simper 23 Likely 25 Antic 26 Care 28 Sup

No 83 - ACROSS: 1 Raffia 7 Bathroom 8 Flee 10 Chalet 11 Crater 14 Col 16 Psalm 17 Stew 19 Hopes 21 Began 22 Lemur 23 Sore 26 Aster 28 Bed 29 Mortal 30 Senile 31 Lean 32 Nauseate 33 Dreams

DOWN: 1 Reacts 2 Follow 3 Abet 4 Sharpen 5 Aorta 6 Smarm 8 Face 9 Eel 12 Ass 13 Elder 15 Mogul 18 Torso 19 Hem 20 Par 21 Berated 22 Let 23 Senate 24 Odin 25 Events 26 Amend 27 Trout 28 Bee 30 Sled

No 84 - ACROSS: 4 Tracts 7 Broccoli 8 Around 10 Rotor 13 Brew 14 Tier 15 Slam 16 Doe 17 Gape 19 Amen 21 Catamaran 23 Rant 24 Irks 26 Ban 27 East 29 Only 32 Inch 33 Gnome 34 Hairdo 35 Rational 36 Lesson

DOWN: 1 Abort 2 Route 3 Scar 4 Tiara 5 Avow 6 Tendon 9 Remark 11 Oil 12 Organ 13 Blemish 15 Spa 16 Den 18 Attend 20 Mason 21 Can 22 Art 23 Ravage 25 Elm 28 Acorn 30 Nouns 31 Yells 32 Iris 33 Grim

No 85 - ACROSS: 3 Place 8 Nasal 10 Angle 11 Nip 12 Start 13 Maniacs 15 Peers 18 Tie 19 Ferret 21 Rampart 22 Tool 23 Aden 24 Diverse 26 Mystic 29 Not 31 Seers 32 Address 34 Earns 35 Ink 36 Alter 37 Added 38 Smash

DOWN: 1 Canal 2 Capital 4 Lots 5 Carpet 6 Enter 7 Flare 9 Sin 12 Sceptic 14 Aim 16 Erode 17 Stone 19 Friends 20 Stems 21 Rouse 23 Astride 24 Disarm 25 Rod 27 Yells 28 Trees 30 Asked 32 Ants 33 End

No 86 - ACROSS: 1 Clash 6 Times 9 Pattern 10 Users 11 Acted 12 Perch 13 Settler 15 Bee 17 Peas 18 Resent 19 Ached 20 Relive 22 Edge 24 Ere 25 Reviser 26 Trait 27 Carat 28 Shuts 29 Leveret 30 Idled 31 Aster

DOWN: 2 Lessee 3 Sprats 4 Has 5 Steer 6 Tracked 7 Inch 8 Eleven 12 Pence 13 Spare 14 Table 15 Bends 16 Ether 18 Reset 19 Averted 21 Errand 22 Eights 23 Gentle 25 Rivet 26 Tale 28 Sea

No 87 - ACROSS: 1 Duffel 7 Alphabet 8 Seen 10 Evaded 11 Steven 14 Gel 16 Trend 17 Tsar 19 Tower 21 Caber 22 Habit 23 Pays 26 Hopes 28 Con 29 Alerts 30 Batons 31 Eden 32 Extremes 33 Titter

DOWN: 1 Detect 2 Feeder 3 Land 4 Chatter 5 Above 6 Stand 8 Saga 9 Eel 12 Err 13 Enemy 15 Robin 18 Spool 19 Tab 20 Wet 21 Castles 22 Her 23 Potent 24 Anon 25 Sister 26 Haven 27 Petty 28 Cad 30 Best

No 88 - ACROSS: 4 Record 7 Espresso 8 Scarce 10 Drake 13 Reap 14 Solo 15 Less 16 Sad 17 Real 19 Toll 21 Mandatory 23 Lung 24 Tend 26 Mad 27 Area 29 Even 32 Aged 33 Crate 34 Adages 35 Tortoise 36 Crisis

DOWN: 1 Lends 2 Appal 3 Cede 4 Roses 5 Clap 6 Racial 9 Cast on 11 Row 12 Koran 13 Related 15 Lad 16 Sly 18 Engage 20 Order 21 Mud 22 Tea 23 Ladder 25 Bet 28 Rests 30 Valid 31 Never 32 Ages 33 Cats

No 89 - ACROSS: 3 Scull 8 Koran 10 Oases 11 Car 12 Staid 13 Bananas 15 Tense 18 Vim 19 Tenets 21 Happier 22 Eden 23 Aria 24 Depicts 26 Crates 29 Out 31 Hones 32 Cuticle 34 Liars 35 Rot 36 Feels 37 Medal 38 Stows

DOWN: 1 Local 2 Caravan 4 Cots 5 Loiter 6 Laden 7 Least 9 Ran 12 Samples 14 Nip 16 Nears 17 Essay 19 Tedious 20 Perch 21 He-man 23 Attired 24 Desist 25 Cut 27 Roses 28 Tells 30 Altar 32 Crow 33 Cod

No 90 - ACROSS: 1 Prism 6 Rouse 9 Terrier 10 Afoot 11 Marry 12 Spool 13 Freight 15 Two 17 Amid 18 Assist 19 Forge 20 Abhors 22 Erse 24 Lot 25 Corsair 26 Below 27 Snood 28 Tango 29 Nonstop 30 Harem 31 Never

DOWN: 2 Reform 3 Stolid 4 Met 5 Crept 6 Remorse 7 Oral 8 Straws 12 Shoos 13 Fatal 14 Eight 15 Tiara 16 Other 18 Aglow 19 Freedom 21 Bosnia 22 Escape 23 Single 25 Coast 26 Bone 28 Ton

No 91 - ACROSS: 1 Collie 7 Pavement 8 Tree 10 Arrive 11 Minute 14 Ice 16 Tines 17 Asps 19 Vital 21 Camel 22 Fetid 23 Feed 26 Taken 28 Tor 29 Agents 30 Torrid 31 Apes 32 Becoming 33 Settle

DOWN: 1 Canada 2 Lyrics 3 Epee 4 Recital 5 Begun 6 Sties 8 Trip 9 Eve 12 Nil 13 Terse 15 Limit 18 Scrag 19 Vat 20 Ted 21 Centime 22 Fen 23 Forest 24 Errs 25 Diddle 26 Tabby 27 Ketch 28 Top 30 Tags

No 92 - ACROSS: 4 Allots 7 Loiterer 8 Gropes 10 Grave 13 Boot 14 Silo 15 Dent 16 Pet 17 Gail 19 Aver 21 Supporter 23 Step 24 Veer 26 Sly 27 Lied 29 Save 32 Send 33 Petal 34 Debase 35 Pretence 36 Aspect

DOWN: 1 Flags 2 Rival 3 Cede 4 Argon 5 Loot 6 Teeter 9 Rotate 11 Rib 12 Vogue 13 Beloved 15 Dip 16 Per 18 Apples 20 Verse 21 Sty 22 Red 23 Sleeps 25 Ova 28 Inept 30 Atone 31 Elder 32 Same 33 Pits

No 93 - ACROSS: 3 Stars 8 Calms 10 Apple 11 Rib 12 Crate 13 Breaths 15 Inert 18 Lea 19 Rotate 21 Smarten 22 Rots 23 Bear 24 Monster 26 Street 29 Oar 31 Trend 32 Engaged 34 Salts 35 Ten 36 Annul 37 Meter 38 Essay

DOWN: 1 Tarry 2 Embalms 4 Tors 5 Ration 6 Spent 7 Alert 9 Lie 12 Chariot 14 Tea 16 Eager 17 Tears 19 Reasons 20 Trust 21 Store 23 Berated 24 Medals 25 Tag 27 Trunk 28 Ensue 30 Tenet 32 Etna 33 Get

No 94 - ACROSS: 1 Stage 6 Crook 9 Restore 10 Fatal 11 Aspen 12 Crest 13 Reptile 15 Leo 17 Ores 18 Report 19 Stood 20 Sleuth 22 Cede 24 Ear 25 Hoarder 26 Treat 27 Stair 28 Easel 29 Restart 30 Added 31 Reads

DOWN: 2 Trader 3 Grants 4 Eel 5 Stare 6 Crashed 7 Rest 8 Opener 12 Cloth 13 Rouse 14 Peter 15 Loved 16 Other 18 Robot 19 Starred 21 Lasted 22 Create 23 Defend 25 Haste 26 Tire 28 Err

No 95 - ACROSS: 1 Closes 7 Lacerate 8 Pane 10 United 11 Ticker 14 Pet 16 Roses 17 Shed 19 Loses 21 Fetid 22 Later 23 Sped 26 Stool 28 Sea 29 Chatty 30 Satire 31 Idol 32 Exhorted 33 Enfold

DOWN: 1 Clouts 2 Seated 3 Sled 4 Desired 5 Sacks 6 Seers 8 Pipe 9 Net 12 Cos 13 Eerie 15 Hotel 18 Heath 19 Let 20 Sir 21 Falters 22 Lot 23 Set off 24 Pail 25 Deemed 26 Screw 27 Oaths 28 Sad 30 Side

No 96 - ACROSS: 4 Sister 7 Evaluate 8 Emends 10 Stiff 13 Drop 14 Till 15 West 16 Bap 17 Aces 19 Ewer 21 Protected 23 Pier 24 Ruse 26 Gap 27 Sett 29 Dove 32 Lens 33 Usual 34 Traits 35 Unsettle 36 Statue

DOWN: 1 Beast 2 Basil 3 Buff 4 Seers 5 Seep 6 Endear 9 Motets 11 Tip 12 Flare 13 Deserts 15 Wet 16 Bed 18 Corset 20 Weeds 21 Pip 22 Cut 23 Parrot 25 Ova 28 Ensue 30 Ousts 31 Elder 32 List 33 Used

No 97 - ACROSS: 3 Brats 8 Harps 10 Atone 11 Cur 12 Tiara 13 Comical 15 Grant 18 Cot 19 Better 21 Contort 22 Chat 23 Fast 24 Craters 26 Motors 29 Tee 31 Spire 32 Alleged 34 Dance 35 Zip 36 Greet 37 Tenet 38 Rebel

DOWN: 1 Tacos 2 Apricot 4 Rail 5 Target 6 Start 7 Inane 9 Rum 12 Tatters 14 Con 16 Atlas 17 Trite 19 Brittle 20 Scams 21 Cacti 23 Freezer 24 Create 25 Eel 27 Opera 28 Order 30 Repel 32 Ache 33 Gin

No 98 - ACROSS: 1 Strap 6 Coped 9 Samovar 10 Ditty 11 Pause 12 April 13 Horrors 15 Pet 17 Eden 18 Parade 19 Mural 20 Rescue 22 Stir 24 Die 25 Redeems 26 Caber 27 Shout 28 Aspen 29 Textile 30 Cried 31 Idled

DOWN: 2 Tripod 3 Astern 4 Pay 5 Romps 6 Capital 7 Oral 8 Ensued 12 Argue 13 Heard 14 Reuse 15 Paste 16 Tears 18 Paper 19 Mutated 21 Either 22 Sensed 23 Impede 25 Rests 26 Cute 28 Ali

No 99 - ACROSS: 1 Camped 7 Ancestor 8 Feat 10 Crease 11 Ripens 14 ESP 16 Sides 17 Else 19 Haven 21 Sated 22 Upset 23 Mess 26 There 28 Red 29 Stance 30 Canine 31 Emit 32 Ring road 33 Eclair

DOWN: 1 Creche 2 Please 3 Date 4 Devised 5 Steed 6 Cross 8 Fees 9 Asp 12 Pin 13 Nears 15 Cater 18 Light 19 Has 20 Vet 21 Spectre 22 Urn 23 Menial 24 Edit 25 Seeker 26 Tsars 27 Earns 28 Ram 30 Cede

No 100 - ACROSS: 4 Salads 7 Transmit 8 Edicts 10 Iraqi 13 Peer 14 Peru 15 Germ 16 Oil 17 Oder 19 Earl 21 Stimulate 23 Stem 24 Sent 26 Sly 27 Meet 29 Ion 32 Bend 34 Scope 34 Report 35 Elegance 36 Debtor

DOWN: 1 Strip 2 Radar 3 Asti 4 Steer 5 Lair 6 Detail 9 Demean 11 Rep 12 Quote 13 Perused 15 Gem 16 Ore 18 Dimmer 20 Attic 21 Sty 22 Let 23 Sleeve 25 Hop 28 Enter 30 Count 31 Never 32 Boat 33 Sags

No 101 - ACROSS: 3 Grope 8 Ceded 10 Irate 11 Pig 12 Blare 13 Capable 15 Aches 18 Leo 19 Attest 21 Censure 22 Hers 23 Even 24 Combine 26 Random 29 Ill 31 Dream 32 Takings 34 Learn 35 Via 36 Coped 37 Helps 38 Sylph

DOWN: 1 Sepal 2 Regales 4 Role 5 Pirate 6 Erect 7 Sties 9 Dip 12 Blossom 14 Ben 16 Heave 17 Stand 19 Arabian 20 Shard 21 Crane 23 Enliven 24 Comedy 25 Ilk 27 Arrow 28 Dales 30 Agape 32 Trap 33 Nil

No 102 - ACROSS: 1 Fated 6 Round 9 Noticed 10 Haste 11 Pilot 12 Titan 13 Delight 15 Ale 17 Idol 18 Crater 19 Doors 20 Callow 22 Tale 24 Spy 25 Revised 26 Sated 27 Fleet 28 Pause 29 Retired 30 Asked 31 Peony

DOWN: 2 Amazed 3 Entail 4 Doe 5 Limit 6 Repairs 7 Odin 8 Noodle 12 Throw 13 Discs 14 Lolly 15 Atlas 16 Erred 18 Creed 19 Donated 21 Apples 22 Tirade 23 Lessen 25 Remit 26 Sere 28 Pep

No 103 - ACROSS: 1 Myopia 7 Mushroom 8 Prep 10 Aprons 11 Arcade 14 Odd 16 Model 17 Espy 19 Panes 21 Taper 22 Tenet 23 Prey 26 Salad 28 Boo 29 Tropic 30 Detail 31 Aged 32 Nurtured 33 Attend

DOWN: 1 Mirage 2 Parody 3 Amps 4 Charmer 5 Nomad 6 Impel 8 Prop 9 End 12 Cos 13 Dense 15 Paper 18 Swear 19 Pan 20 Net 21 Tedious 22 Tap 23 Potent 24 Road 25 Yelled 26 Stink 27 Lorry 28 Beg 30 Dada

No 104 - ACROSS: 4 Squibs 7 Overdraw 8 Ocelot 10 Trite 13 Tour 14 Seer 15 Rend 16 Cab 17 Eden 19 Drab 21 Tarpaulin 23 Beta 24 Bred 26 Gen 27 Kiln 29 Glee 32 Mere 33 Leant 34 Valise 35 Nicotine 36 Serene

DOWN: 1 Loots 2 Eerie 3 Edge 4 Swoon 5 User 6 Baobab 9 Cuddle 11 Red 12 Treat 13 Tenable 15 Rep 16 Can 18 Drakes 20 Ridge 21 Ten 22 Urn 23 Berate 25 Hen 28 Irene 30 Latin 31 Ether 32 Mice 33 Look

No 105 - ACROSS: 3 Blade 8 Hoods 10 Enter 11 Rum 12 Damps 13 Enticed 15 Augur 18 Roc 19 Crease 21 Habitat 22 Reel 23 Cede 24 Recital 26 Portal 29 Tar 31 Sited 32 Lantern 34 Rival 35 Oar 36 Seams 37 Enrol 38 Sheer

DOWN: 1 Corny 2 Admiral 4 Lead 5 Depart 6 Ensue 7 Venus 9 Out 12 Decibel 14 Cob 16 Gavel 17 Revel 19 Capital 20 Drops 21 Heart 23 Cartons 24 Radish 25 Tan 27 Oiled 28 Terms 30 Error 32 Lame 33 Ear

No 106 - ACROSS: 1 About 6 Stork 9 Respite 10 Erase 11 Angel 12 Flirt 13 Council 15 Set 17 Rise 18 Beside 19 Shard 20 Strict 22 Mere 24 Say 25 Cabinet 26 Kayak 27 Strew 28 Purse 29 Entreat 30 Jelly 31 Leant

DOWN: 2 Borzoi 3 Ursine 4 Tee 5 Spill 6 Started 7 Tent 8 Reeked 12 Fight 13 Crass 14 Usury 15 Siren 16 Tenet 18 Break 19 Scrawny 21 Tattle 22 Minute 23 Reason 25 Carry 26 Keel 28 Pal

No 107 - ACROSS: 1 Drifts 7 Labourer 8 Wipe 10 Pealed 11 Adders 14 Rep 16 Oasis 17 Sand 19 Robin 21 Sewer 22 Cadet 23 Seep 26 Sitar 28 Ham 29 Trance 30 Ravine 31 Edit 32 Lonesome 33 Dogged

DOWN: 1 Drapes 2 Failed 3 Sled 4 Boudoir 5 Tries 6 Dress 8 Warn 9 Pep 12 Dan 13 Rinse 15 Cower 18 Astir 19 Red 20 Bet 21 Sarcasm 22 Can 23 Saving 24 Emit 25 Peeked 26 Stale 27 Taint 28 Had 30 Reed

No 108 - ACROSS: 4 Feasts 7 Throttle 8 Wreath 10 Elate 13 Neat 14 Rota 15 Sari 16 Beg 17 Bait 19 Said 21 Computing 23 Crop 24 Ring 26 May 27 Elan 29 Erse 32 Oral 33 Creed 34 Opened 35 Ecstatic 36 Stay on

DOWN: 1 Steer 2 Treat 3 Stye 4 Fewer 5 Abet 6 Tutted 9 Raisin 11 Lot 12 Taboo 13 Natural 15 Sip 16 Big 18 Ampere 20 Anger 21 Cry 22 Tin 23 Carpet 25 Use 28 Laden 30 Rents 31 Edict 32 Only 33 Cute

No 109 - ACROSS: 3 Pairs 8 Hails 10 Enemy 11 Too 12 Rhone 13 Banshee 15 Tears 18 Sin 19 Parity 21 Hopeful 22 Adam 23 Deep 24 Mangled 26 Artful 29 Ear 31 Sheet 32 Engaged 34 Taint 35 New 36 Unlit 37 Ogles 38 Dense

DOWN: 1 Natal 2 Blossom 4 Ache 5 Rental 6 Sneer 7 Smart 9 Ion 12 Renewal 14 Hip 16 Aired 17 Sylph 19 Pungent 20 Tapas 21 Haste 23 Derange 24 Mutate 25 Lag 27 Rhino 28 Fetid 30 Sewer 32 Ends 33 Gel

No 110 - ACROSS: 1 Egged 6 Decry 9 Visited 10 Green 11 Means 12 Demon 13 Lantern 15 Pet 17 Onus 18 Reside 19 Speed 20 Regale 22 Bold 24 Eve 25 Berates 26 Anger 27 Edict 28 State 29 Refusal 30 Asked 31 Years

DOWN: 2 German 3 Events 4 Din 5 Siren 6 Demoted 7 Eden 8 Ranted 12 Drape 13 Loire 14 Nudge 15 Pilot 16 Tends 18 Refer 19 Slanted 21 Evades 22 Battle 23 Letter 25 Begun 26 Acre 28 Say

No 111 - ACROSS: 1 Chaste 7 Rehearse 8 Argo 10 Unties 11 Ribald 14 OBE 16 Mates 17 Same 19 Moved 21 Haven 22 Tenet 23 Dart 26 Sitar 28 Pen 29 Crepes 30 Renown 31 Iron 32 Respires 33 Eleven

DOWN: 1 Clouts 2 Scribe 3 Eros 4 Regimen 5 Treat 6 Leads 8 Atom 9 Gee 12 Bad 13 Lemur 15 Loves 18 Astir 19 Man 20 Vet 21 Heretic 22 Tap 23 Denote 24 Anon 25 Tendon 26 Scare 27 Tense 28 Per 30 Rise

No 112 - ACROSS: 4 Amoeba 7 Ruthless 8 Please 10 Trips 13 Dear 14 Hero 15 Cent 16 Ace 17 Star 19 Tint 21 Pertinent 23 Peri 24 Dare 26 Sow 27 Peep 29 Rage 32 Tors 33 Utter 34 Decode 35 Capitals 36 Street

DOWN: 1 Truth 2 Stair 3 Ales 4 Aspen 5 Over 6 Bisect 9 Latter 11 Red 12 Poser 13 Derides 15 Cat 16 Ant 18 Tripod 20 Inert 21 Pew 22 Nap 23 Potent 25 Age 28 Erect 30 Atlas 31 Erase 32 Tome 33 Unit

No 113 - ACROSS: 3 Spurt 8 Nacre 10 Error 11 Boa 12 Truce 13 Restart 15 Enter 18 Ira 19 Endure 21 Compact 22 Clan 23 Cite 24 Veteran 26 Bestir 29 Lip 31 Steer 32 Topical 34 Rayon 35 Tan 36 Being 37 Fatal 38 Sound

DOWN: 1 Caber 2 Oration 4 Port 5 Recent 6 Trend 7 Poser 9 Cos 12 Trapper 14 Arm 16 Turin 17 Rebel 19 Echelon 20 Scabs 21 Cause 23 Capital 24 Virago 25 Rip 27 Ether 28 Terns 30 Banal 32 Town 33 Cat

No 114 - ACROSS: 1 Stout 6 Robes 9 Rambler 10 Waist 11 Pelts 12 Seats 13 Changed 15 Arc 17 Lyre 18 Blazer 19 Belie 20 Slogan 22 Grew 24 Sew 25 Cowherd 26 Mason 27 Stain 28 Ethic 29 Cabinet 30 Urges 31 Longs

DOWN: 2 Trashy 3 Ursine 4 Tat 5 Ebbed 6 Reptile 7 Ores 8 Entire 12 Seven 13 Class 14 Arrow 15 Azure 16 Crowd 18 Bison 19 Bananas 21 Letter 22 Ghetto 23 Erring 25 Comic 26 Mice 28 Eel

No 115 - ACROSS: 1 Blames 7 Embattle 8 Anon 10 Repent 11 Facade 14 Ere 16 Gamut 17 Lass 19 Caper 21 Motor 22 Motet 23 Ewer 26 Nonet 28 Bra 29 Erotic 30 Naming 31 Unit 32 Extended 33 Events

DOWN: 1 Barrel 2 Miners 3 Sent 4 Manager 5 Steam 6 Tenet 8 Apes 9 One 12 Car 13 Dunce 15 Water 18 Abhor 19 Cot 20 Pot 21 Motions 22 Met 23 Ermine 24 Wait 25 Rights 26 Never 27 North 28 Ban 30 Nude

No 116 - ACROSS: 4 Pickle 7 Trombone 8 Errand 10 Grade 13 Crop 14 Ease 15 Lost 16 Bet 17 Mien 19 Amid 21 Motivated 23 Tuna 24 Ewes 26 Led 27 Lore 29 Sage 32 Mint 33 Pylon 34 Tonics 35 Everyone 36 Ascent

DOWN: 1 Stage 2 Rotas 3 Able 4 Peers 5 Carp 6 Landed 9 Rotate 11 Rap 12 Demon 13 Convert 15 Lei 16 Bid 18 Italic 20 Messy 21 Mud 22 Awe 23 Tenors 25 Ago 28 Onset 30 Allow 31 Ended 32 Mile 33 Part

No 117 - ACROSS: 3 Chart 8 Macaw 10 Orate 11 Nap 12 Tribe 13 Habitat 15 Untie 18 Tot 19 Astern 21 Contort 22 Cool 23 Dram 24 Arrives 26 Nomads 29 Sad 31 Trash 32 Attuned 34 Sense 35 Cup 36 Never 37 Utter 38 Tense

DOWN: 1 Canal 2 Capitol 4 Hurt 5 Robust 6 Trent 7 Stair 9 Cab 12 Tatters 14 Ton 16 Tears 17 Enemy 19 Artiste 20 Scant 21 Comma 23 Deducts 24 Adhere 25 Vat 27 Order 28 Asset 30 Repel 32 Asks 33 Nut

No 118 - ACROSS: 1 Cache 6 Bench 9 Overall 10 Spite 11 Essay 12 Inane 13 Prelude 15 Pen 17 Eels 18 Decide 19 Salad 20 Recoil 22 Ford 24 Sat 25 Debates 26 Ached 27 Stone 28 Ahead 29 Traduce 30 Erase 31 Trend

DOWN: 2 Aspire 3 Hotels 4 Eve 5 Brine 6 Blended 7 Else 8 Chased 12 Ideal 13 Peers 14 Elect 15 Pilot 16 Needs 18 Dated 19 Sincere 21 Easter 22 Father 23 Remain 25 Deeds 26 Ants 28 Act

No 119 - ACROSS: 1 Tattle 7 Rehearse 8 Oils 10 Settee 11 Divide 14 Ice 16 Satan 17 Etch 19 Ripen 21 Later 22 Tenet 23 Rest 26 Groan 28 Gel 29 Rabbit 30 Locate 31 Eden 32 Nosiness 33 Settle

DOWN: 1 Tussle 2 Twitch 3 Erse 4 Deviser 5 Trait 6 Seven 8 Otic 9 Lee 12 Van 13 Dates 15 Rites 18 Tiara 19 Ran 20 Pet 21 Lenient 22 Tab 23 Recent 24 Elan 25 Thence 26 Grand 27 Obese 28 God 30 Less

No 120 - ACROSS: 4 Sparse 7 Childish 8 Energy 10 Light 13 Veer 14 Lose 15 Bent 16 Ban 17 Ruin 19 Teal 21 Continent 23 Cons 24 Soda 26 Rod 27 Avow 29 Crow 32 Mien 33 Stare 34 Braids 35 Thanking 36 Psalms

DOWN: 1 Scull 2 Rings 3 Edit 4 Sheen 5 Aver 6 Signal 9 Netted 11 Ion 12 Heron 13 Venison 15 Bit 16 Bat 18 Unsaid 20 Enact 21 Cod 22 Now 23 Cobras 25 For 28 Vests 30 Rapid 31 Wedge 32 Mill 33 Send

No 121 - ACROSS: 3 Agile 8 Happy 10 Annoy 11 CIA 12 Laird 13 Cheroot 15 Debit 18 Rag 19 Reduce 21 Forbear 22 Avow 23 Aged 24 Compete 26 Remark 29 Aft 31 Ensue 32 Artisan 34 Gamut 35 Ran 36 Bonus 37 Medal 38 Rents

DOWN: 1 Cache 2 Sparrow 4 Gnat 5 Larder 6 Ended 7 Comic 9 Pie 12 Logbook 14 Oar 16 Bulge 17 Tends 19 Rampart 20 Nacre 21 Forms 23 Attired 24 Crease 25 Eft 27 Endow 28 Augur 30 Banal 32 Aunt 33 Sad

No 122 - ACROSS: 1 Ambit 6 Lambs 9 Mongrel 10 Snipe 11 Messy 12 Teams 13 Succeed 15 Ode 17 Cart 18 Snares 19 Being 20 Repeat 22 Soda 24 Ere 25 Baloney 26 Clerk 27 Taboo 28 Fated 29 Polemic 30 Haven 31 Tents

DOWN: 2 Mantua 3 Impact 4 Toe 5 Ogled 6 Lemming 7 Ales 8 Beside 12 Tenet 13 Scare 14 Crepe 15 Orion 16 Essay 18 Sneak 19 Balloon 21 Errata 22 Solace 23 Detect 25 Breed 26 Cope 28 Fit

No 123 - ACROSS: 1 Bosses 7 Teammate 8 Aide 10 Borrow 11 Groove 14 Ian 16 Arrow 17 Oral 19 Fable 21 Rated 22 Cadet 23 Lied 26 Salad 28 Bar 29 Exotic 30 Retire 31 Ages 32 Stranger 33 Entail

DOWN: 1 Bamboo 2 Spiral 3 Stew 4 Emerald 5 Manor 6 Renew 8 Aria 9 Don 12 Ore 13 Vogue 15 Hates 18 Relax 19 Fad 20 Bet 21 Radiant 22 Cat 23 Latent 24 Iris 25 Diesel 26 Sense 27 Lorry 28 Beg 30 Rare

No 124 - ACROSS: 4 Please 7 Traverse 8 Tinsel 10 Elope 13 Pane 14 Sell 15 Gels 16 Ova 17 Aver 19 Tune 21 Stimulate 23 Seer 24 Salt 26 Ate 27 Iced 29 Edge 32 Glad 33 Drool 34 Spared 35 Disagree 36 Frothy

DOWN: 1 Sties 2 Carol 3 Mere 4 Petal 5 Erne 9 Swerve 9 Instal 11 Let 12 Plate 13 Perused 15 Gem 16 One 18 Virile 20 Utter 21 See 22 Lad 23 Stupor 25 Ago 28 Caddy 30 Doors 31 Elder 32 Grit 33 Dear

No 125 - ACROSS: 3 Tread 8 Rites 10 Gamut 11 Dig 12 Fatal 13 Recital 15 Tepid 18 Mar 19 Reside 21 Debates 22 Thin 23 Move 24 Parapet 26 Freely 29 Tin 31 Forge 32 Lettuce 34 Rapid 35 Ire 36 Andes 37 Tonne 38 Tents **DOWN:** 1 Sides 2 Regimen 4 Real 5 Agates 6 Dales 7 Lurid 9 Tic 12 Faraway 14 Tab 16 Pilot 17 Deter 19 Related 20 Staff 21 Diver 23 Mention 24 Please 25 Pit 27 Round 28 Egret 30 Scent 32 List 33 Urn

No 126 - ACROSS: 1 Crude 6 Ditto 9 Removes 10 Stool 11 Silly 12 Edits 13 Redeems 15 Fed 17 Eros 18 Bolero 19 Story 20 Patois 22 Aces 24 Sty 25 Diocese 26 Shard 27 Limit 28 Cedar 29 Tension 30 Ceded 31 Stash

DOWN: 2 Rotter 3 Droves 4 Eel 5 Lords 6 Destroy 7 Isis 8 Teller 12 Emits 13 Reaps 14 Dotty 15 Fence 16 Douse 18 Braid 19 Sighted 21 Attire 22 Accent 23 Essays 25 Dross 26 Site 28 Cos

No 127 - ACROSS: 1 Pencil 7 Insecure 8 Peso 10 Molten 11 Virago 14 Eat 16 Delay 17 Scan 19 Hated 21 Miser 22 Paste 23 Late 26 Asset 28 Hem 29 Chants 30 Tigers 31 Odin 32 Tutorage 33 Singer

DOWN: 1 Plumes 2 Cretan 3 Lion 4 Decider 5 Mural 6 Decoy 8 Plea 9 Set 12 Red 13 Gaunt 15 Haste 18 Crash 19 His 20 Tee 21 Matters 22 Pen 23 Legion 24 Amen 25 Easter 26 Acute 27 Saute 28 Hid 30 Toes

No 128 - ACROSS: 4 Afford 7 Tortures 8 Prints 10 Lance 13 Peer 14 Ever 15 Pens 16 Kit 17 Aver 19 Upon 21 Overcomes 23 Tier 24 Hues 26 Gel 27 Stet 29 Trip 32 Lead 33 Aside 34 Duress 35 Tarragon 36 Kettle

DOWN: 1 Stale 2 Crane 3 Sure 4 Aspen 5 Fair 6 Retain 9 Resume 11 Ave 12 Crave 13 Perched 15 Per 16 Kos 18 Verses 20 Pests 21 Oil 22 Out 23 Tenure 25 Rid 28 Taste 30 Ridge 31 Penny 32 Left 33 Airs

No 129 - ACROSS: 3 Spade 8 Repel 10 Extra 11 Gum 12 Slope 13 Cabinet 15 Error 18 Gut 19 Entire 21 Contend 22 Rued 23 Clue 24 Retinue 26 Trader 29 Vet 31 Hares 32 Feelers 34 Turin 35 Ale 36 Harem 37 Osier 38 Ready

DOWN: 1 Regal 2 Demigod 4 Pelt 5 Depend 6 Exert 7 Prior 9 Pub 12 Settler 14 Nun 16 Rifle 17 Rebel 19 Enliven 20 Truth 21 Cedar 23 Cutlass 24 Resume 25 Nee 27 Radar 28 Deter 30 Creed 32 Find 33 Eli

No 130 - ACROSS: 1 Stash 6 Dents 9 Located 10 Piled 11 Cello 12 Begin 13 Pompous 15 Den 17 Ores 18 Secure 19 April 20 Recaps 22 Scud 24 Sly 25 Tureens 26 Rates 27 Femur 28 Merry 29 Denizen 30 Steel 31 Tenet

DOWN: 2 Tailor 3 Sleeps 4 Hod 5 Mates 6 Decibel 7 Eden 8 Teller 12 Bumps 13 Pours 14 Mercy 15 Dunce 16 Needs 18 Sinus 19 Apparel 21 Eldest 22 Serene 23 Untrue 25 Tepid 26 Rude 28 Met

No 131 - ACROSS: 1 Fulfil 7 Artefact 8 Flaw 10 Relics 11 Recede 14 Ant 16 Roses 17 Date 19 Coped 21 Sated 22 Manor 23 Apes 26 Dream 28 Gnu 29 Editor 30 Signal 31 Ones 32 Elevated 33 Answer

DOWN: 1 Feared 2 Feline 3 Laws 4 Revered 5 Lanes 6 Sties 8 Flat 9 Act 12 Cod 13 Dense 15 Rotor 18 Award 19 Can 20 Per 21 Samovar 22 Mat 23 Angels 24 Puns 25 Seller 26 Defer 27 Eider 28 Gin 30 Soda

No 132 - ACROSS: 4 Assign 7 Trappers 8 Psalms 10 Lease 13 Veer 14 Lash 15 Bend 16 Wit 17 Odin 19 Abet 21 Predicted 23 Rota 24 Sues 26 Bet 27 Loot 29 Oars 32 Tern 33 Impel 34 Record 35 Extolled 36 Stoker

DOWN: 1 Still 2 Tapas 3 Apse 4 Aspen 5 Star 6 Gambit 9 Sedate 11 Ear 12 Short 13 Venison 15 Bid 16 Wed 18 Dealer 20 Besom 21 Pot 22 Cut 23 Recent 25 Ire 28 Order 30 Apple 31 Slide 32 Took 33 Iron

No 133 - ACROSS: 3 Lamps 8 Kudos 10 Ahead 11 Nut 12 Tiara 13 Endears 15 Orbit 18 Pro 19 Cleans 21 Tactile 22 Lard 23 Pair 24 Refusal 26 Rudder 29 Ton 31 Sleet 32 Debated 34 Timid 35 Cob 36 Lever 37 Shout 38 Reply

DOWN: 1 Funny 2 Notepad 4 Axis 5 Parole 6 Share 7 Cabin 9 Dud 12 Trotter 14 Arc 16 Banal 17 Tsars 19 Clouted 20 Slurs 21 Trade 23 Panache 24 Retire 25 Sob 27 Ulcer 28 Deter 30 Debut 32 Dill 33 Too

No 134 - ACROSS: 1 Waifs 6 Spoil 9 Respite 10 Plait 11 Error 12 Nonet 13 Pelican 15 Let 17 Aped 18 Allude 19 Barge 20 Dismal 22 Sips 24 Ant 25 Spindle 26 Crime 27 Cache 28 Steal 29 Elastic 30 Stows 31 Three

DOWN: 2 Asleep 3 Frigid 4 Set 5 Apron 6 Steeple 7 Pert 8 Ironed 12 Natal 13 Panda 14 Least 15 Lurid 16 Tense 18 Agape 19 Barrels 21 Intact 22 Snatch 23 Please 25 Smash 26 Chew 28 Sit

No 135 - ACROSS: 1 Blades 7 Tolerant 8 Peri 10 Sniper 11 Damage 14 Led 16 Tales 17 Sten 19 Doped 21 Copes 22 Wager 23 Even 26 Sever 28 Axe 29 Cretan 30 Titans 31 Idol 32 Aromatic 33 Kettle

DOWN: 1 Beasts 2 Deepen 3 Stir 4 Relates 5 Fatal 6 Sties 8 Pile 9 Red 12 Mad 13 Genre 15 Hopes 18 Tower 19 Dog 20 Per 21 Caravan 22 Wet 23 Extort 24 Veal 25 Nestle 26 Scrap 27 Venom 28 Aid 30 Tick

No 136 - ACROSS: 4 Vision 7 Untangle 8 Speech 10 Large 13 Stop 14 Tier 15 Chat 16 All 17 Ague 19 East 21 Starlings 23 Peer 24 Vote 26 Lea 27 Amen 29 Near 32 Ages 33 Stale 34 Killer 35 Crescent 36 Choosy

DOWN: 1 Built 2 Stare 3 Once 4 Vesta 5 Seep 6 Occult 9 Potent 11 Ail 12 Grate 13 Shelves 15 Cur 16 Ass 18 Garage 20 Agent 21 Sea 22 Ion 23 Perish 25 Pal 28 Mercy 30 Eager 31 Rests 32 Also 33 So-so

No 137 - ACROSS: 3 Began 8 Cache 10 Sorry 11 The 12 Vents 13 Fiercer 15 React 18 Man 19 Master 21 Capital 22 Roll 23 Safe 24 Cossets 26 Strain 29 Hoe 31 Train 32 Fanatic 34 Devil 35 Lip 36 Harem 37 Steel 38 Dated

DOWN: 1 Latin 2 Thermal 4 Ever 5 Astral 6 Noses 7 Trace 9 Che 12 Venison 14 Cap 16 Atlas 17 Tries 19 Marshal 20 Crest 21 Clara 23 Stealth 24 Cinema 25 Eon 27 Tread 28 Aided 30 Biped 32 Fine 33 Tie

No 138 - ACROSS: 1 Spite 6 Douse 9 Averted 10 Crepe 11 Cites 12 Stain 13 Reverie 15 Ova 17 Used 18 Penned 19 Shard 20 Erupts 22 Temp 24 SOS 25 Quartet 26 Aloud 27 Tract 28 Snide 29 Heretic 30 Added 31 Tenet

DOWN: 2 Purses 3 Tapped 4 Eve 5 Crate 6 Decided 7 Odin 8 Shelve 12 Sighs 13 Runes 14 Venus 15 Onset 16 Adept 18 Proud 19 Stilted 21 Roared 22 Trance 23 Meddle 25 Quiet 26 Ache 28 Sit

No 139 - ACROSS: 1 Hikers 7 Computer 8 Rota 10 Louder 11 Facade 14 Nun 16 Rapid 17 Mass 19 Raven 21 Hotel 22 Tibet 23 Lass 26 Sites 28 Ham 29 Treats 30 Cement 31 Omen 32 Deserted 33 Entire

DOWN: 1 Harlem 2 Exodus 3 Scar 4 Apparel 5 Strap 6 Greed 8 Runs 9 Ten 12 Can 13 Dines 15 Later 18 Astir 19 Rob 20 Vet 21 History 22 Tea 23 Lament 24 Amen 25 Settle 26 Study 27 Tense 28 Hem 30 Code

No 140 - ACROSS: 4 Gambit 7 Languish 8 Across 10 March 13 Unit 14 Plea 15 Gnat 16 Odd 17 Reek 19 Rare 21 Adventure 23 Apse 24 Ouse 26 Use 27 Newt 29 Abet 32 Stan 33 Aside 34 Duress 35 Enormous 36 Rental

DOWN: 1 Slump 2 Snare 3 Lush 4 Ghana 5 Mart 6 Inside 9 Citrus 11 Alp 12 Cards 13 Unknown 15 Gee 16 Ore 18 Events 20 Areas 21 Ape 22 Tut 23 Astute 25 Wed 28 Easel 30 Bison 31 Terse 32 Sent 33 Airs

No 141 - ACROSS: 3 Cross 8 Filch 10 Acute 11 Lea 12 Cable 13 Stilton 15 Inert 18 Dam 19 Unease 21 Perfume 22 Lard 23 Rear 24 Trailer 26 Report 29 Rep 31 Ensue 32 Detains 34 Tapas 35 Irk 36 Beard 37 Orals 38 Essay

DOWN: 1 Kilts 2 Scalded 4 Roan 5 Saline 6 Scene 7 Stars 9 Lei 12 Comfort 14 Tar 16 Eager 17 Tears 19 Umpires 20 Flare 21 Props 23 Repairs 24 Treads 25 Let 27 Enter 28 Outre 30 Ankle 32 Dada 33 Ira

No 142 - ACROSS: 1 Abode 6 Dense 9 Refined 10 Libel 11 Bench 12 Clean 13 Measure 15 Ire 17 Ally 18 Dearer 19 Ceded 20 Enfold 22 Stye 24 Rat 25 Succeed 26 Aught 27 Tract 28 Grill 29 Heretic 30 Owned 31 Needs

DOWN: 2 Beigel 3 Dressy 4 Eel 5 Rifle 6 Debated 7 Eden 8 Secure 12 Creed 13 Maker 14 Aloft 15 Irate 16 Erred 18 Debut 19 Clouted 21 Narrow 22 Scarce 23 Yelled 25 Sheen 26 Ache 28 Gin

No 143 - ACROSS: 1 Chaste 7 Raincoat 8 Eros 10 Demure 11 Reward 14 Ice 16 Genus 17 Date 19 Rated 21 Motor 22 Robin 23 Rust 26 Pilot 28 Ban 29 Erotic 30 Gaping 31 Edit 32 Resonant 33 Sorted

DOWN: 1 Chided 2 Spruce 3 Erse 4 Integer 5 Roman 6 Studs 8 Emit 9 Ore 12 Wed 13 Runes 15 Latin 18 Astir 19 Rob 20 Ton 21 Motions 22 Rot 23 Rapier 24 Unit 25 Tagged 26 Pears 27 Louse 28 Bad 30 Gets

No 144 - ACROSS: 4 Rotate 7 Evidence 8 Chimes 10 Stump 13 Ruin 14 Hose 15 Hart 16 Ace 17 Raid 19 Mine 21 Mendicant 23 Mess 24 Cane 26 Bat 27 What 29 Paid 32 Reel 33 Utter 34 Satire 35 Dangling 36 Recess

DOWN: 1 Leash 2 Minus 3 Keep 4 Recur 5 Thin 6 Thence 9 Hit man 11 Top 12 Meres 13 Radical 15 Hid 16 Ant 18 Answer 20 Inept 21 Met 22 Cat 23 Manage 25 Tie 28 Heeds 30 Attic 31 Drags 32 Ripe 33 Urge

No 145 - ACROSS: 3 Glade 8 Macaw 10 Ended 11 Tap 12 Bumps 13 Habitat 15 Augur 18 Tar 19 Create 21 Contort 22 Till 23 Aged 24 Treacle 26 Grapes 29 Sob 31 Eerie 32 Perused 34 Stars 35 Met 36 State 37 Teeth 38 Erode

DOWN: 1 Fatal 2 Capitol 4 Lout 5 Depart 6 Ensue 7 Debut 9 Cab 12 Barters 14 Tan 16 Gauge 17 Ready 19 Creases 20 Stage 21 Clear 23 Albumen 24 Teeter 25 Cor 27 Rests 28 Piste 30 Petty 32 Prod 33 See

No 146 - ACROSS: 1 Agape 6 Rowdy 9 Reacted 10 Impel 11 Piano 12 Spoon 13 Cornice 15 Let 17 Ales 18 Attire 19 Crows 20 Prison 22 Sips 24 Set 25 Brittle 26 Stare 27 Melee 28 Rival 29 Envelop 30 Slant 31 Tenet

DOWN: 2 Gambol 3 Preens 4 Eel 5 Scope 6 Reports 7 Odin 8 Dinner 12 Scorn 13 Camps 14 Remit 15 Limit 16 Tense 18 Aware 19 Content 21 Reveal 22 Stripe 23 Please 25 Breed 26 Seen 28 Rot

No 147 - ACROSS: 1 Camera 7 Jaundice 8 Soda 10 Draper 11 Befall 14 Gen 16 Gales 17 Does 19 Loped 21 Lever 22 Water 23 Sled 26 Satan 28 Lie 29 Trends 30 Relate 31 Aden 32 Reminder 33 Estate

DOWN: 1 Candid 2 Elopes 3 Ajar 4 Integer 5 Vital 6 Seals 8 Sage 9 Den 12 Fad 13 Lease 15 Moved 18 Oscar 19 Let 20 Per 21 Landing 22 Wan 23 Silent 24 Lean 25 Dredge 26 Start 27 Teems 28 Led 30 Rare

No 148 - ACROSS: 4 Copper 7 Triangle 8 Deride 10 Erect 13 Pant 14 Rota 15 Curt 16 Bra 17 Clan 19 Epee 21 Chattered 23 Rues 24 Erse 26 Rep 27 Tire 29 Raid 32 Pens 33 Aside 34 Recede 35 Pamphlet 36 Strict

DOWN: 1 Steer 2 Rivet 3 Unit 4 Cedar 5 Pert 6 Endure 9 Enters 11 Row 12 Cache 13 Punters 15 Cat 16 Bed 18 Lasted 20 Peers 21 Cup 22 Ere 23 Resent 25 Bid 28 Inept 30 Aisle 31 Dents 32 Peri 33 Alps

No 149 - ACROSS: 3 Waist 8 Gales 10 Error 11 Gel 12 There 13 Failure 15 Enter 18 Bra 19 Endure 21 Confine 22 Pray 23 Deal 24 Pirates 26 Erotic 29 Gem 31 Relic 32 Denotes 34 Andes 35 Nag 36 Maori 37 Minim 38 Acute

DOWN: 1 Pagan 2 Bellboy 4 Ache 5 Serene 6 Trend 7 Power 9 Lei 12 Traffic 14 Urn 16 Tunes 17 Reels 19 Engages 20 Upper 21 Carol 23 Demonic 24 Picnic 25 Ten 27 Relay 28 Tiara 30 Begin 32 Dent 33 Tan

No 150 - ACROSS: 1 Spoon 6 Morse 9 Belated 10 Tenet 11 Nears 12 Tents 13 Removes 15 Pet 17 Odin 18 Polite 19 Divan 20 Seeped 22 Sobs 24 End 25 Brittle 26 Meres 27 Minor 28 About 29 Overall 30 Inane 31 Level

DOWN: 2 Peeled 3 Oberon 4 Net 5 Wages 6 Mention 7 Odes 8 Street 12 Tepid 13 Rouse 14 Mimed 15 Pilot 16 Tense 18 Pairs 19 Deserve 21 Ensign 22 Stable 23 Blouse 25 Beers 26 Moon 28 All

No 151 - ACROSS: 1 Carpet 7 Shrapnel 8 Rota 10 Drover 11 Talons 14 Bed 16 Genus 17 Sten 19 Raged 21 Hopes 22 Tacit 23 Post 26 Strip 28 Dam 29 Thumps 30 Mirage 31 Amen 32 Reminder 33 Entire

DOWN: 1 Chides 2 Proven 3 Tsar 4 Damages 5 Onion 6 Class 8 Robe 9 Ted 12 Led 13 Numbs 15 Rapid 18 Truth 19 Roc 20 Get 21 Happens 22 Tim 23 Parent 24 Oman 25 Thence 26 Store 27 Rummy 28 Dim 30 Mare

No 152 - ACROSS: 4 Social 7 Inhumane 8 Writhe 10 Ropes 13 Deep 14 Apex 15 Perm 16 One 17 Pain 19 Adds 21 Magnified 23 Beta 24 Zone 26 Bet 27 Tier 29 More 32 Fern 33 Aster 34 Medusa 35 Tidiness 36 Adhere

DOWN: 1 Tiara 2 Shape 3 Amps 4 Sewer 5 Chip 6 Athens 9 Remain 11 Opt 12 Ex-pat 13 Denizen 15 Pin 16 Odd 18 Agates 20 Deems 21 Met 22 For 23 Behead 25 Ore 28 Irate 30 Other 31 Erase 32 Fume 33 Amid

No 153 - ACROSS: 3 Steel 8 Curls 10 Rabid 11 Lee 12 Synod 13 Repents 15 Demon 18 Car 19 Tenure 21 Debated 22 Raid 23 Eels 24 Snipers 26 Spaces 29 Ear 31 Siren 32 Astable 34 Limit 35 Tic 36 Scull 37 Widen 38 Sense

DOWN: 1 Rules 2 Fleeced 4 Toys 5 Eroded 6 Laden 7 Minor 9 Rep 12 Strains 14 Nab 16 Mules 17 Nessy 19 Tempest 20 Crass 21 Dinar 23 Erratic 24 Senile 25 Eat 27 Pinch 28 Cells 30 Ulcer 32 Ails 33 Bid

No 154 - ACROSS: 1 Creed 6 Ready 9 Railway 10 Spoon 11 Motor 12 Tenet 13 Cabinet 15 Leo 17 Otic 18 Divest 19 Aspen 20 Delude 22 Side 24 Say 25 Stutter 26 Setts 27 Miser 28 Older 29 Ascribe 30 Agate 31 Enter

DOWN: 2 Repeat 3 Erotic 4 Dan 5 Sleet 6 Ramekin 7 Eyot 8 Droves 12 Tense 13 Cords 14 Billy 15 Legit 16 Otter 18 Dents 19 Adverse 21 Eating 22 Stolen 23 Delete 25 Start 26 Seat 28 OBE

No 155 - ACROSS: 1 Stable 7 Denounce 8 Pale 10 Cretan 11 Sparse 14 Red 16 Aster 17 Stir 19 Ranch 21 Posit 22 Sleep 23 Ruse 26 Canoe 28 Din 29 Isobar 30 Medium 31 Abet 32 Intrepid 33 Ensure

DOWN: 1 Slices 2 Boater 3 Eden 4 Compact 5 Snort 6 Sewer 8 Peri 9 Lad 12 Ash 13 Sears 15 Laser 18 Tapas 19 Roe 20 Nip 21 Pleased 22 Sob 23 Riders 24 Unit 25 Ermine 26 Civil 27 North 28 Deb 30 Made

No 156 - ACROSS: 4 Oxhide 7 Teamwork 8 Adroit 10 Arabs 13 Sped 14 Tina 15 Spiv 16 Old 17 Shoo 19 Oars 21 Gratitude 23 Leap 24 Lard 26 Don 27 Peep 29 Erse 32 Bend 33 Green 34 Ravine 35 Moisture 36 Celery

DOWN: 1 Stoat 2 Pagan 3 Owes 4 Okapi 5 Hard 6 Drills 9 Devour 11 Rip 12 Basra 13 Spoiled 15 Sot 16 Ore 18 Happen 20 Adder 21 Gen 22 Tap 23 Locate 25 Use 28 Enemy 30 Recur 31 Ended 32 Bite 33 Gist

No 157 - ACROSS: 3 Carol 8 Divan 10 Rusts 11 Gin 12 Molar 13 Diagram 15 Tines 18 Man 19 Fedora 21 Haggled 22 Iron 23 Skin 24 Sextets 26 Gasped 29 Ire 31 Sweet 32 Pleaded 34 Stale 35 Lip 36 Drool 37 Steep 38 Seats

DOWN: 1 Rigid 2 Hangman 4 Atom 5 Orated 6 Lurid 7 Steer 9 Via 12 Mangled 14 Rag 16 Nooks 17 Saint 19 Fertile 20 Rings 21 Horse 23 Stealth 24 Settle 25 Ere 27 Aware 28 Pesos 30 Repel 32 Plot 33 Die

No 158 - ACROSS: 1 Stash 6 Beers 9 Puzzled 10 Ensue 11 Sense 12 Train 13 Austere 15 Ode 17 Lets 18 Better 19 Doors 20 Halves 22 Mere 24 Ate 25 Secured 26 Fetid 27 Banal 28 Raven 29 Conceit 30 Sheep 31 Pelts

DOWN: 2 Tongue 3 Spurts 4 Hue 5 Azure 6 Besides 7 Eden 8 Reside 12 Trios 13 Alpha 14 Stole 15 Otter 16 Erred 18 Breed 19 Develop 21 Attach 22 Mutate 23 Recent 25 Since 26 Face 28 Rip

No 159 - ACROSS: 1 Auntie 7 Decorate 8 Brag 10 Choice 11 Parade 14 Ice 16 Towel 17 Able 19 Roved 21 Vapid 22 Totem 23 Sash 26 Civil 28 Rep 29 Lean-to 30 Surely 31 Lees 32 Relegate 33 Weekly

DOWN: 1 Acacia 2 Thrice 3 Edge 4 Rotated 5 Macaw 6 Revel 8 Boil 9 Ace 12 Rod 13 Desks 15 Copes 18 Belie 19 Rat 20 Vim 21 Voltage 22 Tin 23 Serene 24 Apes 25 Heyday 26 Clerk 27 Vault 28 Rue 30 Slew

No 160 - ACROSS: 4 Blasts 7 Anaconda 8 Spoons 10 Reaps 13 Brow 14 Sell 15 Gear 16 Orb 17 Uses 19 Oars 21 Amplitude 23 Tier 24 Dose 26 Mad 27 Ewer 29 Peel 32 Cars 33 Steel 34 Decide 35 Solarium 36 Aspect

DOWN: 1 Pairs 2 Fatal 3 Toss 4 Basra 5 Avow 6 Tenors 9 Porous 11 Eel 12 Plume 13 Besides 15 Gel 16 Ore 18 Spread 20 Adept 21 Aid 22 Tor 23 Tapers 25 Lee 28 Wrest 30 Eerie 31 Llama 32 Cite 33 Star

No 161 - ACROSS: 3 Sense 8 Happy 10 Tried 11 Nip 12 Scour 13 Beneath 15 Poked 18 Ale 19 Virile 21 Alleged 22 Ends 23 Stye 24 Density 26 Nursed 29 Ere 31 Opens 32 Cleaver 34 Aides 35 Men 36 Bears 37 Metre 38 Ether

DOWN: 1 Wanes 2 Appeals 4 Each 5 Stupid 6 Error 7 Revel 9 Pin 12 Steered 14 All 16 Kitty 17 Deter 19 Vessels 20 Beano 21 Adore 23 Steamer 24 Desist 25 Ire 27 Upset 28 Snare 30 Genre 32 Cede 33 Vet

No 162 - ACROSS: 1 Wants 6 Bingo 9 Revised 10 Float 11 Slain 12 Trite 13 Restore 15 Ova 17 Apes 18 Halves 19 Final 20 Chopin 22 Urge 24 Her 25 Blunter 26 Hades 27 Trail 28 Habit 29 Demonic 30 Genes 31 Skein

DOWN: 2 Asleep 3 Traits 4 Set 5 Litre 6 Bestial 7 Idle 8 Grieve 12 Train 13 Ranch 14 Senor 15 Overt 16 Aster 18 Hails 19 Finales 21 Hearse 22 Unpack 23 Gemini 25 Besom 26 Hide 28 His

No 163 - ACROSS: 1 Asylum 7 Applause 8 Asks 10 Arches 11 Trance 14 Hen 16 Issue 17 Aged 19 Leech 21 Socks 22 Fugue 23 Code 26 April 28 Gem 29 Chirpy 30 Camera 31 Open 32 Tributes 33 Tattle

DOWN: 1 Armada 2 Lashed 3 Mass 4 Clerics 5 Burns 6 Melee 8 Ache 9 Ken 12 Ash 13 Cupid 15 Recur 18 Graph 19 Log 20 Eke 21 Sulphur 22 Fir 23 Cement 24 Omen 25 Enable 26 Acute 27 Rigid 28 Gap 30 Cost

No 164 - ACROSS: 4 Tigers 7 Seraglio 8 Trains 10 Erase 13 Deed 14 Rent 15 Romp 16 Sow 17 Odin 19 Atom 21 Animation 23 Apes 24 Tidy 26 Act 27 Mien 29 Even 32 Wand 33 Adore 34 Senile 35 Resolute 36 Attest

DOWN: 1 Aster 2 Organ 3 Ogle 4 Totem 5 Glad 6 Random 9 Repaid 11 Rep 12 Stone 13 Donated 15 Rim 16 Son 18 Dismal 20 Toyed 21 Apt 22 Tin 23 Accent 25 Per 28 Inert 30 Vogue 31 Never 32 Wise 33 Avon

No 165 - ACROSS: 3 Brats 8 Water 10 Eerie 11 Cos 12 Stamp 13 Propels 15 Pause 18 Ire 19 Teller 21 Striker 22 Rune 23 Nero 24 Shudder 26 Slight 29 Rue 31 Solar 32 Fiddler 34 Panel 35 Law 36 Seven 37 Repel 38 Skill

DOWN: 1 Nacre 2 Respite 4 Rots 5 Temper 6 Sepal 7 Rinse 9 Too 12 Sleight 14 Err 16 Ulcer 17 Error 19 Tendril 20 Dross 21 Snail 23 Needles 24 Shrank 25 Dud 27 Loves 28 Gapes 30 Sewer 32 Feel 33 Lap

No 166 - ACROSS: 1 Bliss 6 Farce 9 Tippler 10 Start 11 Scent 12 Broth 13 Blondes 15 Den 17 Rend 18 Priory 19 Blues 20 Storey 22 Polo 24 Sin 25 Also-ran 26 Acids 27 Perch 28 Aided 29 Respect 30 Lyres 31 Tents

DOWN: 2 Little 3 Strand 4 Sit 5 Spars 6 Festers 7 Arch 8 Canter 12 Belly 13 Brass 14 Onion 15 Donor 16 Nylon 18 Peals 19 Benches 21 Timely 22 Polite 23 Lament 25 Adept 26 Acre 28 Act

No 167 - ACROSS: 1 Plasma 7 Relevant 8 Omit 10 Lyrics 11 Matter 14 Ate 16 Tiers 17 Able 19 Rupee 21 Ropes 22 Fewer 23 Prey 26 Shoot 28 Lea 29 Levers 30 Beside 31 Eden 32 Menacing 33 Shapes

DOWN: 1 Paella 2 Semite 3 Arts 4 Berates 5 Haste 6 Stars 8 Oral 9 Ice 12 Tie 13 Erode 15 Dupes 18 Bathe 19 Row 20 Per 21 Retract 22 Foe 23 Peseta 24 Rain 25 Yields 26 Slump 27 Ovine 28 Led 30 Begs

No 168 - ACROSS: 4 Engage 7 Cauldron 8 Shares 10 Large 13 Rued 14 Pier 15 Peer 16 Rep 17 Epic 19 Odes 21 Certified 23 Code 24 Tact 26 Wed 27 Feed 29 Even 32 Lens 33 Crete 34 Report 35 Exposure 36 Stupor

DOWN: 1 Scalp 2 Lucre 3 Edge 4 Ensue 5 Glad 6 Grebes 9 Heroic 11 Ail 12 Greed 13 Recites 15 Pit 16 Red 18 Prefer 20 Deter 21 Cod 22 Fad 23 Cement 25 Wet 28 Enter 30 Venus 31 Never 32 Loop 33 Chop

No 169 - ACROSS: 3 Sport 8 Cocoa 10 Organ 11 Gum 12 Trite 13 Support 15 Andes 18 Awe 19 Attest 21 Treacle 22 Ache 23 Avow 24 Romance 26 Fasten 29 Nee 31 Steel 32 Patrons 34 Panic 35 Big 36 Habit 37 Files 38 Dense

DOWN: 1 Bogus 2 Compare 4 Part 5 Rotate 6 Trent 7 Waves 9 Cup 12 Treason 14 Owe 16 Delve 17 Stows 19 Almanac 20 Waifs 21 Those 23 Acerbic 24 Relate 25 Net 27 Atlas 28 Tepid 30 Anger 32 Pigs 33 Oil

No 170 - ACROSS: 1 Crest 6 Loved 9 Towered 10 After 11 Tense 12 Spots 13 Bellows 15 Sew 17 Axis 18 Unwise 19 Being 20 Retort 22 Aver 24 Ass 25 Slivers 26 Stake 27 Depot 28 Timid 29 Flirted 30 Smite 31 Aspen

DOWN: 2 Reflex 3 Steals 4 Tor 5 Helps 6 Letting 7 Odes 8 Ensues 12 Sweet 13 Basra 14 Lists 15 Sieve 16 Wears 18 Uncle 19 Brittle 21 Esteem 22 Avoids 23 Ermine 25 Skirt 26 Soft 28 Tea

No 171 - ACROSS: 1 Tundra 7 Strangle 8 Seek 10 Whelks 11 Kipper 14 Ale 16 Needs 17 Lots 19 Paper 21 Vices 22 Motet 23 Sate 26 Spool 28 Eli 29 Nimbus 30 Evaded 31 Nets 32 Pondered 33 Sister

DOWN: 1 Trowel 2 Dwells 3 Asks 4 Ravines 5 Agape 6 Seers 8 Seat 9 Eke 12 Per 13 Edict 15 Laces 18 Okapi 19 Pit 20 Pet 21 Volumes 22 Mob 23 Slates 24 Aids 25 Endear 26 Snipe 27 Omens 28 Eve 30 Ends

No 172 - ACROSS: 4 Safest 7 Reproach 8 Editor 10 Stool 13 Veer 14 Till 15 Ain't 16 Bet 17 Ills 19 Ewer 21 Avalanche 23 Fret 24 Gate 26 Tic 27 Eden 29 Lows 32 Onus 33 Skill 34 Ducats 35 Thunders 36 Lashes

DOWN: 1 Trust 2 Spool 3 Tool 4 Sheen 5 Fair 6 Shower 9 Detect 11 Tin 12 Olive 13 Visages 15 All 16 Bee 18 Latent 20 Whelk 21 Arc 22 Nan 23 Fibula 25 Owl 28 Dusts 30 Oiled 31 Slash 32 Oath 33 Send

No 173 - ACROSS: 3 Drops 8 Rebel 10 Apron 11 Bat 12 Sabre 13 Radical 15 Andes 18 Roc 19 Oddest 21 Reshape 22 Rues 23 Dill 24 Utensil 26 Clamps 29 Air 31 Tapas 32 Licence 34 Never 35 Cur 36 Blunt 37 Utter 38 Aside

DOWN: 1 Debar 2 Retires 4 Real 5 Parade 6 Spend 7 Hopes 9 Bad 12 Sachets 14 Cos 16 Devil 17 Still 19 Open-air 20 Tract 21 Recap 23 Directs 24 Upsets 25 Sic 27 Ladle 28 Manna 30 Screw 32 Lead 33 Nut

No 174 - ACROSS: 1 Crave 6 Ready 9 Averted 10 Stone 11 Cents 12 Begin 13 Sectors 15 Sin 17 Pray 18 Facile 19 Final 20 Cavern 22 Scar 24 Ere 25 Happens 26 Annul 27 Suing 28 Aisle 29 Neglect 30 Ideas 31 Tears

DOWN: 2 Rotter 3 Vanity 4 Eve 5 Tries 6 Recital 7 Eden 8 Detail 12 Brain 13 Space 14 Carve 15 Since 16 Nears 18 Fatal 19 Fringes 21 Around 22 Sprite 23 Antler 25 Hurls 26 Anna 28 Act

No 175 - ACROSS: 1 Slopes 7 Pictured 8 Plea 10 Feeler 11 Coyote 14 Gel 16 Lemur 17 Last 19 Tells 21 Ropes 22 Remit 23 Mess 26 Dream 28 Cod 29 Editor 30 Bulges 31 Epee 32 Skeleton 33 Dither

DOWN: 1 Sinful 2 Pellet 3 Spar 4 Strolls 5 Groom 6 Adder 8 Pegs 9 Eel 12 Yes 13 Turns 15 Tepid 18 Award 19 Tom 20 Let 21 Removed 22 Rat 23 Molest 24 Edge 25 Sister 26 Dense 27 Eider 28 Cup 30 Bend

No 176 - ACROSS: 4 Artist 7 Catacomb 8 Banter 10 Mints 13 Robe 14 Path 15 Rota 16 Apt 17 Edit 19 City 21 Premature 23 Seem 24 Task 26 Opt 27 User 29 Edge 32 Ores 33 Ideal 34 Barren 35 Sapphire 36 Unglue

DOWN: 1 Scamp 2 Stunt 3 Aces 4 Abbot 5 Tune 6 Sleepy 9 Abacus 11 Ian 12 There 13 Rotates 15 Rim 16 Ate 18 Demure 20 Irked 21 Pet 22 Tar 23 Sprain 25 Aga 21 Sense 30 Debit 31 Elder 32 Oral 33 Imps

No 177 - ACROSS: 3 Loner 8 Funny 10 Beast 11 Mix 12 Probe 13 Rapiers 15 Idles 18 Ore 19 Inside 21 Cursing 22 Hers 23 Dial 24 Revered 26 Rapped 29 Gel 31 Posed 32 Tedious 34 Sewer 35 Gun 36 State 37 Shrew 38 Smart

DOWN: 1 Human 2 Anxious 4 Oars 5 Ebbing 6 Reeds 7 Asked 9 Nip 12 Pressed 14 Err 16 Livid 17 Sells 19 Integer 20 Sharp 21 Crops 23 Delight 24 Redeem 25 Red 27 Aorta 28 Pests 30 Runes 32 Tear 33 Our

No 178 - ACROSS: 1 Stage 6 Cells 9 Ramadan 10 Sneer 11 Piano 12 Timid 13 Testers 15 Hen 17 Imps 18 Safety 19 Spool 20 Relate 22 Solo 24 Ant 25 Broaden 26 Truly 27 Nadir 28 Binds 29 Repairs 30 Ceded 31 Atone

DOWN: 2 Tandem 3 Greets 4 Ear 5 Saris 6 Capital 7 Enid 8 Linnet 12 Tripe 13 Tiara 14 Spilt 15 Herod 16 Nylon 18 Sorry 19 Stirred 21 Engage 22 Sadist 23 Leaden 25 Bleak 26 Tire 28 Bra

No 179 - ACROSS: 1 Pencil 7 Airedale 8 Arts 10 Limpet 11 Rotate 14 Pen 16 Value 17 Rust 19 Tower 21 Voter 22 Rated 23 Rare 26 Sepal 28 Gem 29 Erotic 30 Hovels 31 Eden 32 Untangle 33 Delete

DOWN: 1 Pallor 2 Carpet 3 Last 4 Recover 5 Fatal 6 Melee 8 Amps 9 Ten 12 Tar 13 Tutor 15 Motet 18 Utter 19 Tot 20 Wed 21 Valiant 22 Rat 23 Reveal 24 Amen 25 Ensure 26 Serum 27 Posts 28 God 30 Heed

No 180 - ACROSS: 4 Peters 7 Relegate 8 Enable 10 Space 13 Grow 14 Pisa 15 Pest 16 Ask 17 Real 19 Itch 21 Avalanche 23 Apes 24 Tier 26 Act 27 Tail 29 Open 32 Fern 33 Swine 34 Molars 35 Overcome 36 Astern

DOWN: 1 Crisp 2 Pleas 3 Ague 4 Peers 5 Thaw 6 Relish 9 Notice 11 Pit 12 Carve 13 Gelatin 15 Pal 16 Ace 18 Easter 20 Throw 21 Apt 22 Nil 23 Across 25 Pen 28 Arson 30 Pilot 31 Never 32 Fate 33 Sort

No 181 - ACROSS: 3 Grate 8 Coven 10 Enter 11 Tic 12 Calms 13 Comical 15 Putty 18 Tor 19 Please 21 Respire 22 Aver 23 Tell 24 Stripes 26 Inures 29 Run 31 Siren 32 Sit down 34 Mince 35 Inn 36 Frail 37 Sneer 38 Tears

DOWN: 1 Rotor 2 Reciter 4 Real 5 Temple 6 Ensue 7 Seats 9 Vim 12 Carpets 14 Cos 16 Takes 17 Yells 19 Prairie 20 Basis 21 Recur 23 Tending 24 Senile 25 Put 27 Nitre 28 Remit 30 Owned 32 Scar 33 One

No 182 - ACROSS: 1 Abuse 6 Radio 9 Problem 10 Stare 11 Vital 12 Lurid 13 Parapet 15 Fir 17 Enid 18 Reduce 19 Avoid 20 Create 22 Cede 24 Eat 25 Citadel 26 Beard 27 Scorn 28 Augur 29 Adamant 30 Edits 31 Tents

DOWN: 2 Batman 3 Spread 4 Ere 5 About 6 Reviled 7 Amid 8 Italic 12 Leave 13 Pence 14 Rivet 15 Fused 16 Revel 18 Rigid 19 Attends 21 Rancid 22 Canute 23 Defect 25 Crime 26 Brat 28 Ant

No 183 - ACROSS: 1 Placed 7 Emergent 8 Flee 10 Scaled 11 Dilute 14 Col 16 Total 17 Stew 19 Tenet 21 Cower 22 Comet 23 Fret 26 Sitar 28 Boa 29 Carton 30 Margin 31 Urge 32 Respects 33 Titter

DOWN: 1 Prises 2 Callow 3 Deed 4 Arbiter 5 Rebut 6 Steel 8 Face 9 Eel 12 Lot 13 Table 15 Fewer 18 Tibia 19 Tom 20 Net 21 Coronet 22 Cat 23 Forget 24 Rage 25 Tender 26 Scare 27 Trust 28 Bar 30 Must

No 184 - ACROSS: 4 Happen 7 Mosquito 8 Precis 10 Treat 13 Reek 14 Eons 15 Less 16 Ace 17 Hail 19 Isle 21 Rectangle 23 Zinc 24 Tone 26 Beg 27 Ever 29 Edge 32 Ones 33 Spool 34 Allots 35 Trombone 36 Stress

DOWN: 1 Smite 2 Aspen 3 Bust 4 Hopes 5 Peek 6 Evince 9 Resign 11 Row 12 Ashen 13 Relates 15 Lit 16 Ale 18 Accent 20 Sleep 21 Rig 22 Nor 23 Zealot 25 Ago 28 Vests 30 Donor 31 Elder 32 Ooze 33 Same

No 185 - ACROSS: 3 Spade 8 Ascot 10 Exits 11 Tom 12 Tribe 13 Respire 15 Armed 18 Ere 19 Attire 21 Treadle 22 Rare 23 Shut 24 Coronet 26 Tendon 29 Hue 31 Elder 32 Bottles 34 Anvil 35 Her 36 Style 37 Ledge 38 Troop

DOWN: 1 Aster 2 Compere 4 Pure 5 Debate 6 Exert 7 Otter 9 Cos 12 Treason 14 Ire 16 Might 17 Dents 19 Alcohol 20 Trite 21 Trend 23 Seethed 24 Corner 25 Nut 27 Elate 28 Dealt 30 Serge 32 Biro 33 Led

No 186 - ACROSS: 1 Smear 6 Swore 9 Beguile 10 Dread 11 Ensue 12 Leant 13 Alludes 15 Vet 17 Lees 18 Deride 19 Rotor 20 Happen 22 Peas 24 Ass 25 Reverse 26 Colon 27 Altar 28 Lurid 29 Stripes 30 Omits 31 Tents

DOWN: 2 Morale 3 Abacus 4 Red 5 Rules 6 Slender 7 Went 8 Roused 12 Lemon 13 Alpha 14 Leaps 15 Viper 16 Tense 18 Dozen 19 Reports 21 Asylum 22 Peruse 23 Assist 25 Robin 26 Cast 28 Let

No 187 - ACROSS: 1 Cosset 7 Envelope 8 Sits 10 Zealot 11 Resent 14 Got 16 Rises 17 Star 19 Never 21 Sited 22 Helix 23 Teem 26 Sweet 28 Row 29 Plants 30 Duress 31 Reps 32 Operetta 33 Gadget

DOWN: 1 Crazes 2 Sailor 3 Test 4 Revered 5 Copes 6 Feats 8 Saga 9 Tot 12 Sir 13 Nerve 15 Fetid 18 Trawl 19 Nil 20 Vex 21 Settled 22 Hen 23 Torpid 24 Ewes 25 Mascot 26 Spool 27 Eager 28 Rue 30 Drag

No 188 - ACROSS: 4 Called 7 Guerilla 8 Narrow 10 Twist 13 Robe 14 Each 15 Beer 16 Ova 17 Open 19 Able 21 Pretended 23 Rots 24 Goes 26 Hit 27 Tied 29 Omen 32 Elms 33 Smile 34 Upkeep 35 Elevator 36 Vessel

DOWN: 1 Agate 2 Relic 3 List 4 Canoe 5 Lure 6 Evolve 9 Abrade 11 Wan 12 Short 13 Reneges 15 Bet 16 Old 18 Pestle 20 Besom 21 Pot 22 Nod 23 Ripple 25 Gel 28 Impel 30 Misty 31 Nears 32 Eels 33 Save

No 189 - ACROSS: 3 Enact 8 Rebel 10 Arson 11 Fur 12 Swine 13 Desists 15 Taste 18 Via 19 Tether 21 Settler 22 Bets 23 Spud 24 Sterile 26 Effete 29 Ale 31 Defer 32 Militia 34 Risen 35 Gin 36 Aspic 37 Cheer 38 Ether

DOWN: 1 Refer 2 Derives 4 News 5 Canter 6 Treat 7 Route 9 Bus 12 Statute 14 Sit 16 Shape 17 Erode 19 Terrain 20 Ebbed 21 Staff 23 Sleighs 24 Strict 25 Ill 27 Feast 28 Eerie 30 Fines 32 Mere 33 Tie

No 190 - ACROSS: 1 Ogres 6 Stash 9 Striker 10 Fancy 11 Reset 12 Serve 13 Smarten 15 Sic 17 West 18 Snatch 19 Agent 20 Avenue 22 Seam 24 Tin 25 Grapple 26 Smile 27 Slate 28 Bison 29 Inhabit 30 Snort 31 Tends

DOWN: 2 Gramme 3 Escort 4 Sty 5 Siren 6 Servant 7 Tree 8 Scenic 12 Serge 13 Sweat 14 Ashen 15 Steep 16 Chime 18 Snare 19 Augment 21 Violin 22 Sprite 23 Almond 25 Gleam 26 Stir 28 Bit

No 191 - ACROSS: 1 Crease 7 Withdraw 8 Wipe 10 Crises 11 Pledge 14 Set 16 Trend 17 Eden 19 Wager 21 Hover 22 Nonet 23 Ache 26 Steer 28 All 29 Potent 30 Ribald 31 Amen 32 Tainting 33 Entire

DOWN: 1 Circle 2 Arisen 3 Ewes 4 Shelter 5 Crude 6 Owned 8 Wise 9 Pet 12 Err 13 Gnash 15 Saved 18 Ditto 19 Won 20 Get 21 Hornets 22 Nee 23 Albert 24 Clan 25 Endure 26 Spite 27 Ethic 28 Aim 30 Rage

No 192 - ACROSS: 4 Tabled 7 Walkover 8 Arrest 10 Slash 13 Died 14 Tent 15 Felt 16 Let 17 Opal 19 Awed 21 Clarified 23 Doer 24 Gone 26 Bed 27 Ache 29 Drab 32 Edit 33 Aside 34 Turret 35 Ethereal 36 Severs

DOWN: 1 Twist 2 Clean 3 Moth 4 Trail 5 Bard 6 Ensued 9 Retain 11 Lea 12 Stole 13 Delight 15 Far 16 Led 18 Parade 20 Weeds 21 Cod 22 Foe 23 Delude 25 Lad 28 Cites 30 Riled 31 Belly 32 Erse 33 Axed

No 193 - ACROSS: 3 Blade 8 Rogue 10 Rabbi 11 Cab 12 Stoat 13 Rosette 15 Geese 18 Lea 19 Bonnet 21 Elation 22 Idea 23 Solo 24 Streaky 26 Stifle 29 Dry 31 There 32 Combine 34 Odium 35 Log 36 Aging 37 Dunes 38 Decay

DOWN: 1 Cocoa 2 Rubella 4 Late 5 Dragon 6 Eaten 7 Abuse 9 Gas 12 Statute 14 Tea 16 Envoy 17 Ethos 19 Boredom 20 First 21 Eerie 23 Sky blue 24 Sledge 25 Arm 27 Thigh 28 Frond 30 Angel 32 Cuba 33 Ion

No 194 - ACROSS: 1 Glass 6 Pitch 9 Placard 10 Hurry 11 Aorta 12 Until 13 Against 15 Bus 17 Rein 18 Finish 19 Agile 20 Allege 22 Ache 24 See 25 Peaches 26 Steer 27 Villa 28 Aural 29 Attains 30 Unite 31 Tends

DOWN: 2 Lounge 3 Sprain 4 Sly 5 Scent 6 Prairie 7 Idol 8 Citrus 12 Usage 13 Areas 14 Aisle 15 Birch 16 Shoes 18 Flier 19 Agitate 21 Lesion 22 Accuse 23 Herald 25 Petal 26 Slat 28 Ant

No 195 - ACROSS: 1 Mystic 7 Arpeggio 8 Asti 10 Person 11 Pennon 14 Cup 16 Rigid 17 Ache 19 Steal 21 Vital 22 Caper 23 Beds 26 Shear 28 Fed 29 Permit 30 Punish 31 Unit 32 Alsatian 33 Tandem

DOWN: 1 Myopia 2 Tissue 3 Cain 4 Several 5 Aging 6 Mound 8 Arch 9 Top 12 Nil 13 Oiled 15 Utter 18 Cache 19 Sip 20 Ear 21 Variety 22 Cam 23 Benign 24 Edit 25 Schism 26 Spear 27 Erase 28 Fun 30 Punt

No 196 - ACROSS: 4 Slogan 7 Transmit 8 Ocelot 10 Elite 13 Gran 14 Peri 15 Army 16 Asp 17 Beta 19 Mile 21 Celebrate 23 Hare 24 Bone 26 Par 27 Crew 29 Musk 32 Stud 33 Aspen 34 Sadism 35 Mnemonic 36 Parody

DOWN: 1 Steep 2 Tapir 3 Isle 4 Storm 5 Oven 6 Arouse 9 Cayman 11 Let 12 Tiber 13 Grabbed 15 Ate 16 Ale 18 Elects 20 Items 21 Car 22 Row 23 Havana 25 Use 28 Rummy 30 Upend 31 Knock 32 Silo 33 Aims

No 197 - ACROSS: 3 Slump 8 Navel 10 Aisle 11 Tin 12 Beats 13 Chatter 15 Utter 18 Row 19 Create 21 Fatigue 22 Hull 23 Etui 24 Achieve 26 Garish 29 Ore 31 Spent 32 Furnace 34 Tunes 35 Ire 36 Cadet 37 Incas 38 Revel

DOWN: 1 Lathe 2 Central 4 Leer 5 Mature 6 Piste 7 Sleet 9 Via 12 Bewitch 14 Tot 16 Taste 17 Remit 19 Curious 20 Thugs 21 Flare 23 Evening 24 Astute 25 Err 27 Appal 28 Inter 30 Ocean 32 Fete 33 Arc

No 198 - ACROSS: 1 Ashen 6 Cider 9 Riddles 10 Sisal 11 Rigid 12 Brats 13 Aileron 15 Amp 17 Stir 18 Ritual 19 Aspen 20 Elicit 22 Suit 24 Rat 25 Regards 26 Impel 27 Fence 28 Bigot 29 Onerous 30 Stint 31 Stash

DOWN: 2 Spirit 3 Eraser 4 Nil 5 Adorn 6 Certain 7 Isis 8 Enigma 12 Boast 13 Aster 14 Licit 15 Augur 16 Plots 18 Repel 19 Ailment 21 Lament 22 Sadist 23 Idiots 25 Rears 26 Icon 28 Bus

No 199 - ACROSS: 1 Shears 7 Indecent 8 Flat 10 Cruise 11 Stigma 14 Rep 16 Annul 17 Rays 19 Prank 21 Front 22 Aloud 23 Buds 26 Prose 28 Pun 29 Asthma 30 Larder 31 Also 32 Aversion 33 Earned

DOWN: 1 Soccer 2 Allies 3 Site 4 Sextant 5 Reign 6 Steal 8 Fury 9 Asp 12 Ink 13 Muted 15 Proud 18 Avers 19 Pro 20 And 21 Flemish 22 Ash 23 Bursar 24 Undo 25 Surged 26 Pagan 27 Otter 28 Pal 30 Lane

No 200 - ACROSS: 4 Lodged 7 Macaroni 8 Lesson 10 Gorse 13 Sack 14 Area 15 Inch 16 Age 17 Memo 19 Ouch 21 Component 23 Wasp 24 Zest 26 Red 27 Lied 29 Iron 32 Boss 33 Close 34 Always 35 Ultimate 36 Change

DOWN: 1 Omega 2 Score 3 Free 4 Lilac 5 Dusk 6 Enough 9 Echoes 11 Orb 12 Samos 13 Snoozes 15 Imp 16 Act 18 Employ 20 Until 21 Cad 22 Ned 23 Wealth 25 Cos 28 Issue 30 Royal 31 Never 32 Barn 33 Clip

No 201 - ACROSS: 3 Feral 8 Smear 10 Sated 11 Err 12 Feast 13 Clamber 15 Eerie 18 Fan 19 Stroll 21 Cuddles 22 Real 23 Semi 24 Snooped 26 Baring 29 Nee 31 Singe 32 Adamant 34 Leans 35 Ire 36 Tenor 37 Entry 38 Osier

DOWN: 1 Smell 2 Harmful 4 Ever 5 Assets 6 Later 7 Devil 9 Era 12 Fending 14 Bad 16 Roved 17 Elvis 19 Seconds 20 Cribs 21 Cairn 23 Seeming 24 Sneers 25 Pea 27 Aided 28 Igloo 30 Inert 32 Ante 33 Art

No 202 - ACROSS: 1 Basil 6 Badge 9 Miniver 10 Scope 11 Sigma 12 Aphid 13 Leaders 15 Ale 17 Urge 18 Agreed 19 False 20 Enters 22 Rise 24 See 25 Redeems 26 Begin 27 Arias 28 Giddy 29 Literal 30 Drama 31 Peter

DOWN: 2 Archer 3 Impede 4 Lie 5 Wisps 6 Besiege 7 Arid 8 Gamble 12 Areas 13 Lutes 14 Agate 15 Aerie 16 Edges 18 Aspen 19 Freesia 21 Nearer 22 Revile 23 Smudge 25 River 26 Balm 28 Gap

No 203 - ACROSS: 1 Sinful 7 Invented 8 Eels 10 Gullet 11 Giving 14 Sea 16 Genie 17 Acer 19 Faint 21 Fells 22 Dowel 23 Cats 26 Upper 28 Dim 29 Street 30 Diners 31 Open 32 Grudging 33 Eraser

DOWN: 1 Stigma 2 Feeler 3 List 4 Resigns 5 Stain 6 Adage 8 Else 9 Lea 12 Vet 13 Night 15 Tales 18 Crypt 19 Few 20 Ill 21 Foreign 22 Dee 23 Cinema 24 Amen 25 Sister 26 Usage 27 Proud 28 Dip 30 Doge

No 204 - ACROSS: 4 Impure 7 Needless 8 Sultan 10 Perky 13 Aunt 14 Solo 15 Fret 16 Top 17 Roar 19 Iron 21 Bartender 23 Tuna 24 Says 26 Urn 27 City 29 Toes 32 Elms 33 Aspic 34 Instep 35 Exercise 36 Menial

DOWN: 1 Snaps 2 Pearl 3 Slay 4 Issue 5 Pelt 6 Reason 9 Untidy 11 Eon 12 Koran 13 Arrests 15 Fat 16 Tor 18 Oracle 20 Rests 21 Bun 22 Nay 23 Trance 25 Lei 28 Impel 30 Optic 31 Screw 32 Etui 33 Airs

No 205 - ACROSS: 3 Bluff 8 Drain 10 Rebut 11 Oil 12 Basil 13 Boredom 15 Doubt 18 Nun 19 Cantor 21 Scenery 22 Pile 23 Neat 24 Stammer 26 Crocus 29 See 31 Super 32 Bonding 34 Demon 35 Lot 36 Label 37 Denim 38 Dying

DOWN: 1 Brood 2 Silence 4 Loam 5 Friday 6 Felon 7 Jumbo 9 Air 12 Bonnets 14 Due 16 Utter 17 Truth 19 Crimson 20 Specs 21 Sloop 23 Needles 24 Surely 25 Men 27 Rural 28 Ceded 30 Untie 32 Boon 33 Ion

No 206 - ACROSS: 1 Cress 6 Stale 9 Chalice 10 Stray 11 Angry 12 Adult 13 Precede 15 Cam 17 Here 18 Relate 19 Petal 20 Teeter 22 Bear 24 Old 25 Divorce 26 Livid 27 Optic 28 Paris 29 Raccoon 30 Sedan 31 Tying

DOWN: 2 Retire 3 Scarce 4 Shy 5 Blade 6 Scalpel 7 Tent 8 Lariat 12 Adder 13 Photo 14 Erred 15 Cater 16 Metre 18 Rapid 19 Pelican 21 Elapse 22 Botany 23 Action 25 Ditch 26 Lira 28 Pot

No 207 - ACROSS: 1 Artful 7 Inundate 8 Rope 10 Aboard 11 Pirate 14 Sty 16 Poker 17 Toes 19 Rigid 21 Saved 22 Lupin 23 Teem 26 Oriel 28 Car 29 Sanity 30 Tulips 31 Open 32 Eternity 33 Settle

DOWN: 1 Aghast 2 Floats 3 Lied 4 Insipid 5 Kayak 6 Never 8 Rose 9 Pry 12 Rod 13 Tense 15 Civil 18 Opera 19 Rap 20 Gen 21 Sultana 22 Lei 23 Talent 24 Erin 25 Mosque 26 Osier 27 Inter 28 Cup 30 Toys

No 208 - ACROSS: 4 Clammy 7 Onlooker 8 Estate 10 Emend 13 Asti 14 Aura 15 Alto 16 Ill 17 Cast 19 Race 21 Archenemy 23 Fret 24 Rode 26 Pet 27 Iced 29 Nous 32 Avid 33 Adore 34 Elated 35 Edginess 36 Tremor

DOWN: 1 Bohea 2 Older 3 Hood 4 Crest 5 Anti 6 Mettle 9 Stored 11 Mug 12 Nacre 13 Altered 15 Ash 16 Icy 18 Active 20 Amend 21 Art 22 Nod 23 Feeler 25 Fur 28 Cider 30 Oozed 31 Sense 32 Atom 33 Acid

No 209 - ACROSS: 3 Cross 8 Birch 10 Apple 11 Duo 12 Brave 13 Ignoble 15 Ingot 18 Toe 19 Inters 21 Meaning 22 Hear 23 Rear 24 Recedes 26 Ousted 29 Rod 31 Steed 32 Attuned 34 Needs 35 Cot 36 Tease 37 Ceded 38 Ember

DOWN: 1 Midge 2 Scooter 4 Rare 5 Saving 6 Spent 7 Floor 9 Run 12 Blended 14 Boa 16 Genes 17 Tsars 19 Inserts 20 Chaos 21 Manse 23 Reduced 24 Redeem 25 Dot 27 Utter 28 Tense 30 Meter 32 Adze 33 Nod

No 210 - ACROSS: 1 Float 6 Erode 9 Disease 10 Cramp 11 Carve 12 Album 13 Century 15 Arm 17 Ores 18 Bounty 19 Tunes 20 Endure 22 Fear 24 Day 25 Catarrh 26 Siren 27 Great 28 Ether 29 Foliage 30 Owner 31 Orate

DOWN: 2 Larder 3 Admits 4 Tip 5 Belly 6 Escudos 7 Ream 8 Divert 12 Argue 13 Coped 14 Needy 15 Anger 16 Myrrh 18 Began 19 Traitor 21 Narrow 22 Faster 23 Ardent 25 Celia 26 Safe 28 Ego

No 211 - ACROSS: 1 Random 7 Outhouse 8 Pits 10 Droves 11 Snares 14 Sea 16 Title 17 Reel 19 Tutor 21 Datum 22 Linen 23 Dart 26 Sages 28 Fan 29 Please 30 Runner 31 Urge 32 Romantic 33 Keeper

DOWN: 1 Raider 2 Drivel 3 Moss 4 Phantom 5 Quart 6 Lease 8 Pose 9 Tea 12 Air 13 Elder 15 Muted 18 Equal 19 Tan 20 Tun 21 Dissent 22 Lea 23 Dangle 24 Anne 25 Terror 26 Spire 27 Germs 28 Fur 30 Ruck

No 212 - ACROSS: 4 Submit 7 Redolent 8 Across 10 Stage 13 Iran 14 Tell 15 Ants 16 Few 17 Oars 19 Used 21 Castigate 23 Lots 24 Pole 26 Bit 27 Arid 29 Edit 32 Lied 33 Spoor 34 Cavils 35 Invented 36 Adjoin

DOWN: 1 Crust 2 Ideal 3 Clue 4 Start 5 Barn 6 Issued 9 Casual 11 Teg 12 Gloat 13 Insipid 15 Art 16 Fee 18 Assail 20 Steep 21 Cot 22 God 23 Lizard 25 Rio 28 Resin 30 Dotty 31 Trade 32 Lido 33 Seem

No 213 - ACROSS: 3 Flaws 8 Mummy 10 Inter 11 Lei 12 Cable 13 Mention 15 Tears 18 Arm 19 Peruse 21 Stepped 22 Rope 23 Rung 24 Blunder 26 Idlers 29 Ail 31 Litre 32 Indents 34 React 35 Air 36 Havoc 37 Aspen 38 Rhino

DOWN: 1 Rules 2 Imitate 4 Lean 5 Wilted 6 Sneer 7 Fears 9 Men 12 Compels 14 Ire 16 Augur 17 Sedge 19 Pennant 20 Frail 21 Spilt 23 Release 24 Breech 25 Did 27 Divan 28 Error 30 Strew 32 Icon 33 Nip

No 214 - ACROSS: 1 Close 6 Gaunt 9 Clement 10 Sleek 11 Aorta 12 Storm 13 Resents 15 Act 17 Odes 18 Dealer 19 Sited 20 Amazed 22 Urge 24 Sin 25 Stunted 26 Booty 27 Cairn 28 Pixie 29 Adhered 30 Jeans 31 Gypsy

DOWN: 2 Lolled 3 Scenes 4 Elk 5 Emits 6 Gnarled 7 Atom 8 Notice 12 Staid 13 Rotas 14 Sedan 15 Alert 16 Tried 18 Deity 19 Seconds 21 Mirage 22 Untidy 23 Genius 25 Steel 26 Bran 28 Peg

No 215 - ACROSS: 1 Scared 7 Opponent 8 Even 10 Throne 11 Parson 14 Old 16 Title 17 East 19 Fried 21 Peers 22 Break 23 Reek 26 Agree 28 Tar 29 Beetle 30 Raisin 31 Apse 32 Shedding 33 Endure

DOWN: 1 Subtle 2 Revolt 3 Done 4 Rotates 5 Yeast 6 Stone 8 Eros 9 End 12 Rid 13 Olive 15 Freak 18 Adage 19 Fee 20 Irk 21 Prelude 22 Bet 23 Raised 24 Erse 25 Kindle 26 Abuse 27 Refer 28 Tap 30 Rage

No 216 - ACROSS: 4 Hobnob 7 Virtuoso 8 Scorch 10 Irate 13 Dear 14 Duke 15 Peas 16 Lid 17 Roam 19 Used 21 Implicate 23 Lost 24 Gale 26 Ton 27 Iron 29 Arcs 32 Load 33 Sleep 34 Quaint 35 Taciturn 36 Stormy

DOWN: 1 Avoid 2 Croak 3 Cure 4 Hosea 5 Boor 6 Orchid 9 Casual 11 Rug 12 Terms 13 Demigod 15 Pal 16 Lee 18 Option 20 Steal 21 Ion 22 Can 23 Locust 25 Ace 28 Ratty 30 Recur 31 Spent 32 Liar 33 Spin

No 217 - ACROSS: 3 Shove 8 Trite 10 Alert 11 Ace 12 Alone 13 Operate 15 Icons 18 Apt 19 Astray 21 Stealth 22 Epee 23 Hero 24 Skilful 26 Fights 29 Elm 31 Steer 32 Stymied 34 Aerie 35 Ink 36 Smile 37 Annoy 38 Steep

DOWN: 1 Graph 2 Iterate 4 Hole 5 Vanish 6 Elect 7 Arena 9 Ice 12 Attacks 14 Ape 16 Oriel 17 Synod 19 Athlete 20 Serfs 21 Serge 23 Humming 24 Street 25 Fly 27 Items 28 Heals 30 Pekoe 32 Site 33 Inn

No 218 - ACROSS: 1 Trust 6 Eager 9 Portent 10 Stale 11 Vocal 12 Denim 13 Teacher 15 Pew 17 Idle 18 Cupola 19 Bears 20 Tremor 22 Ache 24 Say 25 mother 26 Clump 27 Flood 28 Tents 29 Measles 30 Adder 31 Etude

DOWN: 2 Rotted 3 Splice 4 Toe 5 Steer 6 Envious 7 Atom 8 Enamel 12 Defer 13 Tints 14 Alley 15 Pouch 16 Waver 18 Cramp 19 Boulder 21 Railed 22 Attest 23 Heated 25 Smash 26 Come 28 Tee

No 219 - ACROSS: 1 Cudgel 7 Aesthete Pawn 10 Stated 11 Appeal 14 Let 16 Padre 17 Deed 19 Comet 21 Coped 22 Tenet 23 Goal 26 Stein 28 Tea 29 Chants 30 Sorrow 31 Lobs 32 Overrate 33 Walrus

DOWN: 1 Cursed 2 Grated 3 Land 4 Stopped 5 Ceded 6 Belle 8 Pale 9 Wet 12 Pat 13 Aroma 15 Moped 18 Earth 19 Con 20 Met 21 Century 22 Tin 23 Gerbil 24 Oars 25 Lowers 26 Scoop 27 Easel 28 Too 30 Slew

No 220 - ACROSS: 4 Zodiac 7 Overture 8 Blends 10 Glare 13 Dram 14 Sore 15 Gear 16 Run 17 Font 19 Dear 21 Recurrent 23 Mere 24 Aura 26 Bid 27 Lace 29 Clip 32 Fort 33 State 34 Admits 35 Obsolete 36 Sermon

DOWN: 1 Gongs 2 Debar 3 Stye 4 Zebra 5 Deem 6 Ardour 9 Larder 11 Low 12 Refer 13 Detract 15 Gnu 16 Rat 18 Ocelot 20 Enact 21 Red 22 Rue 23 Middle 25 Bit 28 Arson 30 Later 31 Peter 32 Firm 33 Soon

No 221 - ACROSS: 3 Parts 8 Tepee 10 Actor 11 Cos 12 Cable 13 Auditor 15 Enjoy 18 Dam 19 Entire 21 Ferment 22 Bias 23 Rear 24 Snooped 26 Select 29 Rip 31 Enter 32 Ostrich 34 Ridge 35 Err 36 Tulip 37 Askew 38 Ether

DOWN: 1 Recur 2 Besides 4 Ajar 5 Talent 6 Scent 7 Motor 9 Pod 12 Comment 14 Tar 16 Jibed 17 Yearn 19 Endorse 20 Abuse 21 Fault 23 Repress 24 Script 25 Pit 27 Ennui 28 Eerie 30 Screw 32 Ogle 33 Irk

No 222 - ACROSS: 1 Offer 6 Epees 9 Machine 10 Crypt 11 Traps 12 Skirt 13 Soprano 15 Try 17 Twee 18 Vacate 19 Divot 20 Kennel 22 Soul 24 Ely 25 Debtors 26 Upper 27 Opera 28 Aimed 29 Gimmick 30 Adder 31 Tents

DOWN: 2 Furrow 3 Empire 4 Rat 5 Shako 6 Entreat 7 Pert 8 Expert 12 Snail 13 Stake 14 Penny 15 Taboo 16 Yells 18 Voter 19 Despair 21 Eloped 22 Strike 23 Urgent 25 Deems 26 Urge 28 Act

No 223 - ACROSS: 1 Seldom 7 Invasion 8 Anon 10 Docile 11 Valise 14 Red 16 Cider 17 Seer 19 Fight 21 Vague 22 Moron 23 Shed 26 Assay 28 Lee 29 Dental 30 Carafe 31 Edit 32 Grateful 33 Lustre

DOWN: 1 Shades 2 Denier 3 Mine 4 Panache 5 Vivid 6 Inter 8 Acre 9 Old 12 Lit 13 Serge 15 Bigot 18 Erase 19 Far 20 Gun 21 Voyager 22 Mat 23 Series 24 Heat 25 Dredge 26 Adage 27 Sneak 28 Lad 30 Cell

No 224 - ACROSS: 4 Buffet 7 Particle 8 Scrape 10 Lapse 13 Moan 14 Lisp 15 Lump 16 Ale 17 Ices 19 TASS 21 Ferocious 23 Gale 24 Lord 26 Bad 27 Amen 29 Idea 32 Isis 33 Stair 34 Chosen 35 Crackers 36 Breeze

DOWN: 1 Spill 2 Grips 3 Nice 4 Besom 5 Fern 6 Expels 9 Captor 11 Aim 12 Spiel 13 Muscles 15 Leo 16 Ass 18 Crease 20 Audit 21 Fad 22 Ion 23 Gather 25 Lei 28 Mince 30 Dated 31 Arise 32 Isle 33 Sick

No 225 - ACROSS: 3 Drift 8 Wrath 10 Error 11 Die 12 Stale 13 Redeems 15 Layer 18 Pro 19 Sedate 21 Clatter 22 Aloe 23 Shoe 24 Defiant 26 Poster 29 One 31 Sweat 32 Tuneful 34 Nears 35 Rob 36 Peaks 37 Tepee 38 Stool

DOWN: 1 Order 2 Steeple 4 Rats 5 Feller 6 Tread 7 Nonet 9 Aid 12 Smother 14 Era 16 Yacht 17 Rebel 19 Serious 20 Camps 21 Copse 23 Sneered 24 Detest 25 Ann 27 Owned 28 Tanks 30 Tuber 32 Trio 33 Fop

No 226 - ACROSS: 1 Pleat 6 Aside 9 Connect 10 Tasty 11 Curls 12 Taken 13 Blurred 15 Ate 17 Lets 18 Stored 19 Asses 20 Averse 22 Made 24 Tar 25 Advised 26 Musty 27 Harem 28 Aural 29 Neglect 30 Studs 31 Testy

DOWN: 2 Liable 3 Actors 4 Toy 5 Knead 6 Accents 7 Stun 8 Dilute 12 Tense 13 Bloat 14 Utter 15 Areas 16 Edged 18 Seedy 19 Assumes 21 Vacant 22 Minute 23 Depart 25 Atoll 26 Mend 28 Act

No 227 - ACROSS: 1 Gratis 7 Engaging 8 Rife 10 Gropes 11 Formal 14 Low 16 Lisle 17 Tied 19 Creep 21 Bread 22 Layer 23 Bawl 26 Saris 28 Lac 29 Clothe 30 Barrow 31 Idle 32 Muscular 33 Dry run

DOWN: 1 Gadget 2 Tripod 3 Sees 4 Cajoled 5 Films 6 Agile 8 Role 9 Few 12 Rip 13 Allow 15 Green 18 Ideal 19 Cry 20 Ear 21 Bashful 22 Lit 23 Barley 24 Acre 25 Lawman 26 Scamp 27 Rouse 28 Lad 30 Bird

No 228 - ACROSS: 4 Darned 7 Interior 8 Edicts 10 Seeds 13 Jail 14 Type 15 Suds 16 Art 17 Boon 19 Mice 21 Captivate 23 Tart 24 Pile 26 Orb 27 Idea 29 Make 32 Poor 33 Astir 34 Infant 35 Thousand 36 Sherry

DOWN: 1 First 2 Steep 3 Arms 4 Dread 5 Rail 6 Entire 9 Dismal 11 Eye 12 Debar 13 Juniper 15 Sot 16 Ace 18 Option 20 Items 21 Cab 22 Via 23 Trench 25 Ski 28 Dotty 30 Atlas 31 Erode 32 Pair 33 Ague

No 229 - ACROSS: 3 Erupt 8 Bathe 10 Rally 11 Boa 12 Deter 13 Central 15 Foray 18 Tom 19 Retire 21 Debater 22 Stir 23 Plus 24 Venture 26 Elated 29 Ire 31 Ninon 32 Element 34 Nerve 35 Ill 36 Genie 37 Refer 38 Crane

DOWN: 1 Label 2 Chatter 4 Reel 5 Prefer 6 Tarot 7 Clear 9 Ton 12 Damaged 14 Rob 16 Rifle 17 Yeast 19 Reptile 20 Aspen 21 Divan 23 Premier 24 Veneer 25 Ure 27 Liken 28 Tonic 30 Inlet 32 Even 33 Elf

No 230 - ACROSS: 1 Scars 6 Amble 9 Elusive 10 Silly 11 Issue 12 Arias 13 Shovels 15 Age 17 Here 18 Topper 19 Defer 20 Pieces 22 Bare 24 Err 25 Stalled 26 Booth 27 Snort 28 Snail 29 Aerated 30 Added 31 Ashen

DOWN: 2 Cliche 2 Relive 4 Sly 5 Tsars 6 Aviator 7 Mess 8 Lounge 12 Aloes 13 Shape 14 Order 15 Appal 16 Erred 18 Teeth 19 Devoted 21 Ironed 22 Blends 23 Revile 25 Strap 26 Brae 28 Sea

No 231 - ACROSS: 1 Combat 7 Indicate 8 Cite 10 Larder 11 Statue 14 Ale 16 Agent 17 Robe 19 Polka 21 Belie 22 Dared 23 Sure 26 Organ 28 Bog 29 Verbal 30 Ballad 31 Eddy 32 Radiance 3 Forage

DOWN: 1 Cellar 2 Bridle 3 Tier 4 Mistake 5 Waste 6 Beret 8 Crab 9 Tee 12 Aga 13 Under 15 Roles 18 Outre 19 Per 20 Lid 21 Bananas 22 Dab 23 Solder 24 Ugly 25 Endure 26 Overt 27 Grade 28 Bad 30 Beef

No 232 - ACROSS: 4 Casket 7 Hyacinth 8 Images 10 Spice 13 Flan 14 Solo 15 Wily 16 Age 17 Roan 19 Hide 21 Apprehend 23 Rise 24 Some 26 Rum 27 Rasp 29 Plan 32 Made 33 Stare 34 Unwise 35 Particle 36 Advent

DOWN: 1 Chess 2 Basil 3 Nice 4 Chill 5 Swan 6 Emerge 9 Mayhem 11 Pot 12 Corps 13 Finesse 15 War 16 Add 18 Operas 20 Inept 21 Aim 22 Hop 23 Ruined 25 Bar 28 Adept 30 Larch 31 Never 32 Mine 33 Site

No 233 - ACROSS: 3 Sprat 8 Decay 10 Veins 11 Lot 12 Dozen 13 Matured 15 Rebus 18 Out 19 Astern 21 Sunrise 22 Lies 23 Trek 24 Accused 26 Resent 29 Rod 31 Event 32 Venison 34 Shred 35 Oar 36 Argue 37 Nudge 38 Empty

DOWN: 1 Relax 2 Fatuous 4 Prod 5 Averse 6 Tenet 7 Incur 9 Cot 12 Detract 14 Run 16 Beard 17 Snake 19 Assured 20 Flare 21 Sense 23 Tedious 24 Anthem 25 Son 27 Every 28 Ensue 30 Forge 32 Vest 33 Sad

No 234 - ACROSS: 1 Atlas 6 Given 9 Statues 10 Jetty 11 Limps 12 Texas 13 Pleased 15 Art 17 Rely 18 Dinner 19 Liken 20 Tended 22 Tern 24 End 25 Aspired 26 Atone 27 Witch 28 Atoll 29 Recluse 30 Defer 31 Prude

DOWN: 2 Treble 3 Astray 4 Sty 5 Steed 6 Gelatin 7 Isis 8 Expire 12 Tepid 13 Prate 14 Eland 15 Anger 16 Trend 18 Dense 19 Leather 21 Entire 22 Titter 23 Reeled 25 Angle 26 Acre 28 Asp

No 235 - ACROSS: 1 Warmth 7 Once-over 8 Also 10 Failed 11 Rotted 14 Let 16 Teems 17 Last 19 Bohea 21 Coped 22 Rowan 23 Adds 26 Prior 28 Pre 29 Streak 30 Caress 31 Aped 32 Linoleum 33 Patter

DOWN: 1 Wilful 2 Mallet 3 Hood 4 Denoted 5 Ovate 6 Grids 8 Ails 9 Set 12 Tea 13 Emend 15 Topaz 18 Alert 19 Bow 20 Hen 21 Coracle 22 Roe 23 Arrest 24 Deed 25 Sister 26 Psalm 27 Irene 28 Pap 30 Camp

No 236 - ACROSS: 4 Tights 7 Kohlrabi 8 Abroad 10 Pleat 13 Oral 14 Serf 15 Opal 16 Act 17 Tore 19 Line 21 Repentant 23 Sore 24 Aide 26 Old 27 Rain 29 Rags 32 Lair 33 Straw 34 Duress 35 Luncheon 36 Chaste

DOWN: 1 Skips 2 Cheer 3 Fret 4 Tiara 5 Girl 6 Trance 9 Ballad 11 Lea 12 After 13 Open-air 15 Ore 16 Ant 18 Operas 20 Inert 21 Rod 22 Tin 23 Sleuth 25 Aga 28 Aisle 30 Armed 31 Swine 32 Less 33 Sick

No 237 - ACROSS: 3 Askew 8 Bales 10 Galas 11 Got 12 Heart 13 Deposit 15 Eerie 18 Kid 19 Stress 21 Detests 22 Iron 23 Idea 24 Custody 26 Dances 29 Tie 31 Sugar 32 Belated 34 Miner 35 Let 36 Mules 37 Plead 38 Learn

DOWN: 1 Lager 2 Betoken 4 Suet 5 Egrets 6 Water 7 Taxis 9 Lop 12 Hideous 14 Sit 16 Ready 17 Essay 19 Stutter 20 Minds 21 Doing 23 Ideally 24 Cerise 25 Oil 27 Augur 28 Camel 30 Petal 32 Beer 33 Tee

No 238 - ACROSS: 1 Crisp 6 Acrid 9 Tarnish 10 Start 11 Tabby 12 Scoop 13 Predict 15 Ebb 17 Ante 18 Snivel 19 Brand 20 Sudden 22 Acts 24 Ere 25 Spectre 26 Sifts 27 White 28 Amend 29 Average 30 Snare 31 Ended

DOWN: 2 Return 3 Stride 4 Pat 5 Enact 6 Astound 7 Chap 8 Imbibe 12 Scorn 13 Passe 14 Etude 15 Evict 16 Blase 18 Snaps 19 Believe 21 Urchin 22 Acumen 23 Trance 25 Stern 26 Star 28 Age

No 239 - ACROSS: 1 Minder 7 Exercise 8 Acme 10 Reveal 11 Aspect 14 End 16 Totes 17 Dart 19 Rivet 21 Pared 22 Tenet 23 Garb 26 Floor 28 Cab 29 Lean-to 30 Hollow 31 Idle 32 Stirring 33 Hacked

DOWN: 1 Marred 2 Decent 3 Reel 4 Trusted 5 Civet 6 Meets 8 Aver 9 Mad 12 Pot 13 Cedar 15 Fired 18 Agile 19 Ran 20 Vet 21 Perturb 22 Ton 23 Gallic 24 Able 25 Byword 26 Flask 27 Oasis 28 Cod 30 High

No 240 - ACROSS: 4 Sugary 7 Claptrap 8 Ogress 10 Rotor 13 Coal 14 Eden 15 Form 16 Leo 17 Span 19 Bred 21 Terrified 23 Rote 24 Fate 26 Tee 27 Fled 29 Kale 32 Fear 33 Aspen 34 Depart 35 Heritage 36 Severe

DOWN: 1 Score 2 Haste 3 Stir 4 Spoor 5 Girl 6 Rested 9 Gambit 11 Ode 12 Onset 13 Conifer 15 Far 16 Led 18 Prefer 20 Reeks 21 Toe 22 Fad 23 Revere 25 Ale 28 Lathe 30 Appal 31 Enter 32 Fame 33 Acid

No 241 - ACROSS: 3 Score 8 Stern 10 Overt 11 Ore 12 Noise 13 Faraway 15 Trust 18 Sat 19 Geyser 21 Regular 22 Head 23 Feud 24 Panther 26 Rascal 29 Eon 31 Tiers 32 Precise 34 Atlas 35 Ilk 36 Tense 37 Inlet 38 Slink

DOWN: 1 Stoat 2 Creased 4 Cloy 5 Roster 6 Every 7 Arise 9 Err 12 Natural 14 Wag 16 Usher 17 Trade 19 Garters 20 Short 21 Raise 23 Fencing 24 Pastel 25 Hoe 27 Aired 28 Crass 30 Asked 32 Pawn 33 Ill

No 242 - ACROSS: 1 Harsh 6 Fiery 9 Toehold 10 Scare 11 Elegy 12 Melee 13 Admirer 15 Gas 17 Mean 18 Ferret 19 Erred 20 Leeway 22 Asti 24 Eat 25 Dropped 26 Envoy 27 Store 28 Again 29 Asinine 30 Frost 31 Terms

DOWN: 2 Arcade 3 Strain 4 Hoe 5 Sheer 6 Fleeced 7 Idle 8 Reggae 12 Merry 13 Amble 14 Manet 15 Grasp 16 Staid 18 Ferry 19 Earnest 21 Easter 22 Apogee 23 Tedium 25 Downs 26 Eras 28 Ant

No 243 - ACROSS: 1 Flinch 7 Insecure 8 Stop 10 Matins 11 Affect 14 Ace 16 Leers 17 Rare 19 Puree 21 Carat 22 Moron 23 Made 26 Madam 28 Tor 29 Usurps 30 Motive 31 Amid 32 Transfer 33 Kindle

DOWN: 1 Former 2 Notice 3 Hips 4 Leaflet 5 Rupee 6 Tests 8 Star 9 One 12 Fee 13 Crowd 15 Huron 18 Arias 19 Par 20 Ran 21 Compose 22 Mar 23 Motion 24 Arid 25 Emerge 26 Musty 27 Ducat 28 Tom 30 Mark

No 244 - ACROSS: 4 Throbs 7 Interior 8 Around 10 Lathe 13 Iced 14 Area 15 Ants 16 Bun 17 Logs 19 Item 21 Impounded 23 Snap 24 Rues 26 Elk 27 Oven 29 Tags 32 Uses 33 Nylon 34 Genres 35 Tiresome 36 Versus

DOWN: 1 Villa 2 State 3 Free 4 Tract 5 Rood 6 Bunkum 9 Reside 11 Art 12 Halma 13 Insures 15 Ago 16 Bed 18 Oppose 20 Testy 21 Ink 22 Nun 23 Sleeve 25 Ego 28 Vest 30 Allow 31 Sneer 32 Urns 33 Need

No 245 - ACROSS: 3 Chefs 8 Rapid 10 Alley 11 Rig 12 Uncle 13 Retorts 15 Cease 18 Tot 19 Popped 21 Veteran 22 Laid 23 Move 24 Certain 26 Beamed 29 Nil 31 Enrol 32 Selling 34 Lever 35 Inn 36 Power 37 Poker 38 Sylph

DOWN: 1 Dared 2 Bigoted 4 Hens 5 Falcon 6 Sleep 7 Tense 9 Pit 12 Uttered 14 Rot 16 Apron 17 Edges 19 Partner 20 Globe 21 Vicar 23 Million 24 Celery 25 Ail 27 Enjoy 28 Moles 30 Annex 32 Seep 33 Ink

No 246 - ACROSS: 1 Never 6 Phase 9 Ravioli 10 Sprat 11 Elite 12 Sepal 13 Aspects 15 Web 17 Seed 18 Desire 19 Broad 20 Invert 22 Star 24 Cue 25 Delayed 26 Bared 27 Ended 28 Sugar 29 Atelier 30 Heath 31 Enter

DOWN: 2 Expose 3 Erased 4 Rat 5 Dives 6 Pleated 7 Hill 8 Setter 12 Start 13 Aspic 14 Peeve 15 Witty 16 Beard 18 Dated 19 Breadth 21 Nuance 22 Saturn 23 Aerate 25 Deals 26 Beat 28 See

No 247 - ACROSS: 1 Leaves 7 Explicit 8 Horn 10 Traded 11 Snared 14 Nod 16 Dregs 17 Ludo 19 Harem 21 Super 22 Sweep 23 Myth 26 Movie 28 Lee 29 Anorak 30 Senate 31 Lair 32 Coalesce 33 Delves

DOWN: 1 Lintel 2 Voodoo 3 Send 4 Blunder 5 Scare 6 Studs 8 Hand 9 Red 12 Arm 13 Egret 15 Caper 18 Union 19 Hue 20 Rep 21 Sweater 22 Sir 23 Menial 24 Year 25 Hyenas 26 March 27 Vocal 28 Lea 30 Sled

No 248 - ACROSS: 4 Forest 7 Increase 8 Rustle 10 Handy 13 Cant 14 Tier 15 Moll 16 Pea 17 Iran 19 Iced 21 Overtaken 23 Oven 24 Aden 26 Era 27 Trio 29 Tale 32 Main 33 Ashen 34 Perils 35 Elongate 36 Slogan

DOWN: 1 Sight 2 Scone 3 Very 4 Feral 5 Rust 6 Salted 9 Unlike 11 Aim 12 Drive 13 Contain 15 Mar 16 Pen 18 Rental 20 Cents 21 Ova 22 Ado 23 Ordeal 25 Ale 28 Risen 30 Ahead 31 Ended 32 Ming 33 Aunt

No 249 - ACROSS: 3 Elect 8 Kudos 10 Erase 11 Son 12 Alone 13 Pitfall 15 Tales 18 Ice 19 Ardent 21 Intrude 22 Line 23 Prig 24 Fellers 26 Stored 29 Age 31 Hotel 32 Stopped 34 Slate 35 Air 36 Panto 37 Breed 38 Swans

DOWN: 1 Music 2 Confine 4 Lull 5 Centre 6 Tread 7 Ashen 9 Dot 12 Alerted 14 Act 16 Leers 17 Stage 19 Adulate 20 Clash 21 Ingot 23 Prepare 24 Fellow 25 Ego 27 Topaz 28 Rests 30 Beret 32 Stun 33 Pie

No 250 - ACROSS: 1 Panic 6 Regal 9 Dappled 10 Greed 11 Sifts 12 Fruit 13 Swollen 15 Lie 17 Isis 18 Second 19 Slips 20 Guests 22 Cede 24 End 25 Courses 26 Argon 27 Point 28 Atlas 29 Termite 30 Asked 31 Erase

DOWN: 2 Arrows 3 Ideals 4 Cad 5 Spurn 6 Resides 7 Edit 8 Attain 12 Feels 13 Siege 14 Oiled 15 Loves 16 Edges 18 Spoon 19 Started 21 Undoes 22 Crater 23 Decays 25 Corms 26 Ante 28 Ate

No 251 - ACROSS: 1 Landed 7 Unstable 8 True 10 Forest 11 Persia 14 Ace 16 Rusty 17 Rapt 19 Sheet 21 Dared 22 Ratel 23 Task 26 Paris 28 Aim 29 Alight 30 Sirens 31 Plan 32 Stagnate 33 Deemed

DOWN: 1 Loafer 2 Direct 3 Duet 4 Uttered 5 Abyss 6 Delay 8 Trap 9 Use 12 Rut 13 Items 15 Shred 18 Appal 19 Sat 20 Eel 21 Dashing 22 Rig 23 Tirade 24 Amen 25 Kissed 26 Passe 27 Rival 28 Ail 30 Sped

No 252 - ACROSS: 4 Marred 7 Espresso 8 Chimes 10 State 13 Shed 14 Tutu 15 Spar 16 Yet 17 Tear 19 Open 21 Condition 23 Dare 24 Neck 26 Bit 27 Rage 29 Ears 32 Ugly 33 Groan 34 Embryo 35 Narrated 36 Allege

DOWN: 1 Yeast 2 Sprat 3 Fete 4 Mocha 5 Raid 6 Eleven 9 Heroic 11 Tug 12 Tutor 13 Springy 15 Sad 16 Yen 18 Energy 20 Poker 21 Cat 22 Tee 23 Dismal 25 Era 28 Alone 30 Aorta 31 Snide 32 Urge 33 Girl

No 253 - ACROSS: 3 Close 8 Spout 10 Irons 11 Ail 12 Enter 13 Wilting 15 Solid 18 Art 19 Strata 21 Inertia 22 Inca 23 Crib 24 Raucous 26 Linnet 29 Ear 31 Angel 32 Erratic 34 Aerie 35 Tan 36 Learn 37 Bored 38 Strew

DOWN: 1 Spain 2 Sultana 4 Long 5 Siesta 6 Error 7 Unfit 9 Oil 12 Entreat 14 Ire 16 Lairs 17 Daubs 19 Sincere 20 Villa 21 Icing 23 Curator 24 Relent 25 Oar 27 Inter 28 Nears 30 Lines 32 Eire 33 Tar

No 254 - ACROSS: 1 Abhor 6 Coats 9 Pontoon 10 Crypt 11 Ultra 12 Every 13 Pensive 15 See 17 Aloe 18 Agents 19 Adore 20 Sledge 22 Visa 24 Eel 25 Royalty 26 Slain 27 Agate 28 Aimed 29 Asphalt 30 Years 31 Lying

DOWN: 2 Barrel 3 Oppose 4 Rot 5 Stove 6 Courage 7 Only 8 Turret 12 Evade 13 Passe 14 Novel 15 Snail 16 Essay 18 Argon 19 Ageless 21 League 22 Vanity 23 Strewn 25 Right 26 Star 28 All

No 255 - ACROSS: 1 Forbid 7 Escalate 8 Fore 10 Cougar 11 Career 14 Nun 16 Bands 17 Lode 19 Sharp 21 Shape 22 Rhyme 23 Sate 26 Argue 28 Cur 29 Steely 30 Rapier 31 Area 32 Esoteric 33 Embers

DOWN: 1 Fiscal 2 Brogue 3 Deer 4 Macabre 5 Haven 6 Fears 8 Fund 9 Ran 12 Rap 13 Edict 15 Shame 18 Overt 19 Shy 20 Ape 21 Shelved 22 Rue 23 Superb 24 Aria 25 Errors 26 Ashen 27 Genoa 28 Car 30 Race

No 256 - ACROSS: 4 Saddle 7 Strength 8 Action 10 Goats 13 Tray 14 Edna 15 Shed 16 Wit 17 Pair 19 Even 21 Distorted 23 Mars 24 Nest 26 Boy 27 Used 29 Chat 32 Iris 33 Shade 34 Chosen 35 Gangster 36 Freeze

DOWN: 1 Usage 2 Urban 3 Onus 4 Share 5 Duty 6 Look in 9 Cadets 11 Odd 12 Tapir 13 Thrones 15 Sit 16 Wed 18 Assure 20 Vetch 21 Day 22 Red 23 Mother 25 Sad 28 Singe 30 Hasty 31 Tears 32 Isle 33 Sign

No 257 - ACROSS: 3 Sylph 8 Stoic 10 Rends 11 Hid 12 Altar 13 Holdall 15 Novel 8 Lit 19 Ignore 21 Demeans 22 Cars 23 Keen 24 Deletes 26 Relied 29 Nee 31 False 32 Adapted 34 Spurs 35 Ion 36 Ensue 37 Sneer 38 Erase

DOWN: 1 Ethos 2 Riddles 4 Yell 5 Prangs 6 Heron 7 Adder 9 Oil 12 Altered 14 Aim 16 Votes 17 Leans 19 Intends 20 Scarf 21 Drill 23 Keeping 24 Deeper 25 Tea 27 Earns 28 Issue 30 Tenet 32 Arms 33 Toe

No 258 - ACROSS: 1 Alias 6 Lever 9 Shutter 10 Daisy 11 Ankle 12 Snare 13 Leering 15 Ass 17 Urge 18 Hearth 19 Coped 20 Chat up 22 Dope 24 Ham 25 Against 26 Barge 27 Carat 28 Child 29 Revenue 30 Edges 31 Brash

DOWN: 2 Leader 3 Assure 4 Shy 5 Sting 6 Learned 7 Erne 8 Enlist 12 Snoop 13 Lunch 14 Egham 15 Arson 16 Sheet 18 Hedge 19 Curates 21 Hazard 22 Dither 23 Psalms 25 Agree 26 Bare 28 Cub

No 259 - ACROSS: 1 Rather 7 Inverted 8 Snap 10 Cattle 11 Senior 14 Eel 16 Range 17 Lewd 19 Grasp 21 Beige 22 Title 23 Mast 26 Baton 28 Cab 29 Elands 30 Wallet 31 Idle 32 Intended 33 Enters

DOWN: 1 Rascal 2 Hinted 3 Ripe 4 Reverse 5 Stain 6 Adore 8 Stew 9 All 12 Nap 13 Ogres 15 Drill 18 Equal 19 Get 20 Age 21 Binding 22 Ton 23 Mallet 24 Able 25 Tutors 26 Belie 27 Taste 28 Cad 30 Wide

No 260 - ACROSS: 4 Topics 7 Confetti 8 Absent 10 Trash 13 Iris 14 Each 15 Snag 16 Boy 17 Abet 19 Open 21 Protested 23 Mien 24 Nest 26 Tot 27 Nose 29 Tegs 32 Mere 33 Nylon 34 Pirate 35 Ancestor 36 Indeed

DOWN: 1 Acute 2 Anzac 3 Mesh 4 Tiara 5 Pass 6 Cannon 9 Bigots 11 Rat 12 Share 13 Intense 15 Set 16 Bed 18 Bonnet 20 Petty 21 Pit 22 See 23 Motion 25 Ago 28 Oread 30 Elate 31 Snort 32 Make 33 Need

No 261 - ACROSS: 3 Alias 8 Clout 10 Baron 11 Owl 12 Divot 13 Atelier 15 Diced 18 Art 19 Denote 21 Creases 22 Curd 23 Tell 24 Snipped 26 Nudges 29 Aid 31 Store 32 Minimal 34 Amber 35 Oar 36 Serve 37 Muted 38 Edges

DOWN: 1 Cloth 2 Dullard 4 Lair 5 Abodes 6 Satin 7 Comet 9 Owe 12 Detains 14 Ire 16 Coped 17 Deals 19 Despair 20 Scans 21 Credo 23 Tedious 24 Seemed 25 Pin 27 Utter 28 Grave 30 Cared 32 Mere 33 Mat

No 262 - ACROSS: 1 Crass 6 Ashen 9 Hammock 10 Stray 11 Cider 12 Beret 13 Grabber 15 Tea 17 Levy 18 Attend 19 Signs 20 Shrine 22 Seep 24 Set 25 Descent 26 Lower 27 Droop 28 Lives 29 Reveres 30 Tweed 31 Amass

DOWN: 2 Retire 3 Shabby 4 Say 5 Ember 6 Accepts 7 Skit 8 Eleven 12 Belie 13 Glass 14 Avert 15 Tepee 16 Adept 18 Anger 19 Snooped 21 Hebrew 22 Schism 23 Enters 25 Defer 26 Lore 28 Lea

No 263 - ACROSS: 1 Slopes 7 Position 8 Peri 10 Stolen 11 Locate 14 Led 16 Sores 17 Aged 19 Riots 21 Fable 22 Rapid 23 Does 26 Spear 28 Rid 29 Chatty 30 Loving 31 Eden 32 Prevents 33 Sitter

DOWN: 1 Siesta 2 Peeled 3 Spin 4 Riposte 5 Dinar 6 Andes 8 Pole 9 Red 12 Cos 13 Tense 15 Tibia 18 Graph 19 Rap 20 Old 21 Farther 22 Rat 23 Divert 24 Odin 25 Signor 26 Scope 27 Eager 28 Rod 30 Less

No 264 - ACROSS: 4 Stripe 7 Hyacinth 8 Offset 10 Leech 13 Bout 14 Polo 15 Bits 16 Hit 17 Poet 19 Ibis 21 Pendulous 23 Best 24 Many 26 Got 27 Iced 29 Elan 32 Amen 33 Grape 34 Hitmen 35 Trounced 36 Leases

DOWN: 1 Whelp 2 Lapel 3 Wish 4 Shoot 5 Rift 6 Precis 9 Fusion 11 Eon 12 Copes 13 Bitumen 15 Bed 16 His 18 On time 20 Buyer 21 Pet 22 Lad 23 Bovine 25 Tap 28 Cents 30 Larch 31 Needy 32 Amps 33 Grub

No 265 - ACROSS: 3 Brats 8 Beret 10 Apple 11 Cos 12 Cable 13 Auditor 15 Envoy 18 Dam 19 Entire 21 Segment 22 Rips 23 Digs 24 Snooped 26 Select 29 Rap 31 Enter 32 Ostrich 34 Ridge 35 Err 36 Tulip 37 Askew 38 Ether

DOWN: 1 Recur 2 Besides 4 Rear 5 Talent 6 Spent 7 Floor 9 Rod 12 Comment 14 Tag 16 Vivid 17 Yeast 19 Endorse 20 Arise 21 Spilt 23 Depress 24 Script 25 Pat 27 Ennui 28 Eerie 30 Screw 32 Ogre 33 Irk

No 266 - ACROSS: 1 Wheat 6 Ended 9 Recline 10 Crate 11 Taupe 12 Start 13 Soprano 15 Try 17 Trey 18 Palate 19 Divot 20 Fennel 22 Soul 24 Fry 25 Debtors 26 Upper 27 Tiara 28 Aimed 29 Gimmick 30 Lever 31 Teeth

DOWN: 2 Horror 3 Artery 4 Tee 5 Pluto 6 Entreat 7 Neat 8 Expert 12 Snail 13 Staff 14 Penny 15 Taboo 16 Yells 18 Power 19 Despair 21 Ermine 22 Strike 23 Urgent 25 Deems 26 Urge 28 Act

No 267 - ACROSS: 1 Plasma 7 Inactive 8 Shed 10 Futile 11 Refine 14 Ask 16 Alder 17 Term 19 Roomy 21 Calls 22 Tamed 23 Part 26 Steal 28 Lam 29 Nearly 30 Cinema 31 Open 32 Conjuror 33 Ensure

DOWN: 1 Profit 2 Schism 3 Aide 4 Screams 5 Livid 6 Refer 8 Star 9 Elk 12 Fly 13 Never 15 Roles 18 Elite 19 Ram 20 Old 21 Callous 22 Tar 23 Panels 24 Amen 25 Trance 26 Snack 27 Earns 28 Lip 30 Core

No 268 - ACROSS: 4 Scarce 7 Admonish 8 Assent 10 Busby 13 Epee 14 Erse 15 Slew 16 Dry 17 Ripe 19 Ague 21 Synagogue 23 Pals 24 Area 26 Law 27 Erne 29 Vase 32 Stet 33 Valet 34 Spouse 35 Dog-eared 36 Breezy

DOWN: 1 Maybe 2 Amass 3 Inky 4 Shape 5 Apse 6 Centre 9 Sewage 11 Urn 12 Beryl 13 Elegant 15 Spa 16 Due 18 Insets 20 Guava 21 Saw 22 Ore 23 Pamper 25 Use 28 Reedy 30 Alarm 31 Etude 32 Sure 33 View

No 269 - ACROSS: 3 Odour 8 Woman 10 Rugby 11 Gap 12 Cigar 13 Furious 15 Naive 18 Tar 19 Dulcet 21 Various 22 Opal 23 Once 24 Buffing 26 Taurus 29 Ere 31 Stein 32 Present 34 Dives 35 Tan 36 Mango 37 Heron 38 Entry

DOWN: 1 Bogus 2 Capital 4 Dais 5 Uranus 6 Rural 7 Above 9 Mar 12 Curious 14 Oar 16 Icing 17 Ethel 19 Duffers 20 Hoots 21 Vague 23 One-step 24 Bunion 25 Ire 27 Atlas 28 Ridge 30 Annoy 32 Pear 33 Ear

No 270 - ACROSS: 1 Acute 6 Assay 9 Hostage 10 Yearn 11 Aesop 12 Again 13 Success 15 Dew 17 Oboe 18 Astute 19 Dealt 20 Sprain 22 Acid 24 Era 25 Hapless 26 Spear 27 Enrol 28 Demur 29 Backlog 30 Messy 31 Needy

DOWN: 2 Cherub 3 Thrice 4 Eon 5 Stags 6 Against 7 Seen 8 Avocet 12 Aspen 13 Souse 14 Cobra 15 Dunce 16 Weeds 18 Altar 19 Display 21 Prince 22 Allege 23 Issued 25 Hacks 26 Sobs 28 Don

No 271 - ACROSS: 1 Harass 7 Paramour 8 Fire 10 Primed 11 Athens 14 Lap 16 Lines 17 Tall 19 Gaped 21 Sated 22 Allow 23 Harm 26 Peace 28 Web 29 Advent 30 Sealed 31 Here 32 Largesse 33 Dry run

DOWN: 1 Hotpot 2 Animal 3 Sped 4 Battled 5 Dozen 6 Dress 8 Fill 9 Rep 12 Hid 13 Never 15 Baton 18 Armed 19 Gal 20 Pew 21 Slender 22 Ace 23 Hearty 24 Able 25 Modern 26 Pails 27 Avert 28 Wee 30 Shed

No 272 - ACROSS: 4 Sinful 7 Withdraw 8 Astern 10 Funds 13 Imps 14 Tree 15 Emir 16 Usk 17 Bulb 19 Oast 21 Disfigure 23 Moth 24 Bite 26 Cot 27 Even 29 News 32 Bred 33 Valet 34 Forest 35 Clarinet 36 Hearth

DOWN: 1 Swift 2 Stone 3 Odes 4 Swami 5 Nuts 6 Unrest 9 Sprout 11 Urn 12 Debit 13 Imbibed 15 Elf 16 Use 18 Ushers 20 Arena 21 Dot 22 Gin 23 Morose 25 Owe 28 Vetch 30 Eland 31 State 32 Beer 33 Very

No 273 - ACROSS: 3 Swans 8 Tower 10 Ether 11 Tap 12 Altar 13 Contest 15 Tales 18 Irk 19 Report 21 Cleaner 22 Ache 23 Aged 24 Acquire 26 Demote 29 Moo 31 Agent 32 Tenuous 34 Sited 35 Sat 36 Lever 37 Refer 38 Terms

DOWN: 1 Motor 2 Reptile 4 Wilt 5 Neater 6 Strap 7 Newer 9 Wan 12 Askance 14 Ere 16 Lodge 17 Study 19 Resumed 20 Panda 21 Chime 23 Aroused 24 Attire 25 Ion 27 Egret 28 Onset 30 Muted 32 Team 33 Oaf

No 274 - ACROSS: 1 False 6 Patch 9 Panther 10 Stoat 11 Reaps 12 Aroma 13 Cossack 15 Ale 17 Once 18 Stream 19 Bogus 20 Appear 22 Sole 24 Lee 25 Stopper 26 Chute 27 Spoof 28 Ideas 29 Vulture 30 Creel 31 Error

DOWN: 2 Action 3 Sparse 4 Eat 5 Stork 6 Permits 7 Area 8 Cupola 12 Actor 13 Coral 14 Scope 15 Aesop 16 Ember 18 Suite 19 Bashful 21 Pepper 22 Spider 23 Legato 25 State 26 Cove 28 Ire

No 275 - ACROSS: 1 Camber 7 Outhouse 8 Etna 10 Rasher 11 Endure 14 Pet 16 Duped 17 Toys 19 Green 21 Visor 22 Canon 23 Rhea 26 Tenor 28 See 29 Origin 30 Legend 31 Yard 32 Conjuror 33 Extort

DOWN: 1 Carrot 2 Bathes 3 Roar 4 Thunder 5 Run up 6 Ceded 8 Espy 9 Net 12 Dun 13 Revue 15 Arson 18 Outer 19 Gin 20 Eon 21 Various 22 Cog 23 Regret 24 Heed 25 Ardent 26 Touch 27 Ninny 28 Sea 30 Lyre

No 276 - ACROSS: 4 Thread 7 Euphoria 8 Blends 10 Irate 13 Coal 14 Data 15 Poor 16 Act 17 Leer 19 Dart 21 Component 23 Lone 24 Nark 26 Rat 27 Reap 29 Loom 32 Ages 33 Verge 34 Draper 35 Inferior 36 Sledge

DOWN: 1 Tepid 2 Sprat 3 Rove 4 Taboo 5 Reel 6 Abduct 9 Larder 11 Raw 12 Talon 13 Coronas 15 Pep 16 Art 18 Emerge 20 Ankle 21 Cot 22 Nap 23 Laurel 25 Bog 28 Eerie 30 Orbit 31 Merry 32 Aped 33 Veer

No 277 - ACROSS: 3 Flats 8 Recap 10 Elvis 11 Rot 12 Arena 13 Obscene 15 Night 18 Hat 19 Finish 21 Serious 22 Cold 23 Plan 24 Curious 26 Aspire 29 Our 31 There 32 Cuticle 34 Oasis 35 Tot 36 Burnt 37 Satan 38 Seven

DOWN: 1 Herbs 2 Matched 4 Lure 5 Tennis 6 Slain 7 Sighs 9 Cos 12 Antique 14 Ear 16 Girls 17 Think 19 Furious 20 Eclat 21 Slope 23 Puritan 24 Create 25 Out 27 Shout 28 Irons 30 Altar 32 Cite 33 Cot

No 278 - ACROSS: 1 Offer 6 Scope 9 Saunter 10 Unity 11 Cable 12 Buxom 13 Tuneful 15 Sea 17 Ream 18 Adults 19 Flags 20 Boiled 22 Cede 24 Err 25 Snooped 26 Itchy 27 Leash 28 Leech 29 Learner 30 Utter 31 Atone

DOWN: 2 Fondue 3 Esteem 4 Ray 5 Annul 6 Seconds 7 Cram 8 Pullet 12 Build 13 Tribe 14 Nadir 15 Sleep 16 Asked 18 Agony 19 Feather 21 Orient 22 Covert 23 Deacon 25 Share 26 Isle 28 Lea

No 279 - ACROSS: 1 Starch 7 Inviting 8 Spin 10 Export 11 Pirate 14 Use 16 Zones 17 Sore 19 Rated 21 Baton 22 Lance 23 Feed 26 Cheer 28 Moa 29 Attire 30 Sorted 31 Togs 32 Medicine 33 Puddle

DOWN: 1 Steers 2 Repose 3 Hint 4 Citizen 5 Titan 6 Ogles 8 Spur 9 Ire 12 Rod 13 Tense 15 Watch 18 Ought 19 Ran 20 Toe 21 Barrack 22 Lei 23 Forged 24 Eats 25 Deduce 26 Calms 27 Etude 28 Moo 30 Step

No 280 - ACROSS: 4 Invest 7 Rattling 8 Litter 10 Globe 13 Ions 14 Side 15 Anon 16 Shy 17 Sort 19 Aloe 21 Tormented 23 Rome 24 Need 26 Fop 27 Gust 29 Gape 32 Note 33 Jewel 34 Parent 35 Excision 36 Terror

DOWN: 1 Dregs 2 Stood 3 Glue 4 Igloo 5 Vats 6 Seethe 9 Innate 11 Lip 12 Besom 13 Intense 15 Arm 16 Sod 18 Oregon 20 Ledge 21 Top 22 Net 23 Rotate 25 Ape 28 Utter 30 Await 31 Eland 32 Near 33 Jail

No 281 - ACROSS: 3 Amass 8 Marry 10 Piers 11 Tot 12 Laden 13 Cabinet 15 Agent 18 Set 19 Preach 21 Tatters 22 Roan 23 Heir 24 Trusted 26 Elopes 29 Eel 31 Let on 32 Snapped 34 Idiot 35 Ion 36 False 37 Undue 38 Erred

DOWN: 1 Fatal 2 Artisan 4 Meat 5 Spears 6 Singe 7 Franc 9 Rob 12 Letters 14 Net 16 Eased 17 Therm 19 Present 20 Creel 21 Tarot 23 Helping 24 Tender 25 Tea 27 Legal 28 Poise 30 Venue 32 Sole 33 Pod

No 282 - ACROSS: 1 Credo 6 Sitar 9 Insight 10 Slave 11 Aerie 12 Realm 13 Averted 15 Cos 17 Pert 18 Forest 19 Gloat 20 Lassos 22 Lace 24 Ere 25 Severed 26 Flaps 27 Vogue 28 Anvil 29 Strange 30 Cross 31 Edged

DOWN: 2 Relive 3 Divert 4 One 5 Fired 6 Shallot 7 Item 8 Amigos 12 Reels 13 Apple 14 Erase 15 Cedar 16 Steed 18 Fares 19 Goblets 21 Armour 22 Leaned 23 Cerise 25 Speak 26 Fuss 28 Age

No 283 - ACROSS: 1 Reward 7 Organdie 8 Came 10 Brakes 11 Caller 14 Sew 16 Fiend 17 Eden 19 Tired 21 Vases 22 Wiped 23 Fire 26 Satin 28 Son 29 Pretty 30 Circus 31 Itch 32 Arrogant 33 Endure

DOWN: 1 Rubble 2 Awaken 3 Does 3 Carafes 5 Addle 6 Beard 8 Case 9 Mew 12 Lid 13 Enter 15 Miser 18 Dinar 19 Tap 20 Red 21 Vintage 22 Wit 23 Forced 24 Inch 25 Ensure 26 Spray 27 Terry 28 Sit 30 Cite

No 284 - ACROSS: 4 Perish 7 Alfresco 8 Sonnet 10 Ideal 13 Pert 14 Curl 15 Barn 16 Wry 17 Diet 19 Away 21 Generated 23 Lord 24 Iced 26 Bat 27 Eyot 29 Gasp 32 Meet 33 Meter 34 Armada 35 Renowned 36 Platen

DOWN: 1 Basic 2 Offer 3 Fell 4 Poser 5 Rant 6 Sherry 9 Ornate 11 Due 12 Alder 13 Patriot 15 Bee 16 Wad 18 Indeed 20 Wedge 21 Got 22 Act 23 Laurel 25 Use 28 Yearn 30 Atone 31 Pride 32 Mast 33 Mood

No 285 - ACROSS: 3 Spoor 8 Trout 10 Races 11 Err 12 Essay 13 Keepers 15 Tonic 18 Oar 19 Genial 21 Estates 22 Role 23 Scam 24 Mistake 26 Tic-tac 29 Ely 31 Enter 32 Bellows 34 Royal 35 Ale 36 Torso 37 Order 38 Ended

DOWN: 1 Green 2 Purpose 4 Pass 5 Orates 6 Rayon 7 Sepia 9 Ore 12 Erratic 14 Eat 16 Niece 17 Clump 19 Genteel 20 Brute 21 Elect 23 Skylark 24 Maroon 25 All 27 Ingot 28 Terse 30 Sweet 32 Bare 33 Old

No 286 - ACROSS: 1 Ashen 6 Sully 9 Let-down 10 Pilaw 11 Odour 12 Taboo 13 General 15 Tea 17 Lead 18 Herald 19 Aided 20 Divest 22 Mere 24 Ere 25 Trainer 26 Pilot 27 Under 28 Auger 29 Ailment 30 Adorn 31 Testy

DOWN: 2 Soiree 3 Elated 4 New 5 Ideal 6 Swooped 7 Undo 8 Laurel 12 Tacit 13 Glide 14 Naive 15 Taken 16 Adder 18 Heart 19 Aspirin 21 Ironed 22 Minute 23 Recent 25 Tommy 26 Pear 28 Ant

No 287 - ACROSS: 1 Dotted 7 Relegate 8 Also 10 Instep 11 Strike 14 Tee 16 Heron 17 Grid 19 Freed 21 Cedar 22 Cower 23 Slap 26 Sedan 28 Lea 29 Pretty 30 Reason 31 Oils 32 Idolised 33 Ending

DOWN: 1 Daring 2 Tilted 3 Drop 4 Leather 5 Nadir 6 Seven 8 Asti 9 See 12 Red 13 Koala 15 Order 18 River 19 Few 20 Ear 21 Contain 22 Cat 23 Sealed 24 Lass 25 Pining 26 Sprig 27 Demon 28 Lei 30 Rode

No 288 - ACROSS: 4 Dismal 7 Employer 8 Obeyed 10 Potty 13 Plan 14 Over 15 Salt 16 Ask 17 Idol 19 Tote 21 Persevere 23 Coda 24 Tend 26 Nod 27 Watt 29 Epee 32 Cede 33 Grill 34 Regard 35 Encircle 36 Stated

DOWN: 1 Tempo 2 Spite 3 Pony 4 Droll 5 Seen 6 Averse 9 Batten 11 Ova 12 Tried 13 Palette 15 SOS 16 Ate 18 Drawer 20 Order 21 Pod 22 Vet 23 Covert 25 Gel 28 Added 30 Pinch 31 Elder 32 Cast 33 Grip

No 289 - ACROSS: 3 Steam 8 Testy 10 Vicar 11 Lei 12 Lemon 13 Hearsay 15 Ceded 18 Rot 19 Serene 21 Benefit 22 Read 23 Glum 24 Latches 26 Sorrel 29 Eon 31 Tines 32 Breezes 34 Issue 35 Rim 36 Seine 37 Happy 38 Snubs

DOWN: 1 Melee 2 Stirred 4 Trey 5 Avocet 6 Miner 7 Haven 9 Sea 12 Lateral 14 Son 16 Deals 17 Deems 19 Sincere 20 Frost 21 Bairn 23 General 24 Lessen 25 Hoe 27 Oiled 28 Reins 30 Tempo 32 Bulb 33 Zip

No 290 - ACROSS: 1 Cling 6 Islam 9 Augment 10 Begun 11 Hurts 12 Ashen 13 Beneath 15 Art 17 Idea 18 Pilfer 19 Fault 20 Cellos 22 Refs 24 Hay 25 Leveret 26 Tepid 27 Styes 28 Sauce 29 Receipt 30 Brine 31 Yeast

DOWN: 2 Leered 3 Nausea 4 Gun 5 Smash 6 Inherit 7 Stun 8 Attire 12 Atlas 13 Birch 14 Newly 15 After 16 Trust 18 Plied 19 Foresee 21 Easter 22 Relate 23 Fences 25 Liver 26 Tern 28 Spy

No 291 - ACROSS: 1 Crisis 7 Imbecile 8 Rift 10 Meagre 11 Writer 14 Shy 16 Alert 17 Rapt 19 Speck 21 Skirt 22 Flier 23 Date 26 Canoe 28 Rep 29 Reaper 30 Weasel 31 Idle 31 Flowered 33 Earthy

DOWN: 1 Calmer 2 Slight 3 Site 4 Retract 5 Piste 6 Heart 8 Rasp 9 Fry 12 Ilk 13 Erect 15 Spiel 18 Algae 19 Ski 20 Err 21 Sleeper 22 Fop 23 Dealer 24 Apse 25 Eulogy 26 Croft 27 Nabob 28 Red 30 Wide

No 292 - ACROSS: 4 Stated 7 Encroach 8 Opened 10 Acute 13 Rear 14 Lute 15 Jest 16 Apt 17 Poem 19 Omit 21 Pictorial 23 Made 24 Rust 26 Pew 27 Lost 29 Clue 32 Cove 33 Short 34 Coyote 35 Rebelled 36 Cygnet

DOWN: 1 Feral 2 Scout 3 Sore 4 Shoes 5 Aver 6 Exempt 9 Patois 11 Cur 12 Tepid 13 Remorse 15 Jet 16 Ail 18 Ocelot 20 Match 21 Paw 22 Rut 23 Melody 25 Fur 28 Overt 30 Lowly 31 Etude 32 Coin 33 Seep

No 293 - ACROSS: 3 Crypt 8 Rapid 10 Laird 11 Gas 12 Anger 13 Missals 15 Aorta 18 Oil 19 Esteem 21 Immense 22 Hide 23 Skin 24 Females 26 Placed 29 Pan 31 Solid 32 Repairs 34 Dozed 35 Toe 36 Meter 37 Money 38 Rally

DOWN: 1 Magic 2 Lissome 4 Runs 5 Please 6 Tarot 7 Trite 9 Pas 12 Alleged 14 Aim 16 Reeks 17 Amend 19 Escaped 20 Chips 21 Ideal 23 Senator 24 Fedora 25 Lap 27 Loved 28 Cider 30 Breed 32 Reel 33 Ion

No 294 - ACROSS: 1 Wants 6 Rinse 9 Relates 10 Pleat 11 Pints 12 Fools 13 Granule 15 Pea 17 Less 18 Scared 19 Genoa 20 Stairs 22 Edge 24 Sam 25 Pioneer 26 Salad 27 Begin 28 Diets 29 Decider 30 Asked 31 Never

DOWN: 2 Allure 3 Trains 4 Set 5 Canoe 6 Replica 7 Isis 8 Settee 12 Flies 13 Glass 14 Assam 15 Pride 16 Adder 18 Solid 19 Groaned 21 Tapers 22 Entire 23 Gentle 25 Panic 26 Side 28 Den

No 295 - ACROSS: 1 Arises 7 Clear-cut 8 Gala 10 Neater 11 Tirade 14 Sea 16 Repel 17 Asps 19 Raged 21 Jibes 22 Rebel 23 Area 26 Bogus 28 Ave 29 Agents 30 Speaks 31 Tend 32 Harangue 33 Whelks

DOWN: 1 Agenda 2 Slates 3 Scar 4 Satires 5 Scrap 6 Steel 8 Gasp 9 Lea 12 Red 13 Delve 15 Caber 18 Sprog 19 Rib 20 Gel 21 Jesting 22 Run 23 Avenue 24 Read 25 Assets 26 Bathe 27 Genre 28 Ape 30 Stew

No 296 - ACROSS: 4 Almost 7 Tribunal 8 Gather 10 Globe 13 Care 14 Solo 15 Poem 16 Old 17 Rain 19 Adds 21 Undecided 23 Bred 24 Imam 26 Ban 27 Lisp 29 Used 32 Mere 33 Arena 34 Cicada 35 Tasteful 36 Cheese

DOWN: 1 Stags 2 Tirol 3 Pure 4 Algae 5 Mute 6 Swells 9 Armada 11 Log 12 Borne 13 Concise 15 Pie 16 Odd 18 Addled 20 Demur 21 Urn 22 Imp 23 Banish 25 Gen 28 Irate 30 Serfs 31 Dally 32 Make 33 Ante

No 297 - ACROSS: 3 Cream 8 Arrow 10 Sitar 11 Eat 12 Amiss 13 Letters 15 Eerie 18 Art 19 Arrest 21 Against 22 Hove 23 Send 24 Hateful 26 Worsen 29 Top 31 Later 32 Kippers 34 Panic 35 Owe 36 Devil 37 Press 38 Adder

DOWN: 1 Green 2 Cottage 4 Rams 5 Assert 6 Miser 7 Saris 9 Rat 12 Artisan 14 Era 16 Rebel 17 Etude 19 Ascetic 20 Shawl 21 Avert 23 Support 24 Herald 25 Fop 27 Oases 28 Sepia 30 Dress 32 Kite 33 Ewe

No 298 - ACROSS: 1 Staff 6 Psalm 9 Rollmop 10 Genie 11 Sabre 12 Under 13 Pennant 15 Ant 17 Reed 18 Orange 19 Sifts 20 Deduct 22 Purr 24 Ely 25 Hearsay 26 Cover 27 Ideal 28 Mimic 29 Marries 30 Idler 31 Never

DOWN: 2 Teepee 3 Friend 4 Foe 5 Glint 6 Poseurs 7 Spar 8 Luring 12 Unfit 13 Pride 14 Needy 15 Angus 16 Terry 18 Otter 19 Scholar 21 Eluded 22 Praise 23 Ravine 25 Heart 26 Came 28 Men

No 299 - ACROSS: 1 Paused 7 Escallop 8 Lane 10 Scared 11 Slants 14 Sew 16 Epsom 17 Sets 19 Chart 21 Moors 22 Bosom 23 Muck 26 Occur 28 Bar 29 Stones 30 Burned 31 Asks 32 Absolves 33 Hatred

DOWN: 1 Passes 2 Spares 3 Deed 4 Callers 5 Glens 6 Spasm 8 Last 9 New 12 Apt 13 Topic 15 Shoot 18 Eject 19 Cos 20 Arm 21 Morello 22 Bun 23 Market 24 Urns 25 Kidded 26 Oscar 27 Copse 28 Bus 30 Bash˘

No 300 - ACROSS: 4 Infant 7 Retiring 8 Lawyer 10 Place 13 Born 14 Soya 15 Soot 16 Elm 17 Poor 19 Free 21 Perpetual 23 Cord 24 Doll 26 Bat 27 Eton 29 Laws 32 Cram 33 Nylon 34 Caress 35 Tea-break 36 Mantle

DOWN: 1 Traps 2 Stray 3 True 4 Igloo 5 Fawn 6 Needle 9 Artful 11 Lop 12 Caper 13 Boredom 15 Sop 16 Eel 18 Orders 20 Rally 21 Pot 22 Ton 23 Canada 25 Two 28 Taste 30 Alien 31 Snake 32 Cent 33 Nabs

No 301 - ACROSS: 3 Paths 8 Motet 10 Atone 11 Ran 12 Balsa 13 Battery 15 Start 18 Roe 19 Sleuth 21 Panache 22 Nail 23 Ruin 24 Shudder 26 Menace 29 Out 31 Epoch 32 Sweater 34 Tests 35 Ion 36 Besom 37 Sneer 38 Rears

DOWN: 1 Moral 2 Central 4 Away 5 Hassle 6 State 7 Inert 9 Tat 12 Breathe 14 Eon 16 Augur 17 Think 19 Shadows 20 Gnome 21 Piano 23 Retains 24 Scheme 25 Due 27 Epees 28 Actor 30 Tenet 32 Stir 33 Toe

No 302 - ACROSS: 1 Scope 6 Cower 9 Learner 10 Steal 11 Reign 12 Swats 13 Baleful 15 Age 17 Apes 18 Silver 19 Talon 20 Angler 22 Tine 24 Lee 25 Divided 26 Speed 27 State 28 Earth 29 Astound 30 Heart 31 Defer

DOWN: 2 Catnap 3 Plates 4 Eel 5 Crawl 6 Certain 7 Ores 8 Engage 12 Sugar 13 Banal 14 Ledge 15 Avoid 16 Erred 18 Solid 19 Tempest 21 Nestle 22 Tirade 23 Nettle 25 Depot 26 Star 28 End

No 303 - ACROSS: 1 Shrink 7 Inspects 8 Opal 10 Modern 11 Looted 14 Elk 16 Sieve 17 Ness 19 Hotel 21 Tepid 22 Dense 23 Bite 26 Ashen 28 Bud 29 Peanut 30 Sidles 31 Edge 32 Adequate 33 Passed

DOWN: 1 Salmon 2 Impels 3 Kiln 4 Opposed 5 Acute 6 Aside 8 Odes 9 Ark 12 Oil 13 Event 15 Copse 18 Erase 19 Hen 20 Tie 21 Tenuous 22 Den 23 Budges 24 Idle 25 Ensued 26 Appal 27 Hated 28 Bid 30 Seep

No 304 - ACROSS: 4 Canvas 7 Infernal 8 Estate 10 Sweep 13 Gate 14 Tarn 15 Aura 16 Pet 17 Rest 19 Tour 21 Constrict 23 Cult 24 Each 26 Hot 27 Earn 29 Romp 32 Arms 33 Femur 34 Cruise 35 Nonsense 36 Teased

DOWN: 1 First 2 After 3 Trip 4 Clear 5 Note 6 Anther 9 Static 11 Wag 12 Enrol 13 Gutters 15 Ass 16 Put 18 Enters 20 Ochre 21 Cut 22 Ran 23 Coerce 25 Emu 28 Amend 30 Omens 31 Preen 32 Aims 33 Fuss

No 305 - ACROSS: 3 Final 8 Swine 10 Carry 11 Act 12 Jests 13 Freedom 15 Oscar 18 Nay 19 Arouse 21 Address 22 Eats 23 Tend 24 Advises 26 Dangle 29 Sum 31 Steal 32 Stepped 34 Tunes 35 Lit 36 Alder 37 Meter 38 Seedy

DOWN: 1 Swarm 2 Intends 4 Item 5 Actors 6 Lasso 7 Areas 9 Ice 12 Joy-ride 14 Dad 16 Cures 17 Rends 19 Assists 20 Bends 21 Atone 23 Temples 24 Allure 25 Sue 27 Atoll 28 Gates 30 Deter 32 Send 33 Pit

No 306 - ACROSS: 1. Sweat 6. Sense 9. Command 10. Elect 11. Igloo 12. Barge 13. Meander 15. Let 17. Edit 18. Debase 19. Steer 20. Guests 22. Ages 24. End 25. Athlete 26. Hills 27. Vixen 28. Muddy 29. Receded 30. Ceded 31. Terse

DOWN: 2. Wilted 3. Accent 4. Tot 5. Smear 6. Snigger 7. Edge 8. Scores 12. Beats 13. Merge 14. Aided 15. Large 16. Tense 18. Dents 19. Stained 21. Unwise 22. Allude 23. Etudes 25. Alter 26. Here 28. Met

No 307 - ACROSS: 1 Defend 7 Exchange 8 Scan 10 Canopy 11 Direct 14 Art 16 Vases 17 Dope 19 Covet 21 Cares 22 Cadet 23 Rose 26 Serum 28 Sex 29 Proper 30 Capers 31 Open 32 Two-faced 33 Enters

DOWN: 1 Danced 2 Encore 3 Deny 4 Thrives 5 Knees 6 Feats 8 Snap 9 Apt 12 Rat 13 Cells 15 Bored 18 Otter 19 Cad 20 Vet 21 Cameras 22 Cup 23 Repent 24 Oxen 25 Ensues 26 Spite 27 Robot 28 Sap 30 Code

No 308 - ACROSS: 4 Shrill 7 Runner-up 8 Armour 10 Trust 13 Bias 14 Halt 15 Tent 16 Bet 17 Iron 19 Haul 21 Blameless 23 Felt 24 Fork 26 Ire 27 Trip 29 Else 32 Slat 33 Adopt 34 Fennel 35 Lopsided 36 Leeway

DOWN: 1 Broth 2 Annul 3 Pert 4 Spain 5 Rams 6 Laurel 9 Rather 11 Raw 12 Still 13 Benefit 15 Tom 16 Bus 18 Rattle 20 Asked 21 Bee 22 Lop 23 Frieze 25 Asp 28 Rally 30 Loads 31 Etude 32 Snow 33 Apse

No 309 - ACROSS: 3 Thump 8 Steel 10 Eased 11 Rep 12 Beast 13 Careers 15 Shell 18 Aye 19 Sesame 21 Pleases 22 Ills 23 Veto 24 Shatter 26 Clasps 29 Ion 31 Sidle 32 Tonight 34 Eaten 35 See 36 Steer 37 Doted 38 Psalm

DOWN: 1 Stray 2 Repeals 4 Hues 5 Messes 6 Paths 7 Realm 9 Eer 12 Breaths 14 Eye 16 Eager 17 Lemon 19 Section 20 Discs 21 Plead 23 Venison 24 Spears 25 Ton 27 Lists 28 Sleep 30 Sheep 32 Tell 33 Get

No 310 - ACROSS: 1 Gaffe 6 Fibre 9 Refuted 10 Anvil 11 Elite 12 Tulle 13 Ensnare 15 Lea 17 Aged 18 Enters 19 Sting 20 Trance 22 Ante 24 Hen 25 Devised 26 Rated 27 Scrap 28 Limps 29 Certain 30 Cedes 31 Egret

DOWN: 2 Awning 3 Friend 4 Eel 5 Fugue 6 Feeling 7 Idle 8 Rotter 12 Trite 13 Earth 14 Sedan 15 Leans 16 Asked 18 Ended 19 Scrapes 21 Rescue 22 Ailing 23 Temple 25 Delta 26 Race 28 Lie

No 311 - ACROSS: 1 Concur 7 Approach 8 Pelt 10 Places 11 Recall 14 The 16 Noted 17 Epee 19 Sated 21 Appal 22 Plain 23 Sane 26 Mural 28 Fir 29 Adored 30 Tariff 31 Area 32 Esoteric 33 Tussle

DOWN: 1 Couple 2 Creche 3 Rats 4 Arsenal 5 Carat 6 Child 8 Pate 9 Lee 12 Cod 13 Let on 15 Rapid 18 Proud 19 Spa 20 Tan 21 Alleged 22 Par 23 Sirens 24 Aria 25 Efface 26 Mares 27 Robot 28 Far 30 Tact

No 312 - ACROSS: 4 Cuckoo 7 Hyacinth 8 Eludes 10 North 13 Daub 14 Tree 15 Sups 16 Woo 17 Peke 19 Tart 21 Similarly 23 Ride 24 Lied 26 Tip 27 Reed 29 Emit 32 Aged 33 Erode 34 Dinner 35 Infamous 36 Ignite

DOWN: 1 Chant 2 Sabre 3 High 4 Cheap 5 Club 6 Ocelot 9 Lustre 11 Ore 12 Tepid 13 Duelled 15 Ski 16 Wry 18 Emerge 20 Alder 21 Sip 22 Aid 23 Rising 25 Rid 28 Eerie 30 Motor 31 Terse 32 Anti 33 Edam

No 313 - ACROSS: 3 Tiers 8 Wares 10 Early 11 Fit 12 Aloft 13 Reports 15 Eyrie 18 Kit 19 Errant 21 Regains 22 Oman 23 Hind 24 Snorted 26 Closes 29 Eel 31 Hired 32 Tadpole 34 Valet 35 Fat 36 Rivet 37 Mural 38 Rears

DOWN: 1 Wafer 2 Betoken 4 Ills 5 Refers 6 Satyr 7 Slain 9 Rip 12 Attains 14 Rig 16 Rapid 17 Etude 19 Entreat 20 Torch 21 Razor 23 Helpful 24 Sedate 25 Ted 27 Livid 28 Sever 30 Altar 32 Tear 33 Oar

No 314 - ACROSS: 1 Thyme 6 Eerie 9 Ancient 10 Stand 11 Voids 12 Begin 13 Feelers 15 Ace 17 Idle 18 Gusset 19 Dozes 20 Dodged 22 Mere 24 Sue 25 Cruiser 26 Score 27 Stale 28 Admit 29 Anemone 30 Adept 31 Twine

DOWN: 2 Hatred 2 Mangle 4 End 5 Wiles 6 Envious 7 Eton 8 Induce 12 Brood 13 Finds 14 Elude 15 Asses 16 Ether 18 Genre 19 Descent 21 Ousted 22 Mildew 23 Resign 25 Crime 26 Slap 28 Ant

No 315 - ACROSS: 1 Damson 7 Armchair 8 Beam 10 Averse 11 Season 14 Ark 16 Alert 17 Deny 19 Blame 21 Seeps 22 Chest 23 Tore 26 Argue 28 Per 29 Stream 30 Berate 31 Earl 32 Evidence 33 Firmly

DOWN: 1 Demand 2 Sherry 3 Name 4 Screams 5 Passe 6 Grant 8 Bean 9 Ask 12 Ale 13 Order 15 Flesh 18 Evert 19 Bee 20 Apt 21 Sheaves 22 Cue 23 Terror 24 Oral 25 Energy 26 Askew 27 Grain 28 Pea 30 Beef

No 316 - ACROSS: 4 Onrush 7 Mischief 8 Topple 10 Gaudy 13 Debt 14 Epee 15 Tent 16 Oil 17 Bawl 19 Aura 21 Favourite 23 Mare 24 Dent 26 Bar 27 Need 29 Ease 32 Fund 33 Cruel 34 Outlet 35 Envisage 36 Flower

DOWN: 1 Image 2 Issue 3 Whey 4 Often 5 Rapt 6 Salvia 9 Obtain 11 Ape 12 Debar 13 Deluded 15 Two 16 Ore 18 Avenue 20 Utter 21 Far 22 Red 23 Manual 25 Use 28 Enter 30 Aural 31 Elder 32 Flaw 33 Crib

No 317 - ACROSS: 3 Shrub 8 Ratty 10 Never 11 Nor 12 Sprig 13 Scrimps 15 Quiet 18 Pal 19 Runner 21 Retinue 22 Eras 23 Read 24 Stutter 26 Scares 29 Lap 31 Turin 32 Senegal 34 Viper 35 And 36Creel 37 Study 38 Tense

DOWN: 1 Lance 2 Stripes 4 Hops 5 Unique 6 Begun 7 Melee 9 Tor 12 Splints 14 Mat 16 Inter 17 Trade 19 Rustler 20 Beast 21 Radar 23 Repeats 24 Senile 25 Tan 27 Curry 28 Rivet 30 Caddy 32 Sets 33 Gnu

No 318 - ACROSS: 1 Smash 6 Spite 9 Hospice 10 Great 11 Ashen 12 Skirt 13 Reverie 15 Sol 17 Alas 18 Desire 19 Habit 20 Guitar 22 Mean 24 End 25 Against 26 Bingo 27 Comic 28 Runes 29 Dovecot 30 Tenet 31 Beano

DOWN: 2 Marvel 3 Shapes 4 Hot 5 Spoke 6 Scarlet 7 Pest 8 Tremor 12 Sitar 13 Range 14 Valid 15 Siren 16 Leant 18 Dingo 19 Haricot 21 Undone 22 Minute 23 Astern 25 Agree 26 Bide 28 Rob

No 319 - ACROSS: 1 Chaser 7 Airedale 8 Sari 10 Slogan 11 Locate 14 Den 16 Sates 17 Star 19 Taper 21 Rages 22 Merit 23 Bred 26 Sides 28 Lea 29 Carton 30 Carped 31 Abet 32 Relation 33 Titles

DOWN: 1 Crisis 2 Stager 3 Rain 4 Reposes 5 Carat 6 Cedes 8 Soda 9 Ran 12 Car 13 Terse 15 Magic 18 Tibia 19 Tar 20 Pet 21 Resorts 22 Met 23 Bereft 24 Rapt 25 Dodges 26 Scarf 27 Droll 28 Lab 30 Cant